INSTRUCTOR GUIDE

Kayla Rihani

Department of Biology, Northeastern Illinois University

Environmental**Science**

TOWARD A SUSTAINABLE FUTURE 11e

Richard T. **Wright** • Dorothy F. **Boorse**

Benjamin Cummings

Boston   Columbus   Indianapolis   New York   San Francisco   Upper Saddle River
Amsterdam   Cape Town   Dubai   London   Madrid   Milan   Munich   Paris   Montréal   Toronto
Delhi   Mexico City   São Paulo   Sydney   Hong Kong   Seoul   Singapore   Taipei   Tokyo

Executive Editor: Chalon Bridges
Project Editor/Development Editor: Nora Lally-Graves
Executive Director of Development: Deborah Gale
Editor-in-Chief: Beth Wilbur
Vice President and Editorial Director: Frank Ruggirello
Executive Marketing Manager: Lauren Harp
Managing Editor, Chemistry and Geosciences: Gina M. Cheselka
Project Manager: Ed Thomas
Operations Specialist: Maura Zaldivar
Supplement Cover Designer: Paul Gourhan
Cover Photo Credit: Barbara Walton/epa/Corbis

Printed in the United States of America

10   9   8   7   6   5   4   3   2   V036

ISBN-13:   978-0-321-65171-6

ISBN-10:   0-321-65171-5

Benjamin Cummings
is an imprint of

Table of Contents
Instructor Guide for Environmental Science: Toward a Sustainable Future, 11e

Content	Page(s)

Overview of the Instructor's Resource Manual

Environmental Science: The Way the World Works is designed around three central themes: sustainability, stewardship, and sound science. This manual was written to complement the textbook and help you to design a course that will be useful to environmental science majors, non-science majors, engineers, and others.

Each chapter of the Instructor's Resource Manual contains the following sections: Chapter Outline, Instructional Goals, Concepts and Connections, Concepts in Context, Key Terms and Vocabulary, Discussion Topics, Suggested Lecture Format, Review Questions: Possible Answers, and Thinking Environmentally Questions: Possible Answers. You will find a detailed description of each section below.

Chapter Outline

This section is an outline overview of the chapter contents. Major headings and subheadings are listed to enable you to quickly determine the focus of the chapter. If you wish to select portions rather than the complete chapter for use in your course, the chapter outline should help you with your initial selections.

Instructional Goals

The major instructional objectives for each chapter are located in this section. Specific learning objectives are provided for the concepts presented in the chapter. The learning objectives are concept oriented rather than fact oriented. In most chapters, at least one instructional goal makes connections between the material presented in the chapter, other course material, and the world. The instructional goals are themes that can be emphasized in each chapter and can be used to develop lecture materials and active learning exercises.

Concepts and Connections

The Concepts and Connections section links chapter materials to issues in everyday life. These issues may have a direct environmental focus or may connect to other issues in science. For example, there are concerns about the impact of genetic engineering on biodiversity as well as ethical, biomedical, and legal concerns. Making connections between the concepts discussed and everyday life will help non-majors see the importance of understanding scientific ideas and will help majors see the interconnectedness of science and society. Both science and non-science majors benefit from understanding how integral science is to society.

Concepts in Context

This section provides information about how material in other chapters connects to the material in the current chapter. You can link material presented earlier in the semester to the current material and future lectures. Some chapters have more links than other chapters but nearly every concept taught in environmental science can be linked to other concepts.

Key Terms and Vocabulary

Key Terms and Vocabulary for each chapter are listed. These words and phrases are the basic tools the students need to understand the concepts presented. It can be difficult to convince non-majors that learning terms and vocabulary is anything more than a waste of time and effort. Without the terms and vocabulary, an individual is limiting her/his ability to understand concepts. Discussing with the students the need to learn a minimum amount of vocabulary in every major discipline may help to motivate them.

Discussion Topics (Discussion, Activities, and Labs)

Active learning has been increasingly emphasized as a means to improve learning outcomes. Each chapter contains at least two suggested activities. The goal of all the exercises is to engage the student and encourage them to think about the concepts being learned. These assignments encourage students to interact with the outside environment, to discover the connections between environmental issues and everyday life, and to observe the world around them.

Some activities require more time than others do. Some suggestions may not be practical due to class size, physical structure of the classroom, or type of outside environment. An attempt has been made to consider these types of limitations and most suggestions are adaptable to any environment. If an activity suggestion is not appropriate for your classroom, it may be adaptable to an activity done by students outside of class.

Suggested Lecture Format

For each chapter an outline of the chapter with a quote or description from each subsection has been provided. The outline summarizes the chapter and can be used as a logical structure for lectures based on this text. Figures from each chapter are integrated into the lecture format outline. Within each outline suggestions have been made for the placement of group/class Discussion Topics; these are highlighted in bold.

Review Questions: Possible Answers

Answers have been provided for the Review Questions at the end of each chapter. These questions are an excellent way to review the material in the chapter. Many students have not learned how to read a science textbook well so they may not know how to pull the important concepts out of their reading. You may wish to discuss with your students the purpose of chapter titles, headers, sub-headers, and bold words. Using these cues will make it easier to find the "answers" to the questions at the back of the textbook.

Many of the answers to the questions are partial or complete quotes from the corresponding chapter in the textbook. This has been done this for two reasons. First, if you wish to use one of these questions on an exam, you will know the exact information provided by the authors in answer to the question. Secondly, because many students tend to copy information directly from the textbook, using this guide as a reference for what the text says exactly will help you to detect plagiarism and advise students to re-word or quote the text as appropriate.

Thinking Environmentally: Possible Answers

Answers have been provided for the Thinking Environmentally questions at the end of each chapter. If the question asks for the student's opinion, information have has been provided to help with evaluating answers you might be given, if possible. Other questions in the section require the student to obtain information that is specific to a local situation. Again, if possible, some information that may help the students find the information or help you evaluate their answers has been provided.

Supplemental Resources for Environmental Science

Books

- A Theory of Education, Joseph D. Novak, Cornell University Press, 1977.
- Collaborative Learning and College Teaching, K. Bosworth and S. Hamilton, Eds. Jossey-Bass, 1994.
- Environmental Science Activities, Dorothy B. Rosenthal. John Wiley and Sons, 1995.
- Learning How to Learn, Joseph D. Novak and D. Bob Gowin. Cambridge University Press, 1984.
- Serendipity: Accidental Discoveries in Science, Royston M. Roberts. John Wiley and Sons, 1989.

Journals

- American Biology Teacher, the official journal of the National Association of Biology Teachers.
- Environmental Education, published by Heldref Publications.
- Issues in Science and Technology, published by the National Academy of Sciences and the Cecil and the Ida Green Center for the Study of Science and Society at the University of Texas at Dallas.
- Journal of College Science Teaching, published by the National Science Teachers Association.

Internet Resources

- National Center for the Teaching of Case Studies
  http://ublib.buffalo.edu/libraries/projects/cases/ubcase.htm#ecology
- Effective Teaching in the Agricultural and Life Sciences—
  www.ais.msstate.edu/TALS
- Mississippi State University, New Mexico State University and North Carolina State University collaborated to create this web site of wonderful information on how to teach more effectively.
- Earth System Research Laboratory
  http://www.esrl.noaa.gov/gmd/
- Total Ozone Mapping Spectrometer
  http://jwocky.gsfc.nasa.gov/
- Energy Information Administration
  http://www.eia.doe.gov/emeu/aer/contents.html
- U.S. Census Bureau – IDB Populations Pyramids
  http://www.census.gov/ipc/www/idbpyr.html
- Water use calculation
  http://ans.engr.wisc.edu/eic/WaterForm.html
  http://ga.water.usgs.gov/edu/sq3.html
  http://www.mrhall.org/science/waterusecalc/waterusecalc.htm
  http://ans.engr.wisc.edu/eic/WaterForm.html
- National Pesticide Information Center
  http://npic.orst.edu/

Other Resources

- National Parks, published by the National Parks and Conservation Association
- National Wildlife, published by the National Wildlife Federation
- Science News

Sample Syllabi-Quarter Term

Quarter Term (10 weeks, 2 lectures per week, 3 exams) - Issues Approach

Lecture	Topic
Chapter 1	Introduction: Toward a Sustainable Future
Chapter 18 (part)	Global Climate Change (ozone depletion)
Chapter 3	Basic Needs of Living Things
Chapter 18 (part)	Global Climate Change
Chapter 4	Populations and Communities
Chapter 6	Wild Species and Biodiversity
Chapter 5	Ecosystems: Energy, Patterns, and Disturbance (relate to biodiversity)
Exam 1	**Chapters 1, 3-6, and 18**
Chapter 8	The Human Population
Chapter 9	Population and Development
Chapter 12	The Production and Distribution of Food
Chapter 11	Soil: Foundation for Land Ecosystems
Chapter 13	Pests and Pest Control
Exam 2	**Chapter 8-9, and 12-13**
Chapter 20	Water Pollution and Its Prevention
Chapter 10	Water: Hydrologic Cycle and Human Use
Chapter 19	Air Pollution
Chapter 14	Energy from Fossil Fuels
Chapter 15	Nuclear Power
Chapter 16	Renewable Energy
Exam 3	**Chapter 10, 14-16 and 19-20**

Quarter Term (10 weeks, 2 lectures per week, 3 exams) -Traditional approach

Lecture	Topic
Chapter 1	Science and the Environment
Chapter 3	Basic Needs of Living Things
Chapter 4	Populations and Communities
Chapter 5	Ecosystems: Energy, Patterns, and Disturbance
Chapter 6	Wild Species and Biodiversity
Chapter 7	The Use and Restoration of Ecosystems
Exam 1	**Chapters 1 and 3–7**
Chapter 8	The Human Population
Chapter 9	Population and Development
Chapter 10	Water: Hydrologic Cycle and Human Use
Chapter 11	Soil: Foundation for Land Ecosystems
Chapter 12	The Production and Distribution of Food
Chapter 13	Pests and Pest Control
Exam 2	**Chapter 8–13**
Chapter 14	Energy from Fossil Fuels
Chapter 15	Nuclear Power
Chapter 16	Renewable Energy
Chapter 18	Global Climate Change
Chapter 19	Air Pollution
Chapter 20	Water Pollution and its Prevention
Exam 3	**Chapters 14-16, and 18-20**

Sample Syllabi-Semester Term

Semester Term (14 weeks, 2 lectures per week, 4 exams) - Issues approach

Lecture	Topic
Chapter 1	Science and the Environment
Chapter 18 (part)	Global Climate Change (Ozone Depletion)
Chapter 3	Basic Needs of Living Things
Chapter 18 (part)	Global Climate Change (Climate and Climate Change)
Chapter 4	Populations and Communities
Chapter 6	Wild Species and Biodiversity
Chapter 5	Ecosystems: Energy, Patterns, and Disturbance (relate to biodiversity)
Chapter 7	The Use and Restoration of Ecosystems
Exam 1	**Chapters 1, 3, 4-7, and 18**
Chapter 8	The Human Population: Dimensions
Chapter 9	Population and Development
Chapter 12	The Production and Distribution of Food
Chapter 11	Soil Foundation for Land Ecosystems
Chapter 13	Pests and Pest Control
Exam 2	**Chapters 8-9, and 12-13**
Chapter 21	Municipal Solid Waste: Disposal and Recovery
Chapter 22	Hazardous Chemicals
Chapter 20	Water Pollution and Its Prevention
Chapter 10	Water: Hydrologic Cycle and Human Use
Chapter 17	Environmental Hazards and Human Health
Chapter 19	Air Pollution
Exam 3	**Chapters 10, 17, 19, and 20-22**
Chapter 14	Energy from Fossil Fuels (relate to atmospheric pollution)
Chapter 15	Nuclear Power (a suggested solution to global warming)
Chapter 16	Renewable Energy (a suggested solution to global warming)
Chapter 2	Economics and Public Policy
Chapter 23	Sustainable Communities and Lifestyles
Exam 4	**Chapters 2, 14-16, and 23**

Semester Term (14 weeks, 2 lectures per week, 4 exams) - Traditional approach

Lecture	Topic
Chapter 1	Science and the Environment
Chapter 2	Economics and Public Policy
Chapter 3	Basic Needs of Living Things
Chapter 4	Populations and Communities
Chapter 5	Ecosystems: Energy, Patterns, and Disturbance
Chapter 6	Wild Species and Biodiversity
Chapter 7	The Use and restoration of Ecosystems
Exam 1	**Chapters 1-7**
Chapter 8	The Human Population
Chapter 9	Population and Development
Chapter 10	Water: Hydrologic Cycle and Human Use
Chapter 11	Soil: Foundation for Land Ecosystems
Chapter 12	The Production and Distribution of Food
Chapter 13	Pests and Pest Control
Exam 2	**Chapters 8-13**
Chapter 14	Energy From Fossil Fuels

Semester Term (14 weeks, 2 lectures per week, 3 exams) - Traditional approach, continued

CHAPTER 1
Science and the Environment

Chapter Outline:

I. The State of the Planet
    A. Increasing Population Growth and Declining Human Well-Being
    B. The Decline of Ecosystems
        1. Millennium Ecosystem Assessment
    C. Global Climate Changes
        1. The Kyoto Protocol
    D. Loss of Biodiversity
        1. Risks of Losing Biodiversity
II. Environmental Science and the Environmental Movement
    A. Environmental Science
    B. The Environmental Movement
        1. The Modern Environmental Movement
        2. Environmentalism Acquires its Critics
III. Three Unifying Themes
    A. Sound Science
        1. The Scientific Method
            i. Assumptions
            ii. Observation
            iii. Experimentation
            iv. Theories
            v. Natural Laws and Concepts
            vi. The Role of Instruments in Science
        2. The Scientific Community
        3. Junk Science
        4. Evaluating Science
    B. Sustainability
        1. Sustainable Societies
        2. Sustainable Development
            i. An Ideal
        3. An Essential Transition
    C. Stewardship
        1. Who are the Stewards?
        2. Justice and Equity
            i. Justice for the Developing World
IV. Moving Toward a Sustainable Future
    A. Economic Changes
    B. Environmental Changes
    C. A New Commitment

Key Topics:

1. The State of the Planet
2. Environmental Science and the Environmental Movement
3. Three Unifying Themes:
4. Moving toward a Sustainable Future

Instructional Goals:

1. Environmental issues are complex. We need to study environmental issues from the perspective of economics, sociology, anthropology, and many other disciplines, which help to explain the problems with which we are faced.

2. Science is a necessary component of environmental decision-making. For the science to be useful it must be sound, and sound science involves scientific peer review.

3. Earth is a finite system, and creating a sustainable lifestyle should allow for indefinite continuation of the human species. Stewardship is the actions and programs that manage natural resources and human well-being for the common good. Sound science is the best method for achieving sustainability and for humans to understand our stewardship role.

4. Environmentalism and environmental problems are not new. Environmental problems caused by human activities have occurred since the dawn of agriculture. The current wave of environmentalism began in 1962 with the publication of *Silent Spring* by Rachel Carson, but its roots can be traced to the 19th century.

Concepts and Connections:

Environmental science is a multidisciplinary field. It is not possible to understand and solve environmental problems when the problems are viewed from a narrow or single disciplinary focus. Discussing the possible contributions from various fields would help draw in students whose primary interests are not the sciences and would help science majors understand the true complexity of environmental science. It is possible to improve how humans interact with our environment from almost any field. Anthropology, archeology, sociology, psychology, and other disciplines that explore how and why people act help a multidisciplinary environmental team determine the most effective way to educate or motivate people to act in environmentally sound ways. Economists and others involved in business decisions influence the quality of the environment around us; many are working to make business decisions "green." Those individuals who transmit culture—actors, writers, musicians—convey values. The values conveyed include how the natural world is perceived and how we should relate to it. Teachers have a special role because they not only transmit concepts (facts) but they also transmit society's values.

Putting the environmental movement in historical context can be very important. Most students think that the current problems are the most severe and may be very upset that adults have not "fixed" these problems. A discussion of success (and failure) stories can be useful. Knowing that people who lived more than 100 years ago cared strongly about the environment can be motivating. Double-edged stories such as John Muir's struggle to save the Hetch Hetchy Valley near Yosemite can be both heartbreaking (because he did not succeed) and enlightening because Muir is an inspiring individual. Another double-edged story involves the first Clean Air Act. To solve the problem of locally high levels of air pollution, the law required the building of tall smokestacks that moved the pollutants to the upper atmosphere, resulting in acid precipitation in areas very far from the pollutant source. We solved the problem of locally severe air pollution, which caused periodic increases in death rates, but moved the problem to places distant from the pollution source. This latter example can be used to demonstrate the need to think through the effects of an action. We may be able to avoid future problems if we try to envision the downstream events that may flow from a decision.

Concepts in Context:

The first chapter is a survey of many of the environmental issues to be covered and the context (sound science, sustainability, and stewardship) in which they will be discussed. We also discuss the historical perspective and the bias and misrepresentations of junk science.

Key Terms and Vocabulary:

Millennium Development Goals (MDGs), goods, services, Millennium Ecosystem Assessment, environmental science, environmental movement, environmentalists, environmentalism, sound science, sustainability, stewardship, scientific method, natural sciences, observation, facts, experimentation, atomic theory, hypothesis, theory, natural laws, concepts, instruments junk science, sustainable yields, development, equity, environmental racism

Discussion, Activities, and Labs:

1. Ask the students to name local environmental controversies. At the same time ask if they know of any local environmental problems that have been resolved; it is important for students to see that there is a continuum between the past and the present. Make two lists of all the suggestions on the board. If they do not have many suggestions, broaden the question to include state, national, and/or international issues. Some examples of national level environmental problems that have been resolved include (1) Air quality: the reduction of lead emissions as a result of the elimination of lead in gasoline, (2) Water quality: the Cuyahoga River, and other rivers, no longer catch on fire, (3) Solid waste: recycling of solid waste is widespread, and (4) Pesticides and hazardous materials/wastes: DDT and most of the persistent organic pollutants are phased out or will be soon.

2. Begin with asking the students to suggest systems (processes) within our society that are sustainable. Have the students provide a justification for why each suggested system (process) is sustainable. Next ask the students to suggest systems within our society that are not sustainable. Have the students provide justification for why the suggested system (process) is not sustainable. Finally, ask the students to summarize the information about sustainable and non-sustainable processes in our society and justify a conclusion about the overall sustainability of our society.

3. Ask the students to suggest examples of sound and junk science. Write all the suggestions on the chalkboard into two lists. If a student suggests an example of sound science but the example is junk science, then put the suggestion within parentheses and discuss as many of these as time allows after the suggestions have ended. Do not interrupt the suggestions to discuss incorrectly placed suggestions.

4. Divide the class into small groups (three to four students). Give each group a small consumer item, (e.g., paper bag, plastic bag, electric hair dryer, toothbrush, disposable pen, disposable razor, or reusable razor). Ask the students to first decide if the item is essential for human survival. (None of the items in my list are essential. None are food, shelter, or clothing.) Then ask the students to list the questions they would like to have answered so that they can decide the environmental impact of their item.

   Take time before the end of class to bring the groups back together and have each group report on their conclusion concerning whether or not the consumer item is essential for survival and their list of questions. After the students have reported their findings, discuss the difference between needs (essential for survival) and wants (perceived to make life easier, more pleasant, and so forth). Discuss how every item used by humans will have some environmental impact. The goal is to reduce an individual's impact.

5. As a follow up to the in-class activity, ask the students to go home and evaluate their food, clothing, and shelter. Much of what we describe as food, clothing, and shelter falls within the category of want, not need. Have students list ten items that are wants (these can include the nonessential food, clothing, or shelter items) that are most important to them. A sentence or two should accompany each item explaining why this item is important. Have students list five items they have that they could live without. A sentence or two should accompany each item explaining why this item was chosen.

Suggested Lecture Format

I. The State of the Planet

    A. Briefly introduce the four topics discussed in the text to provide course context:
        1. Increasing Population Growth and Declining Human Well-Being

2. The Decline of Ecosystems
   i.   Millennium Ecosystem Assessment
3. Global Climate Changes
   i.   The Kyoto Protocol
4. Loss of Biodiversity
   i.   Risks of Losing Biodiversity

B. Mention any local, regional, or state environmental issues if they link to the topics covered during the semester, (e.g., air and water quality, land use planning, solid waste).

C. Use **Discussion Topic #1** to ask the students to suggest local, regional, or state environmental issues.

II. Historical context: Concern about the environment is not new.

A. Discuss some historical environmental movements such as:
1. John Muir and Hetch Hetchy Valley
2   The National Park System and Yellowstone National Park

B. The modern environmental movement
1. *Silent Spring* by Rachel Carson resulted in the movement to reduce exposure to a wide variety of chemicals; chemistry was no longer seen as only beneficial.
2. Environmentalism acquires its critics. Industries began to fight back against regulation.

C. Current issue—tie back to the environmental issues mentioned by the students before you began the historical context discussion.

III. Three Unifying Themes: Sustainability, Stewardship, and Sound Science

A. Sound Science
1. What is science?
    i.   Science seeks to acquire and explain factual knowledge, not just belief and opinion.
    ii.   Science restricts itself to considering objects and events that can be observed in an objective way.
    iii. While religion, ethics, emotions, and so on are important, they cannot be observed in an objective fashion so they are outside the realm of science.
2. Scientific method: a process to gain knowledge; a hierarchical ordering of knowledge from innumerable observations to a few universal natural laws
3. The Universe Functions according to certain basic principles and natural laws that remain consistent through time and space.
    i.   The principles by which we can define and precisely predict the behavior of matter and energy are called natural laws. Examples include: the Law of Gravity, the Law of Conservation of Matter, and the Laws of Thermodynamics
    ii.   Concepts are perfectly valid explanations of data gathered from the natural world, and they can also be predictive, but they never reach the status of laws. They enable us to make qualified predictions of future outcomes.
4. Scientific Instruments perform one of three basic functions:
    i.   They extend our powers of observation. Examples include: Telescopes, Microscopes, X-ray machines, and CAT scans.
    ii.   Used to quantify observations, such as enabling us to measure exact quantities.
    iii. Help us to achieve conditions and perform manipulations required to make certain observations or perform certain experiments.
5. The role of the scientific community and why controversies occur
    i.   New information can be gained from better observations and instrumentation. The ozone hole and the Hubble telescope are examples.

4

ii. Complex Phenomena are hard to conduct experiments with. Examples include enhanced greenhouse gases and global warming as well as the effects of Ozone depletion on ecosystems.

iii. Bias from individuals with vested interests come into play. For example, the tobacco industry and cancer, the chemical industry and ozone depletion, and Agriculture and GMOs

iv. Subjective value judgments may be involved. An example is the debate over the further use of nuclear power.

6. Junk Science-Does not conform to the rigors of sound science (because it doesn't undergo the peer-review process) and it usually includes the selective presentation of desired results. **See Discussion Topic #3**.

i. Politically motivated distortion of scientifically sound papers

ii. The attribution of false information to a respected researcher or research organization. (This occurred in a 1998 *Wall Street Journal* op-ed piece. The editorial claimed the Center for Disease Control (CDC) had found that people who ate organic foods were eight times more likely to suffer food poisoning due to E. coli than those who did not eat organically produced food. When contacted the CDC indicated it had not done any study of organic vs. conventional produce and E. coli or other food-borne pathogens.)

7. Evaluating Science

i. What are the observations underlying the conclusion or explanation? Can they be satisfactorily confirmed?

ii. Do the explanations and theories follow logically from the data?

iii. Does the explanation account for all of the observations?

iv. Are there reasons that a particular explanation is favored? Who profits from having that explanation accepted broadly?

v. Is the conclusion supported by the community of scientists with the greatest competence to judge the work? If not, it is highly suspect.

B. Sustainability

1. Define a sustainable system: a process (or system) that can continue indefinitely without depleting any of the material or energy resources required to keep it running.

i. Use **Discussion Topic #2** to discuss sustainability and its meaning.

2. What is a Sustainable Society?

i. What global trends are the results of not having a sustainable society?

3. What is sustainable development?

i. Like sustainability, the definition of sustainable development differs by perspective.

ii. It's important to uphold sustainable development as an ideal, or goal toward which all human societies should be moving.

4. The transition toward sustainability.

i. There is broad agreement on the following points: 1) A demographic transition from a continually increasing human population to one that is stable. 2) A resource transition to an economy that is not obsessed with growth, but instead relies on nature's income and protects ecosystem capital from depletion. 3) A technology transition from pollution-intensive economic production to environmentally friendly processes. 4) A political/sociological transition to societies that embrace a stewardly and just approach to people's needs and that eliminate large-scale poverty. 5) A community transition from the present car-dominated urban sprawl of developed countries to the "smart growth" concepts of smaller, functional settlements and more livable cities.

C. Stewardship

1. Who are stewards? How does one become a steward of the environment?

2. Justice and equity—define environmental racism.

i. Ask the students if they know examples of environmental racism.

ii. Example: It has been documented that hazardous waste sites (both legal and illegal) are more frequently found in poor and minority neighborhoods. The correlation persists between hazardous waste sites and minority neighborhoods even if land values and other economic parameters are held constant. (If the primary or only factor influencing hazardous waste landfill location was economic, the vast majority of sites would be in white neighborhoods because, in the U.S., there are more white neighborhoods than non-white neighborhoods).

IV. Moving Towards a Sustainable Future

    A. Globalization and the speed of travel for information, people, goods, and diseases are very important.

    B. Economic changes
       1. Examples include the Internet, preferential trade, and transitional corporations.

    C. Environmental changes
       1. Examples: More ecosystem friendly products, the rapid spread of diseases like SARS, H1N1and AIDS, and the global dispersion of exotic species.

    D. A New Commitment
       1. It is not business as usual: "If we don't change direction, we will end up where we are heading".
       2. Some good news: Food production has improved nutrition, there is an increased life expectancy, population growth has slowed, and there is increasing environmental awareness.

Review Questions: Possible Answers

1. *What factors brought about the collapse of Easter Island civilization? How did later contact with the rest of the world affect the islanders?*

    The collapse of the Easter Island civilization was brought about by the overexploitation of resources. Trees were cut to clear land for agriculture, move large stones used for religious icons, and build structures. Trees were cut at a rate faster than they could grow. Eroded soil flowed into the surrounding sea, changing the nutrient level of the water and covering the organisms on the seafloor. The eroded land area was less able to absorb water. Soil, forest, and water resources were degraded. As available resources diminished, conflict between the rich and poor inhabitants of Easter Island due to the unequal distribution of the scarce resources resulted. The environmental situation worsened from the conflict and eventually all inhabitants died from fighting, starvation, or disease.

    When the Rapa Nui (the Easter Islanders) came in contact with the rest of the world in the 19th century, the whalers and other visitors, who were in search of food and water, exposed them for the first time to venereal disease. In the middle of the 19th century, Peruvians who were slavers came to the island and captured individuals to sell them as part of the slave trade. During this time period smallpox was introduced to the islanders, and only 111 Rapa Nui remained by 1877. When Chile annexed the Island in the late 1800s, sheep were brought to the Island and the Rapa Nui were confined to a single village. After archeologists discovered the Rapa Nui, they came to world attention and their situation began to improve. Many of the stone statues have been restored, and the islanders have regained some control over their lives. Unfortunately, unemployment and alcoholism are significant problems.

2. *Cite four global trends that indicate that the health of planet Earth is suffering:*

    "Four global trends of particularly unhealthy: (1) increasing population growth and its detrimental effects on human well-being, (2) a decline of vital ecosystem services, (3) the negative impacts of global climate change, and (4) a loss of biodiversity."

3. *Define environment, and describe the general development and successes of modern environmentalism.*

    The word environment is a broad term and it describes the natural world, human societies, and the human-built world. When the frontier "closed" in the late 19th century people realized that unique wild areas were disappearing. Different groups formed to help popularize the idea of wilderness and preservation of lands. A second wave came after the Dust Bowl, WW I and during the Depression with the CCC and others. After WW

II a technology explosion caused economic (and population) expansion which lead to many environmental problems. New chemicals lead to the decline of bird populations. Rachel Carson's book and others led to the modern environmental movement. A more militant population demanded decreased pollution and increased cleanup. It was a grassroots movement as opposed to a governmental or official one. New groups formed and old ones found new members and new help. Many laws were passed in the late 1960's and the 1970's such as the Clean Air and Clear Water Acts. The EPA was also founded. From there all kinds of things happened, depending on the issues, the government, and the people.

4. What are the concepts behind each of the three unifying themes—sound science, sustainability, and stewardship?

Sound science is based on the rigors of the methods and practice of legitimate science. This means years of observation, experimentation and peer review are behind it. Sound science involves an approach to understanding how the natural world works, an approach that has become known as the scientific method. Careful observation is of utmost importance. Solutions to environmental problems should not be implemented without sound science behind them.

Sustainability is a system or process that can be continued indefinitely, without depleting any of the material or energy resources required to keep it running. A solution to any problem isn't useful if it costs too much money to keep doing, uses too many resources, impairs people's ability to work well and live decently, or puts many companies out of business and people out of work. For example, a decree that no more rain forests can be cut is not sustainable unless a way for the indigenous people to survive and live a decent life style can be found to replace their previous livelihood of slash and burn agriculture. Mandating that all farms are organic and pesticide free is unsustainable if the crop is lost to locusts or other pests year after year. If a system is to be sustainable, it also has to be well thought out and in balance. Like sound science, solutions to environmental problems should not be implemented unless they are sustainable.

Stewardship ties these together. It is the actions and programs that manage natural resources and human well-being for the common good. Stewards are those who care for something—from the natural world or from human culture—that they do not own and that they will pass on to the next generation. Modern-day environmental stewardship, therefore, incorporates an ethic that guides actions taken to benefit the natural world as well as people. Like the other two concepts, environmental solutions should include stewardship as an impetus. We only have one planet and we have to share it with the present population and future populations as well.

5. Explain the role of assumptions, observation, experimentation, and theory formation in the operation of scientific research and thinking.

Most scientific theories, laws, facts, etc., began with observations and assumptions. A simple example is no matter how far you put something into the air, it always falls to the ground—this eventually led to the Law of Gravity. People assumed if they let go of something, it would fall. These observations and assumptions lead to experimentation and conclusions. Conclusions become a theory only after much testing and confirmation that it is logically consistent with all observations—and there is always the possibility that new information or better observation techniques (such as better microscopes or telescopes) will lead to new theories. It is sometimes more informative if a hypothesis is proven wrong then if the data seems to show it is correct. Through logical reasoning, theories will generally suggest or predict certain events. If an event predicted by a theory is observed, the observation provides strong evidence for the truth of the theory. Predictions require experiments, testing, further data gathering, and more observation. Theories, or concepts are perfectly valid explanations of data gathered from the natural world, and they can also be predictive: they model the way we believe the natural world works and enable us to make qualified predictions of future outcomes. For example, if we know that PCBs have a half life of hundreds of years, we can predict that they will be in the Great Lakes and food chains long after we are gone. Scientific thinking and research requires data, quantification, accurate observations and experimentation.

6. What led to the decline of vultures in India and Pakistan? How did scientific work lead to the explanation for the decline?

It was important to look at all the data relating to the decline of vultures. It would have been easy to jump to conclusions. The two key pieces of evidence were (1) the vultures died by kidney failure and (2) they mostly ate dead domesticated animals. But which of numerous factors was causing the failure? There were many culprits, including avian disease, pesticides, polluted waters, metals, or something in their food. It was only

7

after experimenting with captive vultures and using a control group that scientists were able to show that a veterinary drug called diclofenac was causing kidney failure and thus the death of the vultures. Using the scientific method of observation, assumption, experimenting and controls revealed the cause, and phasing out the use of the drug allowed vulture populations to rise and continue the important work of removing dead animal carcasses.

7. *Cite some reasons for the existence of controversies within science, and carefully distinguish between sound science and junk science.*

"There at least four reasons" for controversies in science. First, "we are continually confronted by new observation… (and it) takes some time before all the hypotheses regarding the cause of what we have observed can be adequately tested. During this time, there may be honest disagreement as to which hypothesis is most likely. Such controversies are gradually settled by further observations and testing…." Second, we are looking at complex phenomena that "do not lend themselves to simple tests of experiments…. Gradually, different lines of evidence come to support one hypothesis and exclude another, enabling the issue to be resolved." Third, "there are many vested interests which wish to maintain and promote disagreement because they stand to profit by doing so." Last, "subjective value judgments may be involved."

Sound science has the scientific method behind it. Assumptions and hypotheses have been tested over and over and over, and papers have been reviewed by peers before published. Historic sciences such as astronomy and geology have many careful observations and measurements which are repeated over and over. Junk science does not conform to the rigors of science. It picks only the observations or results that "prove" its point. The material may be published but not in recognized peer reviewed journals.

8. *Define sustainability and sustainable development. What is a sustainable society?*

"A system or process … that can be continued indefinitely, without depleting any of the material or energy resources required to keep it running". By this definition, it would be impossible to run a modern society on fossil fuels. (The rate at which fossil fuels are created is so slow that almost any rate of use would exceed the rate of creation.)

"A sustainable society is a society in balance with the natural world". It is possible for a sustainable society to continue indefinitely because it does not deplete its resource base or produce pollutants in excess of nature's ability to absorb/process them.

9. *List five transitions that are necessary for a future sustainable civilization.*

There is broad agreement on the following major points:
- A demographic transition from a continually increasing human population to one that is stable.
- A resource transition to an economy that is not obsessed with growth, but instead relies on nature's income and protects ecosystem capital from depletion.
- A technology transition from pollution-intensive economic production to environmentally friendly processes.
- A political/sociological transition to societies that embrace a stewardly and just approach to people's needs and that eliminate large scale poverty.
- A community transition from the present car-dominated urban sprawl of developed countries to the "smart growth" concepts of smaller, functional settlements and more livable cities.

10. *Describe the origins of stewardship and its modern applications.*

"Stewardship is a concept that can be traced back to ancient civilizations. A steward was put in charge of the master's household, responsible for maintaining the welfare of the people and the property of the owner. Because a steward did not own the property himself, the steward's ethic involved caring for something on behalf of someone else."

"Applying this concept to the world today, stewards are those who care for something—from the natural world or from human culture—that they do not own and that they will pass on to the next generation. Modern-day environmental stewardship, therefore, incorporates an ethic that guides actions taken to benefit the natural world and other people. It recognizes that even our ownership of land is temporary; the land will be there after we die, and others will own it in turn. Stewardly care is compatible with the goal of sustainability, but is different from it, too, because stewardship deals more directly with how sustainability is to be achieved—what actions are taken, and what values and ethical considerations are behind those actions."

11. *What is an ethic and what are some of the difficult questions confronting the stewardship ethic?*
An ethic tells us something is right and something is wrong. It has moral rules and principles as well as a philosophical or theological base and can be applied to specific cases. For example, the stewardship ethic could be applied to the question of should we drill for oil in the Arctic National Wildlife Refuge. Drilling now would supply oil for the U.S.'s needs, but it could damage the wildlife and the reserve itself so it won't be around for future generations. Also, the oil itself also would not be there for future generations to use and enjoy. In general, the stewardship ethic has to answer how to define the common good. Is cheaper oil good or is preserving wildlife better? It must balance the present needs with future needs, such as preserving species without infringing on property rights. It is difficult to convince people that stewardship is necessary when they are hungry, cold, or homeless. Virtues need to be fostered, and it is hard to limit consumption, especially in more wealthy countries. It's also hard to tell developing countries they can't have cars or electricity or fast food hamburgers when developed countries have all of these things.

12. *What are the concerns of the environmental justice movement?*
The environmental justice movement is concerned not only with caring for the natural world, but also with establishing just relationships among humans. People should not be subject to a disproportionate share of the risks associated with society's activities due to their cultural, racial, political, or economic conditions. For example, hazardous waste sites and polluting manufacturing facilities should not be sited primarily in poor, nonwhite or other disadvantaged neighborhoods. Conversely, due to cultural, racial, political, or economic conditions, people should not receive a disproportionate share of society's benefits, (e.g., new roads, water and sewer projects, fire and police protection, public buildings).

13. *How does justice become an issue between the industrialized countries and the developing countries?*
"Some of the poverty of the developing countries can be attributed to unjust economic practices of wealthy industrialized countries. The current pattern of international trade is a prime example. The industrialized countries have maintained inequities that discriminate against the developing countries by taxing and restricting imports from the developing countries and by flooding the world markets with agricultural products that are subsidized (and, therefore, priced below real costs).

14. *What is globalization? What are its most significant elements?*
Globalization is the accelerating interconnectedness of human activities, ideas, and cultures. The most significant elements are economic changes (such as the dominance of transnational corporations like Nokia and Roche), and environmental changes (including both positive effects like a wider market for environmentally friendly products, and negative effects like the worldwide spread of emerging diseases). An example is how fast the H1N1 virus has spread over the world in 2009. The Monroe Doctrine of keeping to ourselves certainly would not work today. Sustainability is going to have to be the key word if we are going to be working so closely with other countries.

15. *Cite some of the recent developments in the movement toward sustainability.*
A list could include: cap and trade markets to curb carbon emissions, the growth of the wind energy industry, hybrid cars and car-sharing companies, better manufacturing for no waste and carbon neutrality, micro-financing and sustainability investments, international agreements like the Kyoto protocol, sustainable agriculture, and green technology (among others).

Thinking Environmentally: Possible Answers

1. *Imagine a class debate between people representing the developing countries and people representing the developed countries. Characterize the arguments of the two sides in terms of the issues surrounding population growth, energy use, resource use, and sustainable development. Then describe what should be the common interests between the two.*
Developing country viewpoint:
Population growth—On one hand, excessive population growth hinders our development because of the instability it causes. When people do not have jobs or lack access to social services, the impact on the

9

environment can be substantial. On the other hand, people are our major resource. Children increase the economic stability of families because there are more people to bring in money to support the family, and when the parents are too old to work, the offspring will be able to support them. If people do not have assurance that children will live (infant and childhood mortality need to be low), then it is necessary to have a large family. There is no social structure to replace the family as there is in the developed world. We do not have the economic resources to provide that social structure. Population growth, while important, is not more important than curbing the consumption of energy and resources per person. The developed world consumes vast quantities of energy and resources per person, while the developing world consumes very little. For every decrease in environmental impact from the reduction in population growth, the environmental impact from consumption per person should decline. The developing world has decreased in population growth rate steadily since the 1960s while the developed world has continued to increase its consumption rate.

      Energy use— The developed world is the primary user of energy. The developed world has replaced human power with fossil fuels and other forms of energy. To become a developed nation, we need access to the energy that has been historically used by developed countries. In many instances the energy comes from developed nations.

      Resource use—The developed world is the primary user of the world's resources. This is unjust. Many of the resources upon which the developed world depends comes from the developing countries but are controlled by corporations based in the developed countries. Frequently the removal of the resources from developing countries has resulted in severe economic and environmental exploitation. We deserve access to these resources, and the resources have to be extracted in a way that does not damage the environment or the people of the developing countries.

      Sustainable development—The developed world had the opportunity to develop when the environmental costs of their development process was not understood. Because it would be unjust to prevent our development, and because the cost of the progress of the developed world has been borne by the developing world, the developed nations need to assist in our development. This will help the developed world by ensuring that the development is being accomplished in an environmentally acceptable manner. Additionally, as the standard of living in developing countries improves, there will be greater worldwide stability.

Developed country viewpoint:

      Population growth—Many of the developing countries are unable to produce sufficient quantities of food to support their population. When a person is trying to ensure that his/her family has sufficient food to eat tomorrow, he has little time to care about his/her impact on the environment. Tremendous environmental damage would result from attempting to provide those in the developing world the goods and services that those in the developed world have. It is only ethical that those in the developing world should have access to the kinds of things that we in the developed world have. Therefore, it is necessary for population growth to be curbed.

      Energy use—The developed world discovered and continues to discover ways to utilize various energy forms. We cannot be expected to decrease our energy use because the world's economy depends upon our continued economic health, which is dependent on increasing energy use. As new energy forms emerge, especially non-fossil fuel sources, the developing world will have increasing access to energy. It would be environmentally unacceptable for developing countries to begin using fossil fuels, especially coal, to run their economic growth because the environmental impact from the use of coal is too great. The quantity of carbon dioxide would be tremendous and would quickly surpass the release of carbon dioxide from the fossil fuel used by the developed world. The human health impacts from coal use are high. The developed world discovered this during our numerous air pollution disasters of the 1940s and 1950s.

      Resource use—The resources used by the developed world are transformed into goods that can be purchased by those in developing countries.

      Sustainable development—Sustainable development is good for everyone. Those in the developing world need to evaluate their economic growth plans and alter the plans when they are not sustainable. The developed nations need to do the same thing. Because all countries have to change how economic decisions are made and this change will cost money, each country needs to pay for its own sustainable development.

2. Some people say that the concept of sustainable development either is an oxymoron or represents going back to some kind of primitive living. Develop an argument contradicting this opinion, and give your own opinion on sustainable development.

Under the current economic paradigm, sustainable development is an oxymoron because the development model of the last century or more has been dependent upon continued growth; when growth ends, a recession begins. In many ways it is essential that humans develop an economic system that does not require constant growth because constant growth conflicts with natural systems. For example, uncontrolled cell growth is cancer. If taken to its logical extreme our current economic system results in the destruction of natural systems. There is no economic gain associated with not polluting the environment or removing resources at a rate that does not exceed their replacement. Because many industrial processes rely on clean air and/or clean water, polluting these is economically damaging. Yet at the same time there are economic advantages to be gained with releasing wastes into water or air because the cost to clean these resources is not borne by the polluter.

Civilization will not continue without sustainable development. If our current goods and services are produced in a way that destroys the environment, the goods and services provided by the environment will be destroyed and our standard of living will collapse. Therefore, continuation of an economic system that required continuous growth will result in primitive living. The only hope for maintaining our standard of living (health care, education, physical comfort) is to create a way of life that lives within the resources that are available.

3. *Study Table 1–1, pick one of the vital ecosystem services listed there, and investigate the reasons why it is placed where it is by the Millennium Ecosystem Assessment.*

Answers will vary by the service chosen. The overall intent of the MEA project is to build a knowledge base for sound policy decisions and management interventions; it remains for policy makers and managers to act on that knowledge. These three types of services encompass the majority of the resources.

Provisioning services are important because we are overusing and depleting our resources, both renewable and nonrenewable, and they are being replaced with "artificial resources" in agriculture and aquaculture.

Regulating services are important because without them, our environment will be even worse than it is. However, as can be seen by the long list of degraded services, we have a very long way to go.

Cultural services are important because we don't want to forget the aesthetic value of the planet. If we lose our awe of the world around us how can we be expected to want to protect it?

Examples of why a particular service was placed in the degraded, mixed or enhanced column:

Capture fisheries are degraded because of overharvesting, pollution, and invasive species. However, aquaculture is enhanced because of an increase in fish farms. This could likely have been spurred by the increase in price for the commodity caused by the degradation of the capture fish industry.

Wild foods are degraded by the loss of habitat, destruction of forests, and by turning some of these areas into agricultural land (thereby enhancing crop production).

Air quality regulation has degraded globally due to the rush to compete in the global economy. This is evidenced by conditions in China, Eastern Europe, and India. A desire to produce cheap goods quickly has undermined efforts to install clean smokestacks, precipitators, and the like.

4. *Set up a debate between proponents and opponents of building a new coal-fired power plant. Use the strategies of sound science and junk science to conduct the debate, and show how a perverted use of these terms can help to obscure the real issues. Other interesting debate options include the "ozone hoax" and global warming; the Internet can provide ample material for both sides of the debate.*

Pro-Plant Viewpoint

1. Increase in need for electrical power—Debater can cite brownouts and blackouts in California as an example, or the blackout and power grid shut down in the Eastern U.S. in 2003. An example of junk science to support this viewpoint would be: Global warming will cause an increase in demand for air conditioning so more electricity will be needed. But this side will ignore the fact that another coal fired plant will produce more carbon and thus increase global warming even more.

2. Decreased costs to consumer for electrical power—a new power plant can provide more electricity and thus reduce electric prices (using principles of supply and demand).

3. Nuclear Power is unsafe (this is another example of junk science—a selective presentation of results). They can use Three Mile Island and Chernobyl as proof while ignoring all the safe nuclear energy that has been produced.

4. No one is willing to pay for green energy. Wind, solar, biomass, and methane fuel are too expensive, so we need to build a cheaper coal-fired plant.

5. Current precipitators, smoke stacks, and other anti-pollution devices are adequate.

6. Coal mining helps the economy of the region. (This argument ignores or minimizes the environmental damage that coal mining causes to the same region.)

7. Coal ash may be sold to make asphalt and other products.

8. Building the plants will provide construction jobs (about 2,000) and the plant will need workers to run it.

<u>Anti-Plant Viewpoint</u>

1. Coal burning increases the carbon content of the atmosphere and therefore increases global warming.

2. Coal contains sulfur and other gases which cause acid rain and photochemical smog.

3. Coal mining is detrimental to the environment. It causes water pollution, destroys ecosystems, disrupts ground water and displaces people. (This argument ignores or minimizes the economic benefit that a coal plant could bring to the region.)

4. Coal mining is dangerous to the miners (sub-bituminous coal is dangerous to handle; the coal dust may spontaneously combust).

5. Coal dust gets into workers lungs and can cause respiratory illnesses.

6. Coal plants release mercury, which affects the nervous system. In addition, coal contains toxic levels of arsenic.

7. It takes a large amount of energy to mine coal.

8. The displacement of the mountaintops (mountaintop removal) to get to the coal, changes water flow, causing flooding—and where do they put the top of the mountain they've just removed?

9. General high poverty of mining areas.

10. There are viable alternatives in renewable energy facilities (wind, hydropower, and solar plants are being built all over the country).

CHAPTER 2
Economics, Politics, and Public Policy

Chapter Outline:

I. Economics and the Environment
    A. Relationships between Economic Development and the Environment
    B. Economic Systems
        1. The Rulers Decide
        2. The Market Decides
        3. Governments Step In
        4. Is There a Conscience?
    C. International Trade and the World Trade Organization
        1. Free Trade Rules
        2. More Talk
    D. The Need for a Sustainable Economy
II. Resources in a Sustainable Economy
    A. A New Measure of the Wealth of Nations
        1. Complementary Assets
        2. Calculations
        3. Measuring Economic Progress
    B. GDP or GPI to Measure Progress?
        1. Natural Capital Depreciation
        2. Environmental Accounting
        3. Genuine Progress Indicator
    C. Resource Distribution
        1. Essential Conditions
        2. Intergenerational Equity
            i. Use it Up!
III. Environmental Public Policy
    A. The Need for Environmental Public Policy
    B. Policy in the United States
        1. Rules and Regulations
        2. State and Local Levels
    C. Policy Options: Market or Regulatory?
        1. Command and Control
        2. Market Approaches
    D. Public Policy Development: The Policy Life Cycle
            i.   Recognition Stage
            ii. Formulation Stage
            iii. Implementation Stage
            iv. Control Stage
    E. Economic Effects of Environmental Public Policy
        1. Costs of Policies
        2. Impact on the Economy
            i.   Anecdotal Evidence
            ii. Careful Studies
            iii. The Environmental Protection Industry
IV. Benefit-Cost Analysis of Environmental Public Policy
    A. External Costs
    B. Environmental Regulations Impose Real Costs
        1. Costs Go Up

   2. Costs Go Down
  C. The Benefits of Environmental Regulation
   1. Calculating Benefits
    i. Shadow Pricing
   2. The Value of Human Life
  D. Cost-Effectiveness Analysis
  E. Progress
   1. The EPA Checks In
V. Politics and the Environment
  A. Political Parties and the Battle for Control
   1. Special Interest Politics
   2. The Bush Years
    i. Regulatory Reform?
   3. A New Broom
  B. Citizen Involvement

Key Topics:

1. Economics and the Environment
2. Resources in a Sustainable Economy
3. Environmental Public Policy
4. Benefit-Cost Analysis of Environmental Public Policy
5. Politics and the Environment

Instructional Goals:

1. Public policy governs society's interactions with the environment through laws and regulations. These laws and regulations are created by the interactions between the business community, nongovernmental organizations, and the three branches of our government—executive, judicial, and legislative.

2. A nation's wealth is dependent upon produced assets, natural capital, and human resources. Natural capital is the goods and services supplied by ecosystems and the mineral resources in the ground. The natural capital used by a nation is not restricted to the goods, services, and mineral resources found within the nation's borders.

3. Public policy development has a life cycle consisting of four stages: recognition, formulation, implementation, and control.

4. The job versus environment dichotomy is false. A sound economic system is dependent upon a healthy environment. Environmental public policy transfers wealth from polluters to those who control or do not create pollution.

5. Environmental public policy has created a cleaner, healthier, and more enjoyable environment.

6. Society decides how policies are made. In the United States the prevailing decision-making tool is risk-based decision making. This process allows activities until they are proven to be harmful. Many European countries have changed from risk-based decision making to the use of the precautionary principle (if a substance or action has a reasonable probability of causing harm, the lack of scientific data to substantiate the existence of harm can be used as a reason for lack of action). The choice of decision-making tools belongs to the public.

Concepts and Connections:

   All environmental issues function within an economic context. The economy is dependent on the goods and services provided by ecosystems. Minerals and energy are obtained from the environment. To have a sustainable economy the manner in which we use the resources from the environment must be sustainable. When short-term economic decisions are made that leave environmental considerations as externalities, tremendous damage can be done.

There have been many controversies in recent years pitting jobs against the environment. The spotted owl was cited as the reason for the loss of logging jobs, but job loss due to consolidation, non-sustainable logging practices, and shipments of logs out of the country can be documented as the predominant reasons. Recent news concerning the listing of several more salmon species has produced a very different reaction among the residents. There is a tremendous amount of support in the Seattle region for the changes that will be necessary to insure the survival of the native salmon populations. It seems that a possible explanation for this difference is that the people of this region identify with the salmon.

Making connections between a healthy economy and a healthy environment is essential. Links can be made between the services provided by nature—for example, water filtration, groundwater recharge, and atmospheric cleansing—and the amount of money it would cost if we attempted to replace these services. To have a healthy economy we depend on goods from nature, for example, trees, energy, and food. While it is not hard to demonstrate that a healthy economy is dependent on healthy ecosystems, resistance to this idea is common as this recognition complicates our actions. If we cannot ignore nature, life is a bit less simple.

Concepts in Context:

Everything discussed in the textbook has economic implications. Specific discussions in the text include the value of ecosystem goods and services (Chapter 4), biodiversity (Chapter 6), and common property resources (Chapter 11) and the cost to control air pollution (Chapter 21). Human demographic transition (Chapter 8) was discussed as being influenced by economic growth and the reasons for choosing a particular family size (Chapter 9) included the cost to raise children and old-age support.

The remaining topics discussed during the semester can also be linked to economics. The biogeochemical (Chapter 3) and the hydrological (Chapter 10) cycles provide substantial economic services by moving matter. Agriculture (Chapter 12) would not be able to exist without the soil and soil ecosystem (Chapter 11), the hydrological cycle (Chapter 10), and ecosystem goods and services (Chapter 7). Agriculture is affected by pests (Chapter 13), water pollution (Chapter 20), and air pollution (Chapter 19). How we obtain energy and the availability of energy (Chapters 14, 15, and 16) are critical to a healthy economy. Climate regulation (Chapter 18) is a service received from the natural environment that has tremendous influence on the economy and on our ability to grow food.

Adverse human health (Chapter 17) impacts from air pollution (Chapter 19), hazardous waste (Chapter 22), and water pollution (Chapter 20) cost money. Poor use of resources (Chapter 21) costs money.

Key Terms and Vocabulary:

Economics, economy, economic systems, centrally planned economy, free market or capitalist economy, land, labor, capital, Doha Development Round, ecological economists, economic production, produced capital, natural capital, intangible capital, human capital, social capital, knowledge assets, Genuine Progress Indicator (GPI), discount rate, legislative branch, executive branch, judicial branch, Payments for Ecosystem Services (PES), effectiveness, efficiency, equity, benefit-cost analysis, external cost, Regulatory Right to Know Act

Discussion, Activities and Labs:

1. Ask the students to list as many examples as they can of situations where saving (not destroying) the environment is seen as hindrance to the economy. Once the list has been created, challenge the students to think of situations where pitting jobs against the environment would not be a productive way to address the problem. (For example, the attempt to preserve habitat for the spotted owl has been seen by many loggers as an attack on their livelihood. Many economic studies of these areas have indicated that logging was on the decline due to other economic pressures such as exporting and overharvesting, and preserving habitat for the spotted

owl had little to no effect on the local economy. It can be argued that tourism dollars from an intact habitat will be greater than the dollars brought into the area by logging.)

2. Ask students to list as many external costs as possible. Listing specific examples will help students understand this concept and how it is detrimental to reducing human impact on the environment. For example, have the students list all the externalities involved in using the automobile rather than mass transit, bicycles or walking for transportation, or using trucks rather than trains for the movement of goods. Listing all the externalities involved in manufacturing, using, and disposing of a computer could also be an interesting exercise. The same kind of list could be created for the production of food.

3. Have each student search the newspaper for articles linking the economy and the environment. Encourage the students to find as many articles as possible on as many topics as possible. There are at least one or two articles per day on the environment in most major daily papers. With very little imagination it is possible to find an economic link for each article. Ask the students to summarize the information they find. Do the articles pit the environment against the economy?

Suggested Lecture Format

I.   Economics and the Environment

    A.   Public Policy
        1.   What is public policy?
        2.   What role does public policy play in our lives?

    B.   Relationships between Economic Development and the Environment
        1.   A healthy economy needs a healthy environment. **See Discussion Topic #1**
        2.   What is the WTO? Why is it so controversial?

II. Resources in a sustainable society

    A.   The Wealth of Nations
        1.   Natural capital—may obtain from within a country or may be from outside the country
            i.   Human resources include human capital, social capital, and knowledge capital
        2.   Produced assets

    B.   Resource Distribution
        1.   Intergenerational Equity
        2.   Disparities between nations
        3.   Disparities within nations

III. Environmental Public Policy

    A.   Public Policy Development: The Policy Life Cycle (pesticides are used as example in the text; could bring the example back around to the recognition stage by looking at FQPA; could also look at endocrine disruptors as an example of a problem that is in the recognition/formulation stage; air pollution could be used as an example of a pollution issue that has moved through all four stages).
        1.   Recognition Stage
        2.   Formulation Stage
        3.   Implementation Stage
        4.   Control Stage

    B.   Economic Effects of Environmental Public Policy
        1.   Costs of Policies
            i.   Those involving little or no direct monetary cost
            ii. Those involving costs that must be paid by some segment of society. The cost should be borne by those benefiting from the activity that produces the pollution.

2. Impact on the Economy
   i. An economy stimulant
   ii. Creates jobs
   iii. Transfers wealth from polluters to pollution controllers and to less polluting companies

IV. Methods to Evaluated Public Policy Options

A. Benefit-Cost Analysis
   1. The merits of the goal are not necessarily known or accepted. In a cost-benefit analysis the attempt is to determine if the action is worth the cost.
      i. Brings external costs into the equation. **See Discussion Topic #2**
   2. Difficult and controversial to do because the process is filled with value judgements
   3. The Costs of Environmental Regulations
      i. Pollution prevention rather than pollution control to reduce costs and increase compliance
   4. The Benefits of Environmental Regulations
      i. Attempts to quantify benefits have been made, but the task is not easy. The value of human life and non-human environmental components must be considered.

B. Cost Effectiveness
   1. The merits of the goal are accepted. In a cost-effectiveness analysis the attempt is to find the least costly way to achieve the goal.

V. Progress

A. What have we gained through public policy?
   1. Air quality improvements
   2. Water quality improvements
      i. Decreased eutrophication
      ii. Rivers that are not flammable
      iii. Lakes that are recovering from "death"
   3. Improved public health
      i. Decreased blood lead levels
      ii. Decreased incidence of gastrointestinal illnesses
   4. Improved handling of solid and hazardous waste

VI. Politics and the Environment

A. Political Parties and the Battle for Control
   1. How do political parties present their environmental view in contrast to how they portray the "other side"?
   2. Special-interest Politics
   3. The Bush Years
      i. How did this administration "redirect" the environmental movement?
      ii. What was the position on global warming? Mining? Forests?
      iii. What was the result of the regulatory reform of this time?
   4. A New Broom
      i. What is happening under the Obama administration?
      ii. Why is it considered to be a "new broom"?

B. Citizen Involvement
   1. What students can do to help the "cause"
      i. Local involvement
      ii. Work with NGOs
      iii. Work for a pro-environment candidate
      iv. Learn how to stay informed and distinguish between biased and unbiased information.

Review Questions: Possible Answers

1. What is happening these days in the Chinese economy and environment?

The country of China has been experiencing both the benefits and problems of a growing economy. The Chinese economy has doubled in the last decade. It is difficult to avoid the "made in China" label. The Chinese people have a growing middle class with higher literacy, cars, electronics, and all the other material goods and privileges that go along with that status. On the negative side, their environment has suffered greatly. One of the examples is the toxic air. Sixteen of the world's most polluted cities are in China—not a distinction to be proud of. Sulfur dioxide is one of the toxins and many deaths have occurred because of it. Another example is the water pollution that is causing cancers and related to this is the diversion of water for irrigation and other uses. The Three Gorges Dam has displaced millions of people and covered millions of acres of farm land in water. The governmental environmental regulation agency, SEPA, has its hands full and is struggling to keep up. As a result, over 2,000 more local NGOs have been formed in an attempt to slow the pollution down and affect some clean up activities.

2. Three patterns of environmental indicators are associated with differences in the level of development of a nation. What problems decline, what problems increase and then decline, and what problems increase with the level of development?

The proportion of the population without safe water or adequate sanitation declines as per capita income increases. The quantity of municipal wastes and carbon dioxide emission increases as the per capita income increases. As the per capita income increases, the concentration of particulate matter and sulfur dioxide increases and then decreases.

3. Name the two basic kinds of economic systems and explain how they differ.

The two basic kinds of economic systems are centrally planned economies and free-market economies. The two economic systems "differ mostly in how economic decisions are made. In a centrally planned economy, the rulers make all the basic decisions regarding what and how much will be produced where, and by whom." In a pure free-market economy, the market itself determines what will be exchanged." The whole system is in private hands and is driven by the desire of people and businesses to acquire goods, services, and wealth as they act in their self-interest." Neither of the economic systems actually exists as described.

4. What is the role of the World Trade Organization, and how has this role broken down recently?

The World Trade Organization (WTO) was formed in 1993 because of globalization and economic issues laid out by the GATT (General Agreement on Tariff's and Trade). It is supposed to enforce trade rules between nations, but the wealthy nations have been able to dominate. Its power comes by imposing stiff trade penalties on non-complying countries. They have established a reputation for elevating free trade over substantial human rights and environmental resource concerns. In other words, they are sometimes supporting free trade over fair trade. There are incidences of the WTO supporting the economy over the environment, such as when they ruled against the turtle-safe shrimp law of the U.S. Over the years, outside protests and conflicts between developed and developing countries have brought the talks to a halt without reaching any consensus. One of the issues is that developed countries subsidize their agricultural products and therefore developing countries want to impose tariffs to make their own products more competitive. As a result, the goal of free trade and a global economy is yet to be achieved.

5. What are some characteristics of a sustainable economy?

Instead of merely promoting economic growth, a sustainable economy would emphasize improving human well-being. It would value and preserve natural services and goods. It would promote "green" goods and services. Goods would be made more durable, more recyclable, or more reusable. Where possibly more recycled materials would be used to produce goods. The production process would be as nonpolluting as possible. Services would try to use nonpolluting techniques such as using biosolids from a waste treatment plant as fertilizer instead of sending them to a landfill. Overall, a sustainable economy would try to protect the environment as well as promote human well-being.

6. Describe the three components of a nation's wealth. What insights emerge?

The three components of a nation's wealth are produced capital, natural capital and intangible capital. Produced capital is the human-made buildings and structures, machinery and equipment, vehicles and ships, monetary savings and stocks, highways and power lines, and so forth that are essential to the production of economic goods and services. Natural capital refers to the goods and services supplied by natural ecosystems and the mineral resources in the ground. Intangible capital is divided into three elements. The first is human capital which refers to the population and its physical, psychological, and cultural attributes. The second element, social capital is the social and political environment that people create for themselves in a society. The third element is knowledge assets, which is the codified or written fund of knowledge that can be readily transferred to others across space and time.

If you refer to Table 2-1, you can see that although natural capital often ranks third in most countries, this does not mean that it is less important than human resources or produced assets. In particular natural capital plays a more important role in low-income countries, as they develop, and become more dependent on their natural resources, than are wealthier countries.

7. *Why is the gross national product an inaccurate indicator of a nation's economic status? How is it corrected by the Genuine Progress Indicator?*

"The GDP is the GNP minus net income from abroad. The economists who invented GNP as a measuring device years ago, never took into account the depreciation of natural capital—an omission that recently has received a great deal of criticism from ecological economists." The GPI is a measure of progress proposed by the nonprofit organization *Redefining Progress.* It is calculated by assuming that some kinds of economic activity are positive and sustainable and others are not. Some of these activities are not included in the GDP. Several of the positive factors in the GPI—such as labor involved in running the home and volunteering—are considered positive. Negatives in the GPI include factors like the costs of crime, loss of leisure time, costs of pollution, depletion of nonrenewable resources, and loss of farmland. Even though the GDP may steadily rise, the GPI may not because of rising environmental cost as well as depreciation.

8. *What conditions are necessary for a country to make progress in the development of human resources and produced assets?*

"Perhaps the most important reasons relate to the major institutions that coordinate social and political life and that make up the social capital of a society. For example, the definition of rights, the enforcement of those rights, and the facilitation of economic exchange are all considered essential to the successful development of human capital and produced capital. A well-developed body of law, a honest legal system, inclusiveness, broad civic participation, and a free press are essential for maintaining rights within a society. A well-developed market economy and free entry into and exit from markets for people and business are also conducive to development. Functioning communication and transportation networks and viable financial markets are needed to sustain a market economy. History tells us that if these resources are in place, a society will make progress in the development of human resources and produced assets. In societies where such resources are not in place, corruption, inefficiency, banditry, injustice, and intolerance often prevail; continuing poverty and environmental degradation are the predictable outcome."

9. *Explain the importance of considering both intragenerational equity and intergenerational equity in addressing resource allocation issues.*

Intragenerational equity is "the golden rule of making possible for others what is possible for you." If others have the same social awareness the amount of environmental degradation will be less.

Intergeneration equity is about "meeting the needs of the present without compromising the ability of future generations to meet their needs." This is also the definition of sustainability. Intergenerational equity will help us reduce environmental degradation without compromising our own needs.

10. *What is the overall objective of environmental public policy and what are the objective's two most central concerns?*

The objective of environmental public policy is to promote the common good. While it may be difficult to define the common good, the two most central concerns are the improvement of human welfare and the protection of the natural world. Because of this, environmental public policy addresses two sets of environmental issues: One is the prevention or reduction of all types of pollution, and the other is the use of both renewable and nonrenewable natural resources.

11. *Describe the various bodies responsible for environmental public policy at the federal, state, and local levels.*

On the federal level, Congress enacts environmental public policy legislation which the president signs into law. The laws are implemented and enforced by various agencies like the EPA, BLM, Fisheries and Wildlife and others. These agencies also write rules and regulations and otherwise flesh out the laws enacted by Congress. All of this also depends on the budget and appropriations proposed by the President and approved by the Congress. The President also nominates the leaders of these agencies. Many must be approved by Congress. Often, the person appointed has a major say in the direction and views the agency will take.

On the state level, states can enact stricter laws than the federal government. For example, Michigan has tougher wetland laws concerning their use. States also have their own hunting, fishing, and trapping regulations as well as forestry laws about activities such as moving firewood. States also have their own state parks, wildlife refuge and forest systems.

On the local level cities and counties can affect public policy with conservation commissions, planning boards, health boards, water and sewer commissions, and other such agencies and boards. They can set up recycling, hazardous waste collections, green spaces, bike trails and other environmental friendly infrastructure.

12. *What are the advantages and disadvantages of the regulatory approach versus a market approach to policy development?*

Regulatory approach allows for the setting of health-based standards to "protect the health of the most vulnerable members of the population." The regulatory approach also works well with land use issues in which certain values are upheld that will not necessarily be protected by a straightforward market approach. One of the shortcomings of the regulatory approach is that it practically guarantees a certain sustained level of pollution....the policy gives the polluter no incentive to invest in technologies that would keep pollution at lower levels than allowed. A better approach might be to set a standard for air quality or water quality, for example and let the polluter decide how best to achieve the standard. Here there is a command, but control is in the hands of the polluter."

"Market-based policies have the virtues of simplicity, efficiency, and (theoretically) equity. All polluters are treated equally and will choose their responses on the basis of economic principles having to do with profitability." Basically, this is the pay as you pollute principle. If it costs less to be environmentally friendly, or if you will sell more products that way, then the company will chose to do so.

13. *List four stages of the policy life cycle, and show how the discovery of ozone layer destruction and the subsequent responses to it illustrate the cycle.*

The typical life cycle of environmental public policy development has four stages. The stages are recognition, formulation, implementation, and control. **Recognition** is the process through which the early perceptions of an environmental problem occur and a great deal of dissension exists. CFCs were considered miracle chemicals, useful for many processes and seemingly harmless, inert, and nontoxic. That was until two scientists decided to investigate what happens to CFCs in the atmosphere. When they published their theory that CFCs would destroy the ozone they were treated like pariahs and even Russian spies! No one wanted to believe that CFCs were harmful. **Formulation** is the stage where the political weight of those who perceive a problem is increasing. "The public is now aroused, and debate about policy options occurs in the corridors of power." Those that make the policies have listed what may be called the "Three E's" of environmental public policy: effectiveness, efficiency and equity. During this stage, the National Academy of Sciences confirmed the findings of these scientists and CFCs were subsequently banned from aerosol cans. On the international level, the Montreal Protocol was written and required cutting CFC production in half by the year 2000. The process had begun. The **implementation** stage is where "...real political and economic costs are exacted. The policy has been determined, and the focal point moves to regulatory agencies." Companies began developing more benign substitutes for the CFCs while using less CFCs in their processes, refrigerators, and air conditioners. **The control** stage is the final stage. "...Years have passed since the early days of the recognition stage. Problems are rarely completely resolved, but the environment is improving, with things moving in the right direction." The ozone hole appears to be decreasing in size with less CFCs in the atmosphere. CFCs are no longer being manufactured.

14. *What is the conclusion of careful studies regarding the relationship between environmental policies, on the one hand, and jobs and the economy, on the other?*

"Estimated pollution control costs are only 1.72% of value added." Only 0.1% of job layoffs were attributed by employers to environment-related causes, according to a study by the U.S. Bureau of Labor Statistics. ...(S)tates with the strictest environmental regulations also had the highest rates of job growth and economic performance."

15. *Define the term benefit-cost analysis as it relates to environmental regulation. How does this analysis method address external costs? Distinguish it from cost-effectiveness analysis.*

"A **benefit-cost analysis** begins by examining the need for the proposed regulation and then describes a range of alternative approaches. Afterward, it compares the estimated costs of the proposed action and the main alternatives to the benefits that will be achieved. All costs and benefits are given monetary values (where possible) and compared by means of what is commonly referred to as a *benefit-cost* (or *cost-benefit*) *ratio*. A favorable ratio for an action means that the benefits outweigh the costs, and the action is said to be cost effective...."

"By including *all* of the costs and benefits of a project or a regulation, benefit-cost analysis effectively brings the externalities into the economic accounting. One suggestion for accomplishing this is the use of green fees or taxes." This is how benefit-cost analysis can include external costs like pollution, poor health of employees or other negative aspects of doing business. "Cost-effectiveness analysis is an alternative option for evaluating the costs of regulations. Here the merits of the goal are accepted, and the question is: How can that goal be achieved at the least cost? To find out, alternative strategies for reaching the goal are analyzed for costs, and the least costly method is adopted." (Pages 40, 41 and 44)

16. *Discuss the cost-effectiveness of pollution control. How much progress have we made in pollution control in recent years?*

Cost-effectiveness can be applied to the desired level of pollution control. As Figure 2–13 shows, a significant benefit may be achieved by modest degrees of cleanup. Note, however, how differently the cost and benefit curves behave with increasing reduction of pollution. At some point in the cleanup effort, the lines cross, and the costs exceed the benefits. Few additional benefits are realized when cleanup begins to approach 100%, yet costs increase exponentially. This behavior follows from the fact that living organisms—including humans—can often tolerate a threshold level of pollution without ill effect. Therefore, reducing the level of a pollutant below its threshold level will not yield an observable improvement. Optimum cost-effectiveness that meets the efficiency criterion for public policy is achieved at the point where the benefit curve is the greatest distance above the cost curve. However, the perspective of time should be considered in calculating cost-effectiveness (Figure 2–14c). A situation that appears to be cost ineffective in the short term may prove extremely cost effective in the long term. This is particularly true for problems such as acid deposition and groundwater contamination from toxic wastes.

What has been the result of environmental regulation to date? Pollution of air and surface water reached critical levels in many areas of the United States in the late 1960s, and since that time, huge sums of money have been spent on pollution abatement. Benefit-cost analysis shows that, overall, these expenditures have paid for themselves many times over in decreased health care costs and enhanced environmental quality. Consider the phasing out of leaded gasoline as just one example. The project cost about $3.6 billion, according to an EPA benefit-cost report. Benefits were valued at over $50 billion, $42 billion of which were for medical costs that were avoided! (Page 44)

17. *How has the political arena affected environmental public policy in the last few years? What has been the role of special-interest groups? Political parties? Presidents?*

"The 104th Congress (1995–1996) began with an effort to dismantle many key laws, especially the Clean Water Act, the Clean Air Act, and Superfund. When it became apparent what was happening, heavy grassroots work by many environmental organizations and extensive media coverage made it clear that the public did not support this anti-environmental thrust. As a result, most of the anti-environmental legislation died in the Senate or was vetoed by President Clinton. The more recent Congress saw some of the same anti-environmental forces attempting once more to get their legislation through. However, a bipartisan coalition was able to hold off new attempts to weaken environmental laws. One effect of these battles was a failure to reauthorize a number of important laws, such as the Endangered Species Act and Superfund. The laws continued in force nevertheless. The role and power of special interest groups became evident during these struggles. In the 1970s and 1980s, special interests (such as the coal industry and the fisheries industry) would hire lobbyists who would use their influence to try to convince congressional committee members to act in their favor on issues that were important to them. Environmental NGOs would then use the media to expose the issues to the public and call on their constituencies to telephone and send mail to their representatives in Congress. The anti-environmental interests caught on to the NGO strategy and began to mimic what they were doing, but more effectively because they had deeper pockets. Soon a constant battle between special interest groups emerged in which each would use the media and telephone calls (enhanced by phone banks, which can generate thousands of calls to legislators in a short period) to pressure members of Congress. Added to this picture was the massive explosion in campaign contributions, largely from businesses and industry. What all this means is that environmental concerns are often a battle of special interest groups—that environmental protection is seen as one among many interests in American politics." (Page 45)

Thinking Environmentally: Possible Answers

1. Consider the ultimate impact that environmental law has on the economy. Do short-term drawbacks justify long-term goals? If there is a conflict, which should come first—the economy or the environment?

Anecdotal evidence may suggest that environmental laws are detrimental to the economy, but studies show the opposite. Economic performance is highest where environmental public policy is most highly developed. If workers are healthier, the physical plant energy is efficient, and resources are conserved, then the company will see a larger profit and be more competitive. Therefore, the wealth is transferred from polluting companies to those that are less polluting. The environment protection industry itself is good for the economy as it employs people for a variety of jobs.

Developing countries, such as China and the U.S. have followed the precedent that the economy should come first, but are paying for it now with bad air, polluted water, and unhealthy conditions. Given the problems these countries are having, it seems clear that the environment should come first.

2. Research the Doha Round of meetings of the World Trade Organization. Analyze the positions of the developing countries and the industrial countries, and propose a solution that might meet the concerns of both groups.

The Doha Declaration of 2001 was controversial to say the least. One of the issues was the fear that liberalization of agricultural trade would raise food prices and adversely affect the poorer food-importing countries while benefiting the richer food-exporting countries like the U.S. and the European Union. It is believed that reduced tariffs and subsidies will help raise prices with most of the gains going to these countries and Japan. As Bruce Stokes wrote in the National Journal, "The biggest winners among industrial nations would be Japan and the European Union, where incomes stand to grow by $6.5 billion and $5.8 billion, respectively." Among developing nations, the chief beneficiary by far would be China, which would gain $10.3 billion in annual income, or more than four times the increase expected for India. In fact, China's expected benefits account for nearly half of those likely to accrue to the developing world. The biggest losers would be Bangladesh, Malawi, Tanzania, and Uganda and the rest of the nations of sub-Saharan Africa (excluding South Africa). The numbers are so small; however, relative to the size of national economies, that the precise figures are less important than the broad picture they paint. Most farmers in poor countries would suffer because they aren't globally competitive and they wouldn't be well positioned to take advantage of new market opportunities in Europe and the United States. Moreover, many of the poorest nations now enjoy preferential access to rich-country markets, a benefit that will be eliminated in a new trade deal. Furthermore, since a decline in U.S. and other farm subsidies will lead to global price rises for many commodities, developing countries that are net food importers could see their food bills rise. "Countries like India, Indonesia, and Kenya will require exceptions for the products produced by their subsistence farmers if they are to avoid increases in poverty." the Carnegie study concludes. Allowing such countries to exempt their agricultural sector from tariff cuts—a move strongly resisted by American negotiators—would not cost Europe and the United States that much, Polaski contends. And a separate computer model of such a scenario found that India and Vietnam would have slightly greater income gains, while Bangladesh and countries in East Africa would experience less income loss if their subsistence farmers were protected.

(Bruce Stokes, *National Journal*© National Journal Group Inc. Friday, March 17, 2006)

As a result, the industrial countries will benefit from these measures with increased income from agricultural exports and developing countries, with the exception of China, will be harmed in the form of increased food costs and by being less competitive in their food exports. Perhaps a separate subsidy or allowing tariffs in these countries would help equalize the playing field.

On the manufacturing side, the U.S. has little or nothing to gain. However, Mexico has a lot to lose by losing its preferential role created by NAFTA. China will be the big winner on the manufacturing side. The hope is that China will offer the less-developed countries duty-free and quota-free access to its market as the

U.S. and European Union have done. If so, maybe the developing countries can afford the goods to help them increase their standard of living and compete industrially in the future. The Carnegie Model as seen in the *National Journal,* however, sees less benefits for developing countries overall. The World Bank Model is a little more optimistic when it comes to these less developed nations, but overall the consensus is that the Doha Agreement has actually made the gap between poor and rich countries wider instead of succeeding in its attempt to narrow the gap. What should be done about this? Scrap the whole initiative? Delay the time tables? Make separate rules for developed and developing countries?

3. *Examine the three types of capital that make up the wealth of nations. Which do you think is the most valuable? Justify your answer.*

There are three types of capital that determine a nation's wealth. The first is produced capital which is defined as human made items. These items tend to become obsolete. The second is natural capital which is supplied by ecosystems and resources in the ground. These can be either renewable or nonrenewable. The third is intangible capital which includes humans, social capital, and knowledge.

It can be argued that without natural capital (namely resources) a nation cannot build the produced capital—and without produced capital a country may not be able to use its natural resources. However, without adequate intangible capital, a nation does not have the workforce, the knowledge, and the social structure to be able to use the natural resources in an environmentally responsible manner. They also cannot make produced capital which will not become obsolete quickly. Finally, they cannot make capital that is less likely to degrade the environment. Therefore, the best argument would be that intangible capital is the most valuable. Countries can import natural capital and produced goods but they need people with a good social and educational environmental in order to use it.

4. *What different roles do you think the federal and state governments should have in environmental policy?*

Since some problems cross state lines (such as acid rain, water pollution, and ozone depletion), the federal government needs to have a role in environmental policy. Unfortunately, history shows that the administration and political party in power at a particular time has an enormous effect on the way policies are enforced. Through subsidies, and tariffs the federal government can encourage practices that are not environmentally sound. Ideally, the federal government should have the ability to enact and enforce laws but have a limited ability to change or undermine these laws depending on who or what party is in office, or which corporation or interests have the strongest influence. State governments should have the ability to have stronger policies than the federal government. For example, some states have stricter rules on the uses of wetlands or have bottle laws, however states should not have the ability to usurp or undermine federal policy.

5. *Suppose it was discovered that the bleach that is commonly used for laundry was carcinogenic. Referring to the policy life cycle, describe a predictable course of events until the problem is brought under control.*

Recognition would be slow because bleach is a commonly used material and people would be reluctant to give up its use. Eventually, as the number of studies showing the connection between the use of bleach and cancer increased, more people would conclude that something needs to be done.

Formulation of policy would begin as the number of people with political power who support change increases. The arguments in Congress would begin and the companies producing bleach would attempt to stop or soften any proposed legislation. Finally, Congress would pass legislation to address the problem.

Implementation of the policy created by Congress would begin. It is most likely that the EPA would develop the regulations to implement the law passed by Congress and signed by the President.

Control is the final stage where the effects of the policy that was implemented can be seen. Improvements in the cancer rates would be observed as the use of bleach decreased.

CHAPTER 3
Ecology: Basic Needs of Living Things

Chapter Outline:

I.   Organisms in Their Environment
      A.   The Hierarchy of Ecology
          1.   Species
          2.   Populations
          3.   Biotic Communities
          4.   Ecosystems
          5.   Landscapes and Biomes
          6.   Biosphere

II.   Environmental Factors
      A.   Optimums, Zones of Stress and Limits of Tolerance
          1.   A Fundamental Biologic Principle
          2.   Law of Limiting Factors
          3.   Habitat and Niche

III.   Matter in Living and Nonliving Systems
      A.   Basic Units of Matter
          1.   Atoms
          2.   Molecules and Compounds
      B.   Four Spheres
          1.   Atmosphere
          2.   Hydrosphere
          3.   Lithosphere
          4.   Interactions
      C.   Organic Compounds

IV.   Matter and Energy
      A.   Energy Basics
          1.   Laws of Thermodynamics
          2.   Entropy
      B.   Energy Changes in Organisms
          1.   Producers and Photosynthesis
             i.   Within the Plant
            ii.   Cell Respiration
           iii.   Gaining Weight
      C.   One-Way Flow of Energy

V.   The Cycling of Matter in Ecosystems
      A.   The Carbon Cycle
          1.   Human Impacts
      B.   The Phosphorus Cycle
          1.   Human Impacts
      C.   The Nitrogen Cycle
          1.   Nitrogen Fixation
          2.   Denitrification
          3.   Human Impacts
      D.   Comparing the Cycles

Key Topics:

1.   Organisms in Their Environment

2. Environmental Factors
3. Matter in Living and Nonliving Systems
4. Matter and Energy
5. The Cycling of Matter in Ecosystems

Instructional Goals:

1. Humans are dependent on the natural world for survival. Basic needs such as clean air and water are obtained from the natural world. All resources and energy are obtained from the natural world.

2. Limiting factors determine what can live where, and climate is the major abiotic cause of differences between ecosystems.

3. All life on Earth is composed of organic molecules. Organic chemicals, by definition, are molecules with either C-C or C-H bonds. Inorganic chemicals are molecules without either C-C or C-H bonds. Therefore, it is possible to have synthetic (human-made) organic chemicals and natural (nature-made) organic chemicals.

4. The first and second laws of thermodynamics explain how energy flows. The first law of thermodynamics —it takes energy to get energy—explains why there are environmental costs associated with anything we do. The second law of thermodynamics—which says that things become increasingly more dispersed—explains why the availability of high quality (concentrated) energy is declining. A related concept is that it takes the constant input of energy to maintain organisms or ecosystems, because the second law of thermodynamics explains that without energy input things move toward increasing disorder.

5. The movement of matter through the environment can be explained by biogeochemical cycles (phosphorus, carbon, and nitrogen). Human activities have impacted all of these cycles.

Concepts and Connections:

Ecosystems are organizations of the natural world. The universe is made of matter, matter is composed of atoms. Students in an environmental science course will probably be asking themselves why they are required to learn some chemistry and physics. To help them make connections between these two disciplines and environmental science, you could provide many reasons but it would likely be more effective to ask them to think about why they are learning about chemistry in an environmental science course. You should also ask the students why they are learning about the laws of thermodynamics in an environmental science course.

There are chemicals that if found in excessive quantities may result in adverse human or environmental health. Discussing any one of these could provide students with connections between chemistry and environmental science. Examples of chemicals that are possibly linked to adverse human or environmental health outcomes include ozone and asthma rates, carbon monoxide and heart attacks, nitrates/phosphates and Physteria, lead and decreased IQ scores, mercury and neurological disease, and DDT and endocrine disruption. The laws of thermodynamics can be related to food webs, energy use, and pollution.

Limiting factors can be difficult to explain to students because humans have worked so hard to not be governed by them. The inherent non-sustainability of our drive to not be constrained by limiting factors can be shown by the multitude of environmental problems. In the last 20 years the number of Americans moving to the Southwest, in defiance of the limiting factor of the region (water), has created an environmental nightmare. We not only have large quantities of water being extracted from ground and surface sources but the air pollution resulting from air conditioners is tremendous. Water and temperature, both limiting factors in a desert, are being ignored and the result is pollution.

Carbon, phosphorus and nitrogen are vital to life. They are constantly being cycled throughout the spheres. Some of these are very long term cycles and some are rather short term. However, humans are disrupting these cycles and disturbing the balance. As a result, these vital elements are also becoming pollutants in some of their various compounds.

Concepts in Context:

Ecosystems cannot exist without energy provided by the sun. Energy flows and follows the laws of thermodynamics (Chapter 3). The organisms, at their various trophic levels, move nutrients through ecosystems (Chapter 3).

You may use many different current issues to provide the chemistry concepts with a context. Ozone depletion (Chapter 18), global climate change (Chapter 18), acid rain, air pollutants (Chapter 19), and water pollution (Chapter 20) can all provide examples of how chemicals impact our lives. Limiting factors (Chapter 3) can be chemical, (e.g., nitrogen).

The first law of thermodynamics can be discussed in relation to the increasing cost of energy and resources (Chapters 10, 13, 16, 17). Humans initially have always exploited the resources and energy that were the easiest to obtain and the most concentrated. Because it takes more energy to obtain less concentrated energy (shale) or resources, the energy cost to obtain resources has increased over time. The second law of thermodynamics can be related to the dispersion of pollutants (Chapters 13, 18, 19, 20) and the reduced quality of available energy (Chapter 14, 15, 16). The impact of chemicals out of balance (the biogeochemical cycles) can be related to air pollution (Chapter 18, 19) and water pollution (Chapter 20). Current events such as the growth of Physteria can also be discussed.

A number of current environmental problems can be used to put limiting factors into a context. Eutrophication and sewage treatment (Chapter 20) are examples of excessive quantities of limiting factors causing adverse environmental effects. Global warming (Chapter 18) is another example of a limiting factor influencing organism survival. While the current data indicate the temperature of the planet is warming, we have also had ice ages that limited the growth of organisms.

Habitats and niches can be discussed within the context of succession (Chapter 5). An ecosystem with a variety of successional stages, a mosaic, provides the greatest number of niches and habitats. The large number of habitats and niches in a mosaic ecosystem creates the conditions for maximum diversity (Chapter 6).

Key Terms and Vocabulary:

Ecology, species, population, biota, biotic community, abiotic, ecosystem, ecotone, landscape, biomes, biosphere, conditions, resources, optimum, range of tolerance, limits of tolerance, zone of stress, limiting factor, law of limiting factors, synergistic effects, synergisms, habitat, niche, matter, atoms, elements, molecule, compound, atmosphere, hydrosphere, lithosphere, mineral, carbon, hydrogen, oxygen, nitrogen, phosphorus, sulfur, organic, inorganic, natural organic compounds, synthetic organic compounds, energy, kinetic energy, potential energy, chemical energy, calorie, the Law of Conservation of Energy, the first law of thermodynamics, second law of thermodynamics, entropy, oxidation, producers, consumers, photosynthesis, enzymes, cell respiration, biogeochemical cycle, hydrologic cycle, detritus, organic phosphate, nonreactive nitrogen, reactive nitrogen, nitrogen fixation, denitrification, nitrogen cascade

Discussion, Activities, and Labs:

1. After discussing detritus feeders and decomposers, ask the students to discuss what would happen if all detritus feeders and decomposers disappeared tomorrow. Include in the discussion the practice by modern humans to isolate our remains from the environment. How does this influence the flow of nutrients? Are we delaying the movement of nutrients, or are we removing the nutrients from the nutrient cycle?

2. Divide the class into small groups (two to three students) before beginning the lecture and ask the students to provide two reasons why they think it is necessary to know some chemistry/physics when learning about environmental science. Ask them to name environmental issues where they think knowledge of chemistry or physics could help them understand the issues.

3. Divide the class into small groups before beginning the lecture and ask the students to list ten (or as many as you think are appropriate for the amount of time you are providing) environmental issues where a chemical can be stated to be the cause of the problem. (Most environmental issues could be listed because chemicals are the basis of life.)

4. Divide the class into small groups. Ask the students to list 10 examples of situations where the first and second laws of thermodynamics can be used to explain environmental problems.

5. Students typically do not have a good understanding of the relationship between photosynthesis and cell respiration. Plants, according to most students, undergo photosynthesis but do not undergo cell respiration. In class ask the students about their understanding of the processes of cell respiration and photosynthesis. Ask the students to look at the two processes. Ask if they can see similarities between the processes. Ask them to devise an experiment that would test the situation they have described—plants produce oxygen used by animals and animals produce carbon dioxide used by plants. What they are trying to devise is an experiment that would simulate what would happen if there were no animals, or no plants, on the planet. Ask them to predict the results of the experiment based upon their understanding that both animals and plants are necessary for plants to do photosynthesis and animals to respire. A terrarium that they can look at repeatedly over several weeks can be set up to simulate a planet without animals. Ask the students to predict the source of carbon dioxide in the terrarium. Ask the students what happens to the all the oxygen produced by the plants. (The incorrect understanding that only organisms do cell respiration would create a situation where the plants should die if there were no animals in the terrarium.)

6. Divide the class into small groups to discuss a local nutrient cycle problem. If you are living in the Northeast, acid precipitation (excess nitrogen) can be interesting. If you are living in a city, ask the students to discuss the nutrient impact of sewage treatment and effluent release. If you are living in an agricultural area, ask the students to discuss the effect of fertilizer application or large animal feedlots on streams. Students should not only be asked to outline the problem but to develop potential solutions.

7. Bring to class a variety of items having potential, kinetic, and chemical energy. Divide the class into groups of three to four students. Have the students group items by the potential, kinetic, and chemical energy status. The reason for the inclusion of each item in a group should be articulated. If students are uncertain as to the placement of an item, ask them to devise a test that could help them determine an answer. Once the students have created sets of groupings, have them try to change the groupings. For example, coal can be potential or chemical energy. Additionally, coal could be kinetic energy if it is presumed to be burning. Have the students attempt to put items into as many groups as can be logically justified. (Examples of items that can be used include candy bars, nuts, charcoal briquettes, and pictures of water behind a dam, a baseball being thrown, a car idling in traffic, a car speeding down the highway, a plane in the air, a plane on the ground.)

8. Before class begins, put warm water (115^0F) baths containing test tube holders near each student. Give each student a closed vial containing a silverfish and a firebrat. Have the students put their two vials into the water bath. About half way through the class, after you have introduced the concept of limiting factors, ask the students to remove both vials from the water bath. Ask the students to see if both insects are alive. Record on the chalkboard the number of each insect that has died. (About one-half of the silverfish should have died and none of the firebrats.) At the end of the lecture ask the students to again tell you which insects are alive and which insects are dead. Ask the students what these observations tell them about heat as a limiting factor in the survival of firebrats and silverfish.

9. Most students understand the definitions of potential, kinetic, and chemical energy but have a difficult time recognizing objects containing potential energy (and chemical) or kinetic energy (and chemical energy). Discuss with the students the human tendency to put things into categories. These categories are human inventions and they help us to understand the world around us. Tell the students to review the definitions of potential, kinetic, and chemical energy. Instruct them to go home and find everyday items that are potential, kinetic, or chemical energy. They are to list five different everyday items for each type of energy. With each item the students should include an explanation as to why they grouped the item as they did. (Why the item fits in the group where they placed it?) Additionally, if an item could be grouped with a second energy type, then

27

the explanation for why the item can also belong in the second group needs to be provided. Ask the students to state why they think it is useful to group items by the type of energy contained. (The presumption here is that the three groups of energy were created for a rational reason.)

Suggested Lecture Format

I. Organisms in Their Environment

      A. Define the hierarchy of Ecology including the terms:
         1. species, populations, biotic communities, ecosystems, landscapes and biomes and the biosphere

      B. Ecosystems are the biotic and abiotic factors in a specified area that interact with each other.
         1. Understanding the interaction of the biotic and the abiotic factors in an ecosystem can help us to see why particular human activities may be a problem for human survival.
         2. Example: The loss of ozone in the stratosphere increases the quantity of UV radiation on the surface of the planet. In the same way humans experience sunburn from too much sun exposure, so do plants. Excessive UV may damage or destroy plant protein and DNA, killing the plant.

II. Environmental Factors

      A. Optimum levels
         1. Each factor necessary for survival has an ideal range.

      B. Zones of stress
         1. Each factor has a range of values that are above or below the idea but not outside the range allowing survival.

      C. Limits of tolerance
         1. Each factor has an upper and lower limit beyond which the organism cannot survive.
         2. Law of limiting factors: Quantities of any single factor above or below optimum levels necessary for organism growth, reproduction, or survival will limit growth, reproduction, or survival.
            i.   Synergistic effects: Two or more factors interact to cause an effect greater than anticipated from the effects of the factors acting alone.

      D. Habitat and Niche
         1. Habitat is defined by plant community and the physical environment
         2. Niche is the sum of all of the conditions and resources under which a species can live. **See Discussion Topic # 2**

III. Matter in Living and Nonliving Systems

      A. What is matter?

      B. What are the basic units of matter – What is an atom? A molecule? An element?

      C. What are the four spheres and how do they interconnect?
         1. Atmosphere, Hydrosphere, Lithosphere and Biosphere
         2. Interactions
         3. What is the difference between organic and inorganic molecules?
         4. What is the difference between synthetic and natural organic molecules?

      D. Do In-class discussion #2 and #3

VI. Matter and Energy – Energy basics

A. What is energy?

B. What is potential energy?

C. What is kinetic energy?

D. What is chemical energy?
   1. **See Discussion Topic #1**
   2. How do these types of energy relate to each other?

E. Explain the first law of thermodynamics: Energy is neither created nor destroyed; it only changes form. The first law of thermodynamics can be described as "You can't get something for nothing" or "There is no such thing as a free lunch." Ask the students how the "official" definition relates to these unofficial definitions. If you don't have them work to integrate these to forms of the first law, they tend to not understand that all three phrases are saying the same thing.
   i.   It is not possible to destroy energy, so some people have thought it possible to create a perpetual motion machine. The second law of thermodynamics explains why this is not possible.

F. Explain the second law of thermodynamics: Systems will go spontaneously in one direction only, toward increasing entropy. The second law of thermodynamics can be described as "It takes energy to get energy" or "In any energy conversion, you will end up with less usable energy than you started with" or "If you think things are confused now, just wait" or "Everything moves in the direction of increasing disorder." Ask the students how the "official" definition relates to the unofficial definitions. Again, asking that students work to integrate the various forms of the second law improves the understanding of the concepts.
   1. Discuss the ultimate source of energy on our planet—the Sun.
   2. Discuss the "First basic principle of ecosystem sustainability: For sustainability, ecosystems use sunlight as their source of energy." Our planet is sustainable as long as the Sun exists. Ecosystems do not use energy at a rate that is faster than that which is available from the Sun. (The same cannot be said for humans because of our rate of fossil fuel consumption.)
   3. Entropy is the measure of disorder. Discuss how entropy relates to the second law of thermodynamics. Discuss examples of disorder students can relate to such as a messy room or desk.
   4. **See Discussion Topic #4**

G. Energy Changes in Organisms
   1. Make sure the students understand the basic concepts of photosynthesis and cell respiration.
   2. Make sure the students understand the characteristics of a producer, consumer, heterotroph, detritus feeder, and decomposer.
   3. How do weight gain, cellular respiration and photosynthesis relate?
       i.   What does breathing rate have to do with it?

H. One-Way Flow of Energy
   1. Energy flows only one way through ecosystems. The heat will eventually be radiated back out into space.

V. Nutrient Cycles: Discuss how energy flows but nutrients cycle. Discuss again the Law of Conservation of Matter and the first and second laws of thermodynamics. You could discuss how the molecules in an organism will eventually be found in another organism. You could introduce the idea of the movement of nutrients downstream; sewage effluent upstream will be taken up by organisms downstream.

A. Discuss the three most important cycles—carbon, phosphorus, and nitrogen.

1. The carbon cycle: Changing the location of this element is the primary issue in global warming. We are moving carbon from where it has been stored (fossil fuels) to the atmosphere, where it acts to reduce the amount of heat reradiated to space.
    i. Discuss the carbon cycle's storage pools and flows. The rate of movement (flows) between pools can be slow or fast depending upon the nature of the pool.
2. The phosphorus cycle: Changing the location of this element is one of the primary reasons for the increased nutrient load in aquatic ecosystem. We move phosphorus from where it has been concentrated (e.g., guano), and deposit on soil (or in consumer products), where it is released to water.
    i. Discuss the phosphorus cycle's storage pools and flows. The rate of movement (flows) between pools can be slow or fast depending upon the nature of the pool.
3. The nitrogen cycle: Changing the location of this element is the other reasons for the increased nutrient load in aquatic ecosystems. (Nitrogen and phosphorus are limiting factors in aquatic ecosystems.)
    i. Discuss the nitrogen cycle's pools and flows. The rate of movement (flows) between pools can be slow or fast depending upon the nature of the pool.
    ii. Discuss the human impacts on the nitrogen cycle especially as it relates to agriculture.

Review Questions: Possible Answers

1. *Distinguish between the biotic community and the abiotic environmental factors of an ecosystem.*

    The biotic community is the living portion of the ecosystem—plants, animals and microbes—while the abiotic community is the nonliving portion—chemical and physical factors. The abiotic factors support and limit that biotic community. The biotic community members influence each other and will contribute to the abiotic community (such as minerals or carbon dioxide) during decomposition.

2. *Define and compare the terms species, population, and ecosystem.*

    Species are the different kinds of plants, animals, and microbes in the community. A given species includes all those individuals that are like one another and that are distinct from other such groups (robins vs. redwing blackbirds, for example). Similarity in appearance suggests a close genetic relationship. The biological definition of a species is the entire population that can interbreed. A population is the individuals that make up the interbreeding reproducing group within a species. Therefore, the distinction between population and species is that population refers only to those individuals of a certain species that live within a given area, such as all the wolves in Isle Royale National Park, whereas species is all inclusive, such as all of the gray wolves of North America. An ecosystem is an interconnected complex of plants, animals, and microorganism communities and the nonliving environmental interactions as a functional unit within a specified space. Individuals within a species make up a population; there can be more than one population of a species.

3. *Compared with an ecosystem, what are an ecotone, landscape, biome, and biosphere?*

    An ecotone is area between two or more ecosystems, where many of the species and characteristics of the adjacent ecosystems are found plus some unique conditions that support distinctive plant and animal species. An example may be that there is more sunlight where a forest meets a meadow.

    A landscape is a group of interacting ecosystems. Landscapes acknowledge that ecosystems impact each other.

    Biomes are similar or related ecosystems or landscapes often grouped together to form major kinds of ecosystems. Prairies or steppes are examples of biomes. The biosphere is all the ecosystems of the Earth combined. As a result, all of these terms are actually more than one ecosystem.

4. *How do the terms organic and inorganic relate to the biotic and abiotic components of an ecosystem?*

    Organic compounds contain carbon—carbon bonds and/or carbon-hydrogen bonds. Biotic components are related to the term organic as they are living contain organic compounds. However living things also contain inorganic compounds such as sodium chloride and other salts. Likewise, abiotic components of an ecosystem could contain organic compounds, such as those found in oil. The atmosphere, lithosphere and hydrosphere are more likely to contain inorganic compounds. In biogeochemical cycling, the biotic parts of a cycle, namely plants and animals, are likely to use the cycled material (N, C, or P) in organic molecules. In contrast, the material is more likely to be inorganic in the abiotic parts of the cycle. An example would be, the element nitrogen is used to make amino acids and proteins in living things, but are found as ammonia, and nitrates in the soil, and N_2 in the atmosphere.

5. *What are the six key elements in living organisms?*

   Nitrogen, carbon, oxygen, hydrogen, phosphorus, and sulfur are the key elements in nature. Each is found in all living things and detritus. All six elements are found in the different spheres. Carbon is primarily found in the atmosphere. Phosphorus and sulfur are primarily found in the lithosphere.

6. *What features distinguish between organic and inorganic molecules?*

   Inorganic molecules tend to be smaller molecules. They may contain two or three elements but rarely more than that. While they may contain a carbon or hydrogen, they do not have both carbon and hydrogen. Organic molecules can be very large complex molecules. In addition to carbon and hydrogen they may contain P, N, O and other elements.

7. *In one sentence, define matter and energy, and demonstrate how they are related.*

   Matter is anything that occupies space and has mass, while energy is the ability to move matter. On a molecular level, changes in state are actually movements of atoms or molecules. For instance, the degree of heat energy contained in a substance is a measure of the relative motion caused by the vibrations of the atoms and molecules of the substance. More motion results in a higher temperature. The motion of matter takes energy and energy moves matter.

8. *Give four examples of potential energy. In each case, how can the potential energy be converted into kinetic energy?*

   Water behind a dam is an example of potential energy. If the water is released by opening the dam, the water moves and can move things such as debris, a water wheel or maybe turn a generator. These are examples of kinetic energy. Coal is chemical potential energy. Like moving water, burning coal can make steam to turn a generator. A stretched rubber band has potential energy. To convert it to kinetic energy, you would release the rubber band. A leaf attached to a tree has gravitational potential energy and eventually the leaf falls.

9. *State the two energy laws. How do they relate to entropy?*

   The first law of thermodynamics states that energy is neither created nor destroyed, but may be converted from one form to another form. The second law of thermodynamics states that in any energy conversion, some of the usable energy is always lost. Entropy is a measure of the degree of disorder in a system, so increasing entropy means increasing disorder. With energy inputs, everything goes in one direction only—toward increasing entropy. This disorder is the lost energy as described in the second law. In order to keep anything organized, you must put energy in because everything moves to disorder. Energy that has been converted from one form to another may include heat energy. As heat dissipates it disperses, thus becoming more disordered.

10. *What is the chemical equation for photosynthesis? Examine the origin and destination of each molecule referred to in the equation. Do the same for cellular respiration.*

    Photosynthesis: Carbon dioxide plus water plus sunlight gives glucose plus oxygen. The carbon dioxide originates from respiration, including the burning of glucose in cells, decomposition, the burning of biomass and fossil fuels, and so forth. It is obtained by the plant from the atmosphere. Water originates from soil, streams, and so forth in the hydrological cycle. The oxygen that is released is used in combustion and in respiration. The glucose formed is stored and eventually is burned during respiration.

    Respiration: Oxygen plus glucose gives carbon dioxide plus water plus energy. The oxygen and glucose originate from photosynthesis. Oxygen is obtained from the atmosphere, plants use their stored glucose and animals must eat something containing glucose. The exhaled carbon dioxide is used by plants in photosynthesis. Water is used by plants and animals for their processes, and by plants in photosynthesis, and energy is used by the organism whose cells are undergoing respiration for other cellular reactions.

11. *Describe the biogeochemical cycle of carbon as it moves into and through organisms and back to the environment. Do the same for phosphorus and nitrogen.*

Carbon cycle: The carbon cycle "begins" with the two reservoirs: carbon dioxide in the atmosphere and bicarbonate molecules in water. Carbon atoms from carbon dioxide are incorporated into producers through the process of photosynthesis. The carbon in producers is transferred to consumers via the food web. Carbon is released back to the atmosphere through decomposition by decomposers and detritus feeders. Respiration releases carbon as carbon dioxide for land-based organisms and as inorganic carbonate in aquatic ecosystems. Other transfers of carbon include the geological sedimentation of carbon, thereby removing carbon from solution, and the combustion of fossil fuel carbon, thereby releasing carbon to the atmosphere. **Phosphorus cycle:** The phosphorus cycle has several reservoirs: phosphorus in rock and soil minerals. When rocks break down, phosphate and other phosphorus ions are released to soil or water. Plants absorb phosphate from soil or water and incorporate it into the plant's structure. The food web transfers phosphorus from producers to herbivores to carnivores. Phosphorus is found in many important chemicals in living things. Cell respiration and decomposition result in the release of phosphorus ions (in urine or other waste products) to the environment for re-uptake by plants. Phosphorus does not have a gas phase; it is recycled only if the wastes containing it are deposited back to the soil *"from which it came."* (Phosphorus is a limiting factor in aquatic ecosystems.) **Nitrogen cycle:** The nitrogen cycle "begins" with its reservoir: nitrogen dioxide in the atmosphere. Nitrogen gas is "fixed" by bacteria into nitrate compounds or may be "fixed" by lightning. Nitrate compounds are taken up by producers and incorporated into essential organic compounds. Nitrogen is moved through the food web by herbivores consuming producers and carnivores consuming herbivores. Nitrogen is released back to the soil, primarily as ammonium compounds. Various bacteria convert the ammonium compounds to nitrate compounds, which are then available for plant uptake. Humans impact the nitrogen cycle by the fixation of nitrogen gas into chemical fertilizer. Much of the nitrogen fertilizer runs off the land and is added to aquatic ecosystems where nitrogen, like phosphorus, is naturally found in small quantities. (Nitrogen is a limiting factor in aquatic ecosystems.)

12. *What are the major human impacts on the carbon, phosphorus, and nitrogen cycles?*

The major human intrusions into the carbon cycle are the release of carbon through the combustion of fossil fuels and the burning/destruction of forests. Humans disrupt the phosphorus cycle by removing matter from ecosystems such that phosphorus is not returned to the ecosystem from which it came. An example is the removal of trees from tropical rain forests where the recycling of nutrients is nearly 100% efficient and there are few to no reserves of nutrients in the soil. Another way in which humans disrupt the phosphorus cycle is through the addition of chemical fertilizer to lawns and farmland. Much of the phosphorus fertilizer runs off the land and is added to aquatic ecosystems where phosphorus is naturally found in small quantities. The major human intrusion into the nitrogen cycle comes from the use of nitrogen fertilizers including manure and biosolids, the planting of nitrogen fixing crops, and the combustion of fossil fuels "fixing" nitrogen from the air. Humans also alter the nitrogen cycle by burning fossil fuels. High temperature combustion oxidizes nitrogen gas, producing nitrogen oxides. Nitrogen oxides include nitrogen dioxide and the precursors to ozone destruction and acid rain.

Thinking Environmentally: Possible Answers

1. *From local, national, and international news, compile a list of the many ways humans are altering abiotic and biotic factors on a local, regional, and global scale. Analyze ways that local changes may affect ecosystems on larger scales and ways that global changes may affect ecosystems locally.*

Look for articles on waste disposal, hazardous waste and materials, energy consumption and production, pesticide use, land use (such as building homes, business, or parks), road construction, air pollution, water pollution, consumer buying, and so forth. It is possible to find information about how we are altering abiotic and biotic factors on a local, regional, and global scale in a substantial portion of news articles. Any article on cars can be evaluated for energy efficiency, air pollution, resource extraction (petroleum, minerals, and coal) waste disposal, urban sprawl, road construction impacts, water pollution from road and parking lot runoff, and energy consumption due to road building and maintenance, traffic and street lights, and law enforcement.

Local changes may impact ecosystems on a larger scale in a variety of ways. The release of mercury from coal-fired power plants impacts local ecosystems, and the mercury moves from local ecosystems all over the world. Local loss of species impacts on a larger scale because of the loss of biodiversity.

Global changes may impact local ecosystems when overall climate shifts or if the quantity of UV reaching the surface of the planet changes.

2. *Use the laws of conservation of matter and energy to describe the consumption of fuel by a car. That is, what are the inputs and outputs of matter and energy? (Note: Gasoline is a mixture of organic compounds containing carbon-hydrogen bonds.)*

Gasoline and oil are the primary inputs for a car. For the internal combustion engine, oil is used for lubrication so it should not be a part of the fuel, but there are times when the engine is not working properly (oil leaks) and oil is also burned. In addition to the carbon-hydrogen bonds of gasoline, there are contaminates in gasoline. Some of these contaminants are normal constituents of gasoline; others are added during refining. When gasoline is burned using oxygen (another input) from the atmosphere, the contaminants are also released to the atmosphere.

The energy contained in gasoline is released during burning. During this conversion of energy some of the energy is converted to work (forward motion) and some is converted to heat and "lost" to the atmosphere. The first law of thermodynamics is demonstrated by the conversion from gasoline to forward motion and heat. The second law of thermodynamics is demonstrated by the disorder that is created. Gasoline is very concentrated energy. The heat energy is dissipated. Additionally, the contaminants in the gasoline are dispersed. The law of conservation of matter is also at work here; no matter is created or destroyed, it only changes form. The carbon is changed from gasoline to carbon dioxide. Carbon dioxide is a greenhouse gas.

3. *Using your knowledge of photosynthesis and cell respiration, draw a picture of the hydrogen cycle and the oxygen cycle. (Hint: Consult the three cycles in the book for guidance.)*

Carbon dioxide (contains oxygen) and water (contains hydrogen and water) are taken up by plants. Using sunlight, glucose and oxygen are the products. The hydrogen from the water has been incorporated into glucose. The oxygen then is taken up by animals and plants for the burning of glucose during respiration, and carbon dioxide and water are released.

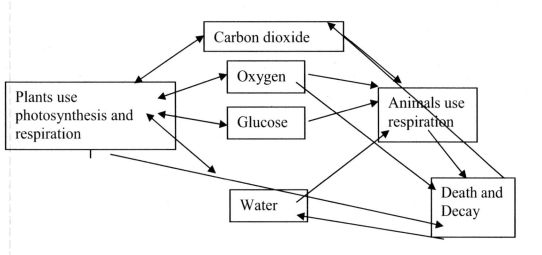

4 *Look up everything you can find about iron seeding of the oceans and see if you can decide what you think we should do.*

Students would have to come up with their own conclusions, but here are some arguments for both sides.
Pro Side
  • It does promote large amounts of phytoplankton growth when tested.

- Huge cores of phytoplankton have been found in ice from various ice ages.
- In the deeper parts of the ocean the carbon would be sequestered for thousands of years.
- Approximately one-half of the photosynthesis takes place in the oceans but oceans make up three-fourths of Earth's surface. Seeding would help equalize this disparity.
- The Earth's warming is reducing the productivity of the oceans. Iron seeding could help reverse this trend.
- The process is simple, dump a tanker of iron into an open part of the ocean.

Con Side
- It promotes large amounts of zooplankton growth.
- Some are also worried that the increased mass of plankton will release additional methane and nitrous oxide, which might increase greenhouse gases, and have a counter-productive effect.
- May give people the feeling they have a "license to pollute" because carbon is being sequestered elsewhere. (I.e. drive more, or use more electricity).
- Iron disperses in the ocean rapidly so it would be a very short term gain and would take huge amounts of iron to sustain bloom activity.
- There is very little regulation of what is done in the ocean so there is a high probability of something going wrong.
- It is 10 to 100 times less efficient than other natural means of carbon sequestering.
- Iron seeding could trigger an ice age (started by a quip by John Martin, the first to suggest iron seeding in 1993). (*Earth Magazine* 1996)
- The amount of iron needed is too expensive in comparison to the benefits.
- May interfere with natural food webs in the area.
- Currents and upwelling from the deep vary from one area of the ocean to another and both must be considered when planning the seeding.

CHAPTER 4
Populations and Communities

Chapter Outline:

I.   Dynamics of Natural Populations
    A.   Population Growth Curves
       1.   Exponential Increase
       2.   Logistic Growth
    B.   Biotic Potential Versus Environmental Resistance
       1.   Environmental Resistance
       2.   Reproductive Strategies
II. Limits on Populations
    A.   Density Dependence and Density Independence
    B.   Critical Number
III. Community Interactions
    A.   Predation
       1.   Parasites
       2.   Regulation of Prey
       3.   Plant-Herbivore Dynamics
          i.   Overgrazing
          ii. Predator Removal
       4.   Keystone Species
    B.   Competition
       1.   Intraspecific Competition
          i.   Territoriality as an Advantage
          ii. Impact on the Species
       2.   Interspecific Competition
    C.   Mutualism
    D.   Commensalism
IV. Evolution as a Force for Change
    A.   Selective Pressure
    B.   Adaptations to the Environment
       1.   The Limits of Change
          i.   Keys to Survival
          ii. Genetic Change
       2.   The Evolution of Species
          i.   Two Species from One
          ii. Darwin's Finches
    C.   Drifting Continents
V.   Implications for Human Management
    A.   Introduced Species
       1.   Rabbits in Australia
       2.   Plants
       3.   Pests
       4.   Lessons
       5.   Remedies

Key Topics:

1.   Dynamics of Natural Populations
2.   Limits on Populations

3. Community Interactions: Population
4. Evolution as a Force for Change
5. Implications for Human Management

Instructional Goals:

1. The fundamental mechanism of population growth provides students with the tools to comprehend why the potential population size of some species is so much greater than the potential population size of other species.

2. All populations are subject to limits placed on them by their environment.

3. A relationship between two species can be characterized as being helpful, harmful, or neutral in regard to each species. The sum of the resulting interactions between species in a given environment helps to shape the ecosystem.

4. The theory of evolution is fundamental to biology. The change in a species' gene pool through time, by differential reproduction, is an essential component of evolution. When faced with selective pressures populations will adapt, migrate, or become extinct (locally or globally). The result of each population's reaction to selective pressures permanently re-shapes the ecosystem. New alleles are produced by random mutations. Speciation, encouraged by our drifting continents over time, occurs when a population is separated and prevented from interbreeding. Further, speciation is encouraged when the selective pressures on each new population differ consistently through time.

Concepts and Connections:

Population dynamics will be interesting to many students. Before beginning the lecture, you can ask students how fast the population sizes of different species grow. Most students will be able to tell you that flies, bacteria, and rats reproduce at rates faster than humans. Discussing the similarities and differences in biotic potential and environmental resistance between humans and other species will help students connect what they already know about population dynamics with the concepts being taught.

Find out if students know that the deer population is too large in many areas. Use this information to discuss plant-herbivore dynamics. Discuss the introduction of rabbits to Australia (effects of an introduced species on population dynamics) and the eventual control of the rabbits by an introduced virus (host-parasite balance).

Explaining how birds use song to designate a territory can help students create conceptual links between habitat loss, territoriality, and critical number. The territory is needed so that the food supply for raising young will be sufficient. Habitat loss can reduce the amount of available territory to a point where the population size drops below the critical number and the birds stop reproducing.

Evolutionary change provides an explanation for why diversity exists. The mosaic of habitats and niches within each ecosystem provides the selection pressure for speciation. The elimination of species reduces the potential for future evolutionary change. Many scientists are currently concerned about the speed of species extinction and the impact that species loss will have on ecosystem stability. E.O. Wilson has been an outspoken advocate for endangered and threatened species. For most species, because they reproduce so slowly, we are unable to see the impact of selection pressures on the diversity of alleles in the gene pool. Fortunately, antibiotic and pesticide resistance provide excellent, short time-scale examples of the impact of selection pressures.

Concepts in Context:

Population dynamics, as discussed in Chapter 4, can be related to human population dynamics discussed in Chapters 8 and 9. Discussions of resource use by individual organisms and humans specifically can be related to the resource availability and use (Chapter 7). The impact of environmental resistance factors on survival can be related to the concept of limiting factors discussed in Chapter 3.

Mechanisms, such as plant-herbivore dynamics, by which a population maintains its equilibrium, can be related to the material in Chapter 6 on biodiversity and how the lack of equilibrium can result in species loss. The impact of habitat loss (Chapter 6) can be discussed in the context of the size of territory needed for reproduction (adequate food supplies for offspring). The disruption of existing plant-herbivore dynamics or the change in the types of plant competition as a result of introduced species can be discussed. Habitat and niches (Chapter 3) provided by the native species have been lost and the diversity of new habitats and niches created by the introduced species is low.

Pesticide resistance (Chapter 13) is an excellent example of the effect of selection pressure on the alleles in the gene pool. Evolutionary processes have produced the tremendous biodiversity (Chapter6) on this planet. The loss of biodiversity decreases overall genetic diversity and reduces the ability of an ecosystem to withstand environmental change (Chapter 3, 4, and 5). As diversity declines we may impact our ability to grow food (Chapter12) because the wild type of domesticated species will be lost. The size of the gene pool is part of the reason for each species having a critical number (Chapter5) of individuals necessary for survival.

Various human activities can impact allele selection. Air pollution (Chapter 19) in England resulted in the color change of a moth species. Climate change and increased UV levels from decreased stratospheric ozone levels (Chapter 18) produce selective pressures. Hazardous wastes (Chapter22), when improperly handled, can eliminate biota.

The impact of disturbance (non-regular events) on the creation of new habitats and niches (Chapter 3) is an increase in the diversity of species found in an ecosystem (Chapter 6). The quantity of resources available to humans and other species is greatest in ecosystems with the greatest diversity of succession (Chapter 7). Soil ecosystems (Chapter11) are the most diverse in ecosystems with a diversity of succession. Nutrient cycling (Chapter 4) is the most efficient and has the fewest losses in an ecosystem in equilibrium.

Key Terms and Vocabulary:

Population, community, population growth, equilibrium, population growth rate, exponential increase, population explosion, J-curve, carrying capacity (K), logistic growth, S-curve, biotic potential, recruitment, environmental resistance, reproductive strategies, *r*-strategists, *K*-strategists, life history, population density, density-dependent, density-independent, critical number, threatened, endangered, predation, interspecific, intraspecific, mutualism, commensalism, predator, prey, carnivores, herbivores, parasites, host, pathogens, keystone species, territory, fitness, natural selection, amensalism, symbiosis, selective pressures, natural selection, biological evolution, fitness, reproductive isolation, plate tectonics, tectonic plates, tsunami, Indo-Australian tectonic plate

Discussion, Activities, and Labs:

1. At the beginning of the lecture (if you have a teaching assistant who can collect and collate the data) or during the previous lecture, ask each student to tell you the sex and how many people in their family (immediate and first cousins) fall within five-year age brackets. This information can be easily obtained if you provide a form with two columns labeled female and male and rows with five-year age brackets, (e.g.; 0–4, 5–9, 10–14, etc.). Tabulate the data into an age structure diagram. Alternatively, you could have the students work in groups to create the age structure diagram from the data.

2. Divide the class into groups of three to four students. Have the students list at least five species that reproduce at fast rates (rats, bacteria, and flies) and list at least three of the similarities between these species (small, short gestation, large number of offspring per generation, short time between productive cycles). Next have the students list at least three species that do not reproduce at fast rates (elephants, humans, and primates) and list at least three similarities between these species (large, long gestation, small number of offspring per generation, long time between productive cycles). Discuss the lists as a class.

3. An alternative to the previous discussion would be providing the students with two lists of species: one with high biotic potential species and the other with low biotic potential species. Have the students list the similarities between the species within each list. Either provide them with a list of environmental resistance factors or ask them to create a list of environmental resistance factors. Have the students list how environmental resistance factors will affect species within each list. (Species with similar biotic potential will typically experience environmental resistance factors in similar ways.) Discuss the lists as a class.

4. If there recently was an unusual cold or hot period or a flood or drought in your area, ask the students about the effect of this abiotic factor on local plants and animals. Have them list the ways the extreme weather could have influenced population growth [limiting food, limiting water needed for drinking, or too hot (overheat), cold (froze), or wet (drown) to survive].

5. This exercise is similar to what occurred in England with the predation of a white moth as the color of tree bark became darker due to pollution. This activity has two parts:

   a. The goal of the first part is to show students how natural selection works. [This process has been proposed to be slow (Darwin) or rapid with intervening periods of quiescence (Gould and Eldredge).] Begin with 0.5-cm dots, 100 blue and 100 green. Give half the students a large piece of blue paper and the other half of students a large piece of green paper. Have the students scatter the blue and green dots across their piece of paper. Simulate predation by a predator that sees prey that don't match the background color by having the students remove 60 of the dots that are a different color than their large piece of paper. Each dot remaining is now duplicated (simulating reproduction). Students with a green piece of paper will add 100 green dots and 40 blue dots. Repeat the process of removing 60 dots of the color not matching the background and duplicating the remaining dots. Next have the students indicate how many more generations it would take for there to be no blue (green) dots. [The exercise can be followed by a more complex version of the same idea. Use different pieces of multicolored, patterned fabric for the habitat. The individuals are a variety of different colored paper dots (use 40 each of 5 colors). Have the students remove 75 dots of any visible color. To reduce inadvertent selection by the students, have them remove the 75 dots as rapidly as possible. Next have the students match each of the remaining dots with a dot of the same color. Scatter the dots across the fabric again and repeat the removal of 75 dots. Ask the students to deduce which color[s] will dominate.]

   b. The goal of the second part of the activity is to show how genetic drift (change due to random chance) and natural selection combine to change the gene pool of a species. Groups for this exercise should be no larger than three. Two students will simulate natural selection while one student will simulate genetic drift. Use the multicolored pattern fabric and the 40 dots of each of 5 colors. In addition to having students simulate predation (natural selection), have students simulate random events. One student in each group, using a glove with double-sided sticky tape on various parts of the glove, places his or her hand on the fabric with the various colored dots. Meanwhile, the other two students are removing 75 visible dots from the fabric as rapidly as possible. Next the students match each of the remaining dots with a dot of the same color. The dots are again scattered across the fabric, and the simulation of genetic drift and natural selection is repeated. Ask students to speculate as to the effect of the random event (removal of dots by the gloved hand) on the variation in dot color. Ask the students to speculate as to the effect of both genetic drift and natural selection on the gene pool.

6. Plant-herbivore dynamics, territoriality, and predator-prey relationships exist in all types of urban, suburban, and rural environments. Find several locations on or near campus where plant-herbivore dynamics (squirrels, insects), territoriality (birds), plant competition (chemical release by eucalyptus or incense cedar, shading, etc.), and predator-prey relationships (insects) can be observed. Ask students to find as many examples of plant-herbivore dynamics, territoriality, and predator-prey relationships as they can. Each example should be labeled (plant-herbivore dynamics, territoriality, predator-prey relationships, etc.) and described. Have the students describe how each of these population equilibrium mechanisms influences population dynamics and ecological succession.

Suggested Lecture Format:

I. Dynamics of Natural Populations-
    Ecosystems and the organisms within them are constantly changing. These changes occur because living organisms within the ecosystem face varying stresses from both living and non-living factors in the environment. Living things must respond to those stresses and their response changes not only the affected population but many others that are tied in some way to the affected population.

    A. Population Growth Curves
        There are three basic scenarios that any given population may find itself in at any given point in time: exponential increase, logistic growth, and constant growth. Constant growth is virtually never seen in nature. See Figure 4-1.
        1. Exponential Increase-J-curve growth. **See Discussion Topic #1.**
        2. Logistic Growth-S curve growth. This occurs when a population is at equilibrium and the number of births + immigration = the number of deaths + emigration.

    B. Biotic Potential Versus Environmental Resistance
        Biotic potential is "the number of offspring (live births, eggs laid, or seeds or spores set in plants) that a species may produce under ideal conditions." A species' biotic potential remains constant despite environmental pressures. Species are not often allowed to reach their biotic potential because of environmental resistance. See Figure 4-3.
        1. Environmental Resistance-is "the combination of all the abiotic and biotic factors that may limit a population's increase". Resistance may increase or decrease depending on population size and it controls a population's size.
        2. Reproductive Strategies- *R*-strategists (r-selected species) "produce massive numbers of young, but then leave survival to the whims of nature". On the other hand, *K*-strategists (K-selected species) "have a much lower reproductive rate (that is, a lower biotic potential), but then care for and protect the young until they can compete for resources with adult members of the population". **See Discussion Topic #2 and #3.**

II. Limits on Populations
    Mortality in a population may be related to either density dependent factors (related to population size per given area) or density independent factors (not related to population size per given area). In either case, when a population faces stress that leads to mortality, a critical number of individuals in that population are necessary for that population to survive in an ecosystem.

    A. Density Dependence and Density Independence-An example of a density dependent factor is food; the more individuals that compete for the same food source the more difficult it is for any one individual to get food. Examples of density independent factors include an unusual heat wave or hard freeze. If a particular limiting factor moves outside an organism's range of tolerance, then the organism dies irrespective of how many individuals there are in the population. **See Discussion Topic #4.**

    B. Critical Number-The minimum number of organisms necessary for a species to survive. If the number of individuals in a population drops below the critical number, density independent factors become very important. It is very difficult to pre-determine what the critical number for a particular population is because of the complexity of ecosystems.

III. Community Interactions
    The interactions between predator and prey and between competing individuals (whether of the same or different species) are important factors that shape an ecosystem. In addition, the survival or death of keystone species is critical in the success of an entire ecosystem.

    A. Predation-Predation can be divided into many sub-categories, but each scenario represents one organism benefiting while the second is harmed by the relationship. As the population size of the prey

or host (in the case of parasites) increases, the population size of the predator or parasite increases. As the predator or parasite population increases, the number of prey or hosts declines because the predators or parasites have "eaten" them. Reference the example of moose and deer on Isle Royale and Figure 4-7.
1. Parasites—Parasites affect their hosts in a density dependent manner.
2. Regulation of Prey
3. Plant-Herbivore Dynamics—Herbivores consume plants and therefore keep the size of a plant population in check. See the example of reindeer on St. Matthew Island and see Figure 4-8.
    i. Overgrazing—If there are too many herbivores, the herbivores can consume the plants at a faster rate than the plants can reproduce.
    ii. Predator Removal—Removal of natural predators can upset the fine balance of an ecosystem and allow the prey (or host) population to grow uncontrollably.
4. Keystone Species—These species have a crucial role in maintaining an ecosystem.

B. Competition—whether between members of the same species or between members of different species, competition is considered environmental resistance and helps shape an ecosystem. Some individuals will be successful and others will need to become subservient or leave an area to survive.
1. Intraspecific Competition-Members of the same species compete for the same resources.
    i. Territoriality as an Advantage
    ii. Impact on the Species
2. Interspecific Competition—Members of different species compete for the same resources. See Figure 4-12.

C. Mutualism—This is a relationship between two types of organisms that is beneficial for both.

D. Commensalism—One organism will benefit from this relationship while the other will be unharmed.

IV. Evolution as a Force for Change
Evolution is in response to environmental pressures that cause change. Species respond to these pressures and to changes in the environment by adapting, migrating, or dying. Adaptation of a species in response to environmental (selective) pressures comes about through a process called natural selection which is a constant selection and "modification of a species' gene pool toward features that enhance survival and reproduction within the existing biotic community and environment."

A. Selective Pressure—"Each factor (that) can affect which individuals will survive and reproduce and which are eliminated". Examples include both biotic (predators, competition, etc.) and abiotic (weather, availability of nutrients, etc.) factors. See examples of environmental resistance in Figure 4-3.

B. Adaptations to the Environment-Include coping mechanisms, adaptations for obtaining food, adaptation for escaping predation, adaptations for pollination, adaptations for finding and attracting mates, and adaptations for seed dispersal. See Figure 4-18.
1. The Limits of Change—All organisms will adapt, migrate, or become extinct.
    i. Keys to Survival—Geographical distribution, specialization to a given habitat, genetic variation, and reproductive rate are all keys to survival selective pressures.
    ii. Genetic Change—Genetic variation is the norm in living things and will occur over generations in a population.
2. The Evolution of Species—Over time the result of adaptations can lead to the formation of new and unique species.
    i. Two Species from One—Prerequisites include geographical separation of individuals in the species and differing selective pressures for each new population. See Figure 4-20.
    ii. Darwin's Finches. See Figure 4-21.

C. Drifting Continents—The drifting of continents over time certainly provided for the geographical isolation and differing selective pressures that separated populations would have needed to undergo speciation. See Figure 4-22.

V. Implications for Human Management
Humans occupy a unique place in the ecosystem. The actions we take in the environment can either benefit or disrupt it.

A. Introduced Species—No other example has given us more insight into the delicate balance of the ecosystem and its members than when introduced species are able to integrate into a previously foreign ecosystem. Often this integration causes a disruption or even devastation to the native inhabitants (invasive species) whereas other times integration is successful and the new species becomes neutralized. Whether by accident or on purpose, most cases of introduced species occur due to human interference in the ecosystem. Some notable examples are listed below.
1. Rabbits in Australia
2. Plants—See Figure 4-24 regarding Kudzu.
3. Pests—See Figure 4-25 regarding Zebra mussels and Ctenophores.
4. Lessons—In some cases introduced species will join the native species of an ecosystem and have a neutral impact on that ecosystem. Other cases will lead to an invasive species that causes harm to the native organisms in the ecosystem. In either case it is generally better to try to prevent the introduction of new species into an ecosystem.
5. Remedies—Introduction of natural enemies to an invasive species can sometimes remedy the situation. However, we must be careful that the natural enemy itself does not become invasive. Because of our limited understanding of each complex ecosystem it can sometimes be very difficult to understanding the far reaching impact that such a "remedy" can have.

Review Questions: Possible Answers

1. *What are three basic population growth curves? When might you see them in nature?*
The three types of population growth curves are the constant population growth rate, the J-curve (exponential growth) and the S-curve (logistic growth). The constant population growth rate remains constant over time and results in a straight line when plotted on a growth curve (population number vs. time). It is highly unlikely that this type of growth would be found in nature. The J-curve demonstrates population growth under optimal conditions, with no restraints. The S-curve shows a population at equilibrium. The J-curve is caused by exponential growth of a population and the absence of mechanisms to cause the population to level off; exponential growth can occur in nature. Humans, for example, have been growing exponentially for many generations now. J-curve growth is not sustainable and the consequence of this type of growth is a population crash and a reduction in the carrying capacity. The S-curve is caused by exponential growth of a population until natural mechanisms cause the population to level off at the carrying capacity (K) and continue in a dynamic equilibrium. The causes of this type of growth are the various biotic and abiotic factors that limit a population's size.

2. *Define biotic potential and environmental resistance, and give factors of each. Which generally remains constant, and which controls a population's size?*
Biotic potential is "the number of offspring (live births, eggs laid, or seeds or spores set in plants) that a species may produce under ideal conditions." A species' biotic potential remains constant. **Environmental resistance** is "(t)he combination of all the abiotic and biotic factors that may limit a population's increase." Environmental resistance may increase or decrease depending upon population size." Environmental resistance controls a population's size.
The biotic potential of a species causes the population size to increase. While the population size is relatively small, the environmental resistance is low and the rate of population growth increases. As population size increases, the environmental resistance increases and the rate of population growth declines. The population size of some species remains relatively level with moderate increases and decreases in population

size. Other species have more dramatic fluctuations in population size.

3. *Differentiate between the terms critical number and carrying capacity. What is density dependence?*

Critical number is the minimum size of a population below which it will not reproduce. The survival of the species is unlikely below the critical number. The **carrying capacity** is a characteristic of an ecosystem and "is the upper limit to the population of any particular species that an ecosystem can support...." Therefore, the critical number is the smallest number of individuals within a species that is required for the species survival while the carrying capacity is the largest number of individuals within a species that an ecosystem can support. Carrying capacity is a characteristic of an ecosystem, while critical number is a characteristic of the species. **Density dependent** factors are those environmental resistance factors that, as the population size increases there is an increase in "mortality, (such) that population growth ceases or declines." As population size decreases, environmental resistance factors decrease as well, allowing the population to grow again. **Density independent** factors are those that cause mortality irrespective of the population density. The population size can be small or large and the factor will have the same effect, (e.g., a sudden, hard freeze will kill plants, seeds, or animals irrespective of the population size).

4. *Explain the difference between r- and K-strategists. Where do these terms come from, and what are the characteristics of each broad category?*

R-strategists (r-selected species) "produce massive numbers of young, but then leave survival to the whims of nature". On the other hand, a *K*-strategist (K-selected species) "have a much lower reproductive rate (that is, a lower biotic potential), but then care for and protect the young until they can compete for resources with adult members of the population".

R-strategists are called so because they usually have high r values (the number of offspring that individuals can produce in a given amount of time if resources are unlimited). *K*-strategists are named as such because "their population sizes are more likely to fluctuate around the carrying capacity", termed *K*.

5. *Describe the predator-prey relationship between the moose and wolves of Isle Royale. What other factors influence these two populations?*

"Fewer wolves represent low environmental resistance for the moose, so the moose population increases. Then, the abundance of the moose represents optimal conditions (low environmental resistance) for the wolves, so the wolf population increases. More wolves means higher predation on the moose (high environmental resistance); again the moose population falls. The decline in the moose population is followed by a decline in the wolf population because now there are fewer prey (high environmental resistance for the wolves)."

Other factors also influence these two populations. Examples given in the text include changes in weather (deep snow) which affected the moose population, deep freezes, parasites, and other natural enemies of both populations.

6. *Distinguish between intraspecific and interspecific competition. How do they affect species as a form of environmental resistance?*

Interspecific competition is competition between species, while intraspecific competition is competition within a species. Interspecific competition occurs when ecological niches overlap. Intraspecific competition occurs because members of the same species are competing for the same resources. Intraspecific and interspecific competition are forms of environmental resistance that limit a population size because these types of competition result from density dependent biotic and abiotic factors that are necessary for survival.

7. *What is meant by territoriality, and how does it limit the effects of competition in nature?*

Territoriality refers to individuals or groups defending a territory against the encroachment of others of the same species. It is a form of intraspecific competition. By establishing a territory, a nesting area or adequate food resources are being defended against others' use. When populations are high some individuals are unable to secure nest sites or areas with adequate food resources, thus limiting the size of a population.

8. *What problems arise when a species is introduced from a foreign ecosystem? Why do these problems occur?*

Introducing species into foreign ecosystems "alter(s) community and population ecology relationships such as competition and predation". These problems can occur because an introduced species typically does not have predators, parasites, and/or grazers. A non-native plant may also release chemicals that exclude native species. A non-native species may find the environment favorable for survival but it is unlikely that it fits in the framework of relationships in the new biotic community."

Examples of exotic species include rabbits introduced into Australia, chestnut blight, Japanese beetles, fire ants, gypsy moth, zebra muscle, kudzu, and spotted knapweed and purple loosestrife introduced into the United States.

9. *What are selective pressures and how do they relate to natural selection?*

Selective pressure is "each factor (that) can affect which individuals survive and reproduce and which are eliminated." These are environmental resistance factors such as predators, parasites, drought, lack of food, and temperature extremes. Individuals that are able to survive (avoid or cope with selective pressures) are those that can reproduce.

10. *Describe several types of adaptations a species might have that would allow it to survive in a dry environment, escape predation, or lower competition with another species.*

Adaptations including those that allow an organism to cope with climatic changes, changes of other abiotic factors, adaptations for obtaining food and water or for obtaining nutrients, energy, and water, adaptations for escaping from or protecting one against predation, adaptations of disease resistance, adaptations for finding and attracting mates or for pollinating and setting seed, and adaptation for migrating or dispersal of seeds could allow for selective survival of individuals.

11. *What factors determine whether a species will adapt to a change or whether the change will render it extinct?*

"There are four key variables among species that will affect whether or not a viable population of individuals is likely to survive new conditions: (1) geographical distribution, (2) specialization to a given habitat or food supply, (3) genetic variation within the gene pool of the species, and (4) the reproductive rate relative to the rate of environmental change."

12. *How may evolution lead to the development of new species (speciation)?*

As selective pressures select from new, randomly generated and existing mutations, new species are possible. It is also possible to obtain two or more species from one. Two prerequisites are necessary for this to occur. First, reproductive isolation is necessary. Reproductive isolation is a result of some physical factor resulting in two or more populations being isolated from each other such that they are unable to interbreed. The second necessary factor is that the different subpopulations must be exposed to different selective pressures. If the selective pressure results in sufficiently different characteristics, then the subpopulations will not be able to interbreed even if they are in contact later.

Speciation is the creation of new species in one of two ways: "the infusion of new variations from mutations and the pressures of natural selection serve to adapt a species to the biotic community and the environment in which it exists" or a species ". . . separates into smaller populations that do not interbreed with one another." Both of these processes increase biodiversity. "Although it can be difficult to imagine, overwhelming evidence from today and patterns from the past inform us that the present array of plants, animals, and microbes has developed through evolution over long periods of time and in every geographic area on earth. This is the source of our current biodiversity".

13. *What is plate tectonics, and how does this theory explain past movement of the continents? How have past tectonic movements affected the present-day distribution of plant and animal species on Earth's surface?*

Plate tectonics is a "grand theory" that "helps us to understand earthquakes and volcanic activity, and is key to understanding the geographic distribution of present-day biota." The lithosphere "can be visualized as huge slabs of rock floating on an elastic layer beneath. This is much like crackers floating next to each other in a bowl of soup. These slabs of rock are called tectonic plates. Some 14 major plates and a few minor ones make up the lithosphere. "Within Earth's semi molten interior, hot material rises toward the surface and spreads out at some locations, while cooler material sinks toward the interior at other locations. Riding atop these convection currents, the plates move slowly, but inexorably, with respect to one another. The spreading process of the past 225 million years has brought the continents to their present positions. It also accounts for the other interactions between tectonic plates. In addition to the periodic catastrophic destruction that may be caused in localized regions by earthquakes and volcanic eruptions, tectonic movement may gradually lead to major shifts in climate in three ways. First, as continents gradually move to different positions on the globe, their climates

43

change accordingly. Second, the movement of continents alters the direction and flow of ocean currents, which in turn have an effect on climate. Third, the uplifting of mountains alters the movement of air currents, which also affect climate." We find every region on Earth occupied by well-adapted living organisms, so it is clear that they have been able to evolve, speciate, and adapt to these geological changes. We can understand the present-day distribution of plants and animals only in light of continental drift and plate tectonics.

Thinking Environmentally: Possible Answers

1. *Describe, in terms of biotic potential and environmental resistance, how the human population is affecting natural ecosystems.*

   Human population is affecting natural ecosystems by increasing the environmental resistance many species face. We may change the pH, nutrient load, or salinity of water; increase the chemical pollutants in water; change the pH, salinity, or nutrient load of soil; contaminate soil with synthetic pollutants; flood or drain land; increase or decrease the chance of fire; or change local or global temperatures. Human actions tend to decrease the probability of survival for most organisms.

   Typically, biotic potential is not altered by human activities. Biotic potential is the number of offspring a species may produce under ideal conditions. Humans are able to increase or decrease the number of offspring produced by domesticated species, but this is more difficult in wild species. Recruitment is not typically changed by human action. The length of "childhood" has been changed for humans, but we have not changed this for other species.

2. *Explain the key differences between r- and K-strategists, their life histories, and their reactions to environmental changes. Where do the r and K come from in population equations? What do they stand for?*

   R-strategists (r-selected species) "produce massive numbers of young, but then leave survival to the whims of nature". On the other hand, a K-strategist (*K*-selected species) "have a much lower reproductive rate (that is, a lower biotic potential), but then care for and protect the young until they can compete for resources with adult members of the population".

   R-strategists typically multiply quickly and have a high mortality rate. They are called *r*-strategists because they usually have high r values (the number of offspring that individuals can produce in a given amount of time if resources are limited).

   K-strategists are typically "larger, longer lived, and well adapted to environmental conditions". They are so named so because "their population sizes are more likely to fluctuate around the carrying capacity", termed *K*.

3. *Consider the various kinds of relationships humans have with other species, both natural and domestic. Give examples of relationships that (a) benefit humans, but harm other species; (b) benefit both humans and other species;(c) benefit other species, but harm humans. Give examples in which the relationship may be changing-for instance, from exploitation to protection. Discuss the ethical issues involved in changing relationships.*

   A relationship that benefits humans but harms other species would be considered predation-any example that the student cites of humans hunting, gathering, or otherwise killing another organism for its benefit and survival would be appropriate. For example, humans hunting and eating wild turkeys is predation. A relationship that benefits both humans and other species would be considered mutualism. Although it may be difficult for students to initially think of examples of mutualism between humans and other organisms, a well known example of mutualism is the relationship between some bacteria that normally reside in the human digestive tract (which receive nutrition as a bi-product of digestion) and the human (which receives crucial vitamin K from the bacteria). If a human was in a relationship that benefited another species but harmed the human it would be considered predation as well. The other species in this case would be benefitting from the relationship and would typically be parasitic (particularly pathogenic). An example of such predation would be any type of disease-causing organism or parasite living in or on a human. Relationships are constantly changing as pressures from the environment are constantly changing. One could imagine that at one point the bacteria found in the digestive tract of the human were parasites that eventually evolved to have a mutualistic relationship with the human. On a completely different level think about how the relationship between cows and humans have changed over time. Initially the relationship was predatory since humans would hunt and kill cows or other similar species. During the transition towards settling and farming humans began to domesticate animals like the cow. The cows eventually became dependent on the humans for food, water, and shelter as more and more generations of cows were born in captivity. This led to a new type of mutualism based on the changing relationship between humans and cows. This raises ethical issues about our place as humans in the biosphere and whether our ability to "conquer" lower animals is really beneficial for them and whether shifting the relationship to "mutualism" because we have created a false new environment for the animals to live in is truly beneficial for them.

4. *Consider the village weaverbird (see "Sound Science: The Village Weaverbird: Marvel or Menace?") and describe how its various traits support its survival and reproduction. How could these traits have been affected by natural selection?*

   The village weaverbird has many traits that make it an excellent invader of new areas, such as the ability to raise several broods of young per season, a generalized diet, and a preference for human-altered environments. It is regularly transported to new areas in the cage bird trade, and often escapes from captivity. In the last two decades the village weaver has been sighted in the wild for the first time in North and South America and Europe. Many of these birds attempted to bread, and some were successful. The village weaverbird's ability to raise several broods of young per season means that it has a good chance of producing at least some young that will survive to reproduce. Its generalized diet means that it can occupy a new ecosystem with relative ease because it will find something to eat. Because it can easily live in human-altered environment it is likely to live wherever we transport it. The monoculture crops of our industrial agricultural system have aided the village weaverbird by providing substantial amounts of food. Small grain production aids their survival. With economic and agricultural diversification it may be possible to reduce (eliminate) the negative impact of the village weaverbird.

   Natural selection works on characteristics that result in reproductive advantages. If a characteristic helps you to obtain more food, you increase your chance to survive to reproductive age. This characteristic is passed on to future generations. If a characteristic reduces the chance that you will die prior to reproductive age, this characteristic will be selected. If a characteristic reduces the chance that you will develop a disease after reproductive age, natural selection will not work to select this trait. The survival of an individual village weaverbird is enhanced by human disturbance and agricultural production. Thus the individuals who have survived will reproduce offspring with the same characteristics.

5. *Describe how a human action such as removing a top predator, or adding a species, can have an impact on many species in an ecosystem.*

   Removing a top predator (which can typically be keystone species) can have a major impact on an ecosystem. Removing such a predator would reduce environmental resistance on their prey which would in turn lead to potential J-curve growth of the prey. This has a trickledown effect on many organisms in the ecosystem. On the other hand, if humans add species to an ecosystem we run the risk of the non-native species becoming invasive and competing with or destroying native species in the ecosystem. This could also have a trickledown effect on many organisms in the ecosystem.

CHAPTER 5
Ecosystems: Energy, Patterns, and Disturbance

Chapter Outline:

I. Characteristics of Ecosystems
    A. Trophic Levels, Food Chains, and Food Webs
    B. Trophic Categories
        1. Producers
        2. Consumers
        3. Decomposers
        4. Limits on Trophic Levels

II. The Flow of Energy in Ecosystems
        1. The Fate of Food
    A. Energy Flow and Efficiency
    B. Aquatic Systems

III. From Ecosystems to Global Biomes
    A. The Role of Climate
        1. Biome Examples
        2. Examples of Aquatic Systems
    B. Microclimate and Other Abiotic Factors
        1. Biome Productivity

IV. Ecosystem Responses to Disturbance
    A. Ecological Succession
        1. Primary Succession
        2. Secondary Succession
        3. Aquatic Succession
    B. Disturbance and Resilience
        1. Fire and Succession
            i. Fire Climax Ecosystems
        2. Resilience

V. Human Values and Ecosystem Sustainability
    A. Appropriation of Energy Flow
    B. Involvement in Nutrient Cycling
    C. Value of Ecosystem Capital
        1. Using Ecosystem Value in Decision Making
            i. A New Look
    D. Can Ecosystems Be Restored?
    E. The Future
    F. Managing Ecosystems

Key Topics:

1. Characteristics of Ecosystems: Matter and energy flow through ecosystems by moving from one broad feeding (trophic) level to another.
2. The Flow of Energy Through the Food Web: Trophic (feeding) pyramids reflect the relative numbers and biomasses of different levels in a food chain.
3. From Ecosystems to Global Biomes: Ecosystems are connected into broad regions called biomes, and certain factors determine their placement on the globe.
4. Ecosystem Responses to Disturbance: Ecological disturbances, such as a fire, are normal in ecosystems and can even be beneficial.
5. Human Values and Ecosystem Sustainability: Humans impact ecosystem services both positively and negatively; therefore, we need to manage ecosystems to protect their components from overuse.

Instructional Goals:

1. All ecosystems contain communities that include a variety of species interacting with each other and with the abiotic factors in the ecosystem.

2. Energy flows from the source (typically the sun) through producers and eventually to higher and higher levels of consumers in each ecosystem. Producers always have the greatest biomass in the environment while each additional feeding level must occupy less biomass.

3. There are patterns in ecosystems throughout global regions. These patterns, based on climate, determine which types of organisms will not only survive but also thrive in each region.

4. Although ecosystems depend on balance, they are also usually able to adjust to disturbances and return to their normal state through the process of succession.

5. Because of the unique place that humans occupy in the ecosystem, our evaluation of the Earth's natural services and our use and/or abuse of the Earth's resources is necessary for sustainable living.

Concepts and Connections:

Processes such as photosynthesis and respiration in organisms lead to the complex interplay between members of an ecosystem, particularly related to feeding. Ecosystems can change over time in response to selective pressures but also in response to natural disturbances and disturbances caused by humans. An ecosystem will be at different stages of succession, usually caused by a disturbance, at any given point in time. The result of different successional stages within an ecosystem is that the ecosystem will be more diverse than an ecosystem in a single stage of succession. Current succession theory does not describe any ecosystem in a single stage of succession. Undisturbed areas, agricultural lands, parks, abandoned fields, golf courses, and landscaped areas around homes or businesses can be compared to provide students with an understanding of the impact of ecosystem simplification.

Concepts in Context:

Ranges of tolerance and limiting factors (Chapter 3) apply not only to individuals and single populations, but also to the larger ecosystem. The concepts of mutualism (Chapter 4) and population dynamics (Chapter 4) will be revisited. The impact of disturbance (non-regular events) on the creation of new habitats and niches (Chapter 3) is to increase the diversity of species found in an ecosystem (Chapter 6). The quantity of resources available to humans and other species is greatest in ecosystems with the greatest diversity of succession (Chapter 7). Soil ecosystems (Chapter 11) are the most diverse in ecosystems with a diversity of succession. Nutrient cycling (Chapter 4) is the most efficient and has the fewest losses in an ecosystem in equilibrium. Links to urban problems beyond land-use issues can also be made to ecological succession. Succession can be adversely impacted by air pollution (Chapter 19), water pollution (Chapters 10 and 20), and the legal and illegal disposal of hazardous waste (Chapter 22).

Key Terms and Vocabulary:

biomes, trophic levels, productivity, consumption, food chains, food web, autotrophs, heterotrophs, chlorophyll, chemosynthesis, primary production, primary consumers, herbivores, secondary consumers, carnivores, omnivores, fermentation, anaerobic, biomass, biomass pyramid, cellulose, temperate deciduous forest biome, grassland biome, prairie biome, desert biome, tropical rain forest, coniferous forest biome, permafrost, tundra biome, microclimate, disturbance, ecological succession, facilitation, climax ecosystem, fire climax ecosystems, resilience mechanisms, incremental value, ecosystem management

Discussion, Activities, and Labs:

1. To discuss how ecological succession can be extended to include human created environments, divide the class into groups of three to four students. Have the students apply ecological succession to the succession process observed in your home city. Examples of succession in cities would include the changes that occur over time including how neighborhoods change, industrial areas changing from manufacturing to providing services, revitalization of downtown areas, open space becoming malls and housing, and so forth. Is the succession observed in cities sustainable? How could you make a city sustainable? What would be an ideal climax urban ecosystem? (Describe the components of a "perfect" city.)

2. Secondary succession can be easily demonstrated if you are willing to begin the process during one class session and check the site periodically over the next month. (This activity needs to be done during a portion of the term when the weather is favorable for plant growth.) Find a location where plants are currently growing. Have each student stake a small area and scrape all the plants from the area. The bare soil should be surrounded by plants that have not been removed. Every few days the area should be watered (if needed) and the students should periodically (at least once per week) record any changes to their area. Within a short period of time plants should return to the bare area, demonstrating the first sequence in secondary succession.

Suggested Lecture Format:

I. Characteristics of Ecosystems
    All ecosystems contain communities that include a variety of species interacting with each other and with the abiotic factors in the ecosystem. "Ecosystems that have a similar type of vegetation and similar climactic conditions are grouped into broader areas called biomes".

A. Trophic Levels, Food Chains, and Food Webs—All of the members of an ecosystem are dependent upon those organisms that have the ability to undergo photosynthesis or chemosynthesis. Food produced by those who do such processes provides food energy for all the consumers in various tropic (eating) levels.

B. Trophic Categories—Organisms can be divided according to the way that they either produce or eat food. See Table 5-3.
1. Producers—Those who can convert carbon dioxide into organic matter for food.
2. Consumers—"All organisms in the ecosystem other than the producers feed on organic matter as their source of energy." Consumers can be divided into primary consumers (herbivores), omnivores, secondary consumers, higher order consumers, and parasites. See Table 5-3.
3. Decomposers—Decomposers include scavengers, detritus feeders, and chemical decomposers. They "use organic matter as a source of both energy and nutrients" by "breaking down detritus into carbon dioxide, water, and mineral nutrients".
4. Limits on Trophic Levels—There is a limit to the number of trophic levels possible in an ecosystem. Each higher level comprises approximately 10% of the biomass of the previous level, making it difficult to have more than three to four levels in a biomass pyramid. See Figure 5-7.

II. The Flow of Energy in Ecosystems
Energy flows from the source (typically the sun) through producers and eventually to higher and higher levels of consumers in each ecosystem. Producers always have the greatest biomass in the environment while each additional feeding level must occupy less biomass.

A. Energy Flow and Efficiency—"When energy flows from one trophic level to the next, only a small fraction is actually passed on." This phenomenon can be explained by three things: "1) much of the preceding trophic level is biomass that is not consumed by herbivores, 2) much of what is consumed is used as energy to fuel the heterotroph's cells and tissues and, 3) some of what is consumed is undigested and passes through the organism as waste".

B. Aquatic Systems—Producers and consumers can also be found in aquatic ecosystems; however, the "transfer of energy is often more efficient in aquatic ecosystems" and "aquatic ecosystems do not result in the same kind of biomass pyramid as the terrestrial ecosystems". Aquatic ecosystems typically have an "upside-down pyramid" compared to terrestrial ecosystems. See Figure 5-8. For examples of major aquatic systems, see Table 5-2.

III. From Ecosystems to Global Biomes
There are patterns in ecosystems throughout global regions. These patterns, based on climate, determine which types of organisms will not only survive but also thrive in each region.

A. The Role of Climate—The average temperature and amount of precipitation that falls each year determine the biome of an ecosystem. Climate determines in large part what the dominant species of an area will be.
1. Biome Examples—Examples include Deserts, Grasslands and Prairies, Tropical Rain Forests, Temperate Forests, Coniferous Forests, and Tundra. See Table 5-1 and Figure 5-10.

B. Microclimate and Other Abiotic Factors—"Abiotic factors such as terrain, wind, and type of soil create different microclimates by influencing temperature and moisture in localized areas." See Figure 5-12.
  1. Biome Productivity-Some biomes are more productive than others. See Figure 5-13.

IV. Ecosystem Responses to Disturbance
  Although ecosystems depend on balance, they are also usually able to adjust to disturbances and return to their normal state through the process of succession.

  A. Ecological Succession-Ecological succession is the transition from one biotic community to another. Because niches and habitats form during the transition from one biotic community to another, circumstances are favorable for the existence of a large number of species. **See Discussion #1.**
    1. Primary Succession—If an area has not been occupied by organisms previously, the initial invasion and progression from one biotic community to the next is called primary succession. Soil and soil organisms do not exist prior to the beginning of the succession process. See Figure 5-14.
    2. Secondary Succession—If an area has been occupied by organisms previously and something has occurred to leave only the bare soil, then the invasion and progression from one biotic community to the next is called secondary succession. Soil and soil organisms exist prior to the beginning of this succession process. See Figure 5-15. **See also Discussion #2.**
    3. Aquatic Succession—Succession can take place in lakes and ponds as well. When soil particles "erode from the land and settle out" they can fill aquatic ecosystems in over time, turning them into ecosystems that are partially terrestrial. See Figure 5-16.

  B. Disturbance and Resilience—Disturbances provide habitat for a wide array of species. In any area, there are likely to be all stages of succession represented because of large and small disturbances.
    1. Fire and Succession—Fire is a necessary factor for a diverse number of species. Certain species, for example the fire pines, are dependent upon fire. Without fire their cones do not open and the bare ground necessary for seed germination does not exist. Other species are adapted to fire conditions. Fire helps to maintain a balance between species or may release nutrients that have not decomposed because of arid conditions. Fire creates pockets of secondary succession.
    2. Resilience—Resilience is the "ability of an ecosystem to return to normal functioning after a disturbance, such as a fire or a food". See Figure 5-19.

V. Human Values and Ecosystem Sustainability
  Due to the unique place that humans occupy in the ecosystem, our evaluation of the Earth's natural services and our use and/or abuse of the Earth's resources is necessary for sustainable living.

  A. Appropriations of Energy Flow—Calculations indicate that approximately 30% of the total annual global net primary production is used by humans.

  B. Involvement in Nutrient Cycling—Human intrusion into the natural cycle of nutrients "is substantial" and "has long term consequences".

C. Value of Ecosystem Capital—"Goods and services we derive from natural systems are ecosystem capital". The Earth provides very important services naturally that would cost us a lot of money to replace. See Table 5-3.

1. Using Ecosystem Value in Decision Making—Once we know the value that natural systems provide we can use that value to make smart decisions about whether to disrupt an ecosystem to replace it with a different one for human benefit. Unfortunately, when we disrupt natural systems we replace them with less efficient and less economical systems.

D. Can Ecosystems Be Restored? Our ability as humans to "fix" mistakes we have made in the ecosystem is determined by whether 1) abiotic factors in the ecosystem are unaltered, 2) viable native species are still available and, 3) lack of introduced species.

E. The Future—"To turn human efforts in a sustainable direction, we need to protect or manage the natural environment in a way that maintains the goods and services vital to the human way of life, and we need to manage ourselves."

F. Managing Ecosystems—"Good ecosystem management is based on understanding how ecosystems function, how they respond to disturbances, and what goods and services they can best provide to the human societies living in or around them."

Review Questions: Possible Answers

1. *What were the biggest surprises from the Yellowstone fires of 1988?*

   It was surprising that within just two weeks of the last fire burning out vegetation began to grow again. Even more surprising though, was that "while wood buildup in the forest does matter to fire intensity, it is actually the climate that primarily drives large fires" like the ones in Yellowstone. "The fire was also much more heterogeneous (variable) than expected. Unburned portions of the forest were close to severely burned portions and provided the seeds for re-colonization in burned patches."

2. *Name and describe the attributes of the two categories into which all organisms can be divided based on how they obtain nutrition.*

   The two categories that organisms can be divided into (based on nutrition source) are autotrophs and heterotrophs. Autotrophs "produce the organic compounds they need to survive and grow. Green plants, photosynthetic single-celled organisms, and chemosynthetic bacteria are autotrophs". Heterotrophs, on the other hand, include all other organisms that "feed on organic matter as their source of energy."

3. *Name and describe the roles of the three main trophic categories that make up the biotic structure of every ecosystem. Give examples from each category.*

   The three main trophic categories are the producers, the consumers, and the decomposers. Producers "capture energy from the Sun or from chemical reactions to convert carbon dioxide to organic matter. Most producers are green plants." Consumers "feed on organic matter as their source of energy". Examples of consumers include all animals, fungi, and most bacteria. Decomposers have the ability to digest and feed off of detritus which includes leaves, grasses, and "fecal wastes and dead bodies from higher trophic levels". Examples of decomposers include scavengers, like vultures, and other detritus feeders like earthworms, some species of fungi and also some bacteria and other microbes.

4. *Give four categories of consumers in an ecosystem and the role that each plays.*

51

Consumers can be divided into primary consumers (herbivores), omnivores, secondary consumers (carnivores), higher orders of consumers, and parasites. Primary consumers "feed directly on producers". "Animals that feed on primary consumers are called secondary consumers". Each level of consumer feeds on the level before. Higher level consumers (like humans) may be found in several levels at the same time. Parasites may become "associated with another plant or animal and feed on it over and extended period of time". Each organism has a place in the food web and such predator-prey relationships help to keep the ecosystem in balance.

5. *Describe different members of the decomposition food web.*

Members of the decomposition food web include scavengers, detritus feeders, and chemical decomposers. "Scavengers eat larger dead things" and "may also eat living (things) some of the time." Detritus feeders are "organisms that feed directly on detritus", and chemical decomposers can include "fungi and bacteria that cause rotting".

6. *Differentiate among the concepts of food chain, food web, and trophic levels.*

Food chains "describe where the energy and nutrients go as they move from one organism to another. The food web is "all food chains" that are "interconnected and form a complex web of feeding relationships". Trophic levels are feeding levels in an ecosystem.

7. *Relate the concept of the biomass pyramid to the fact that all heterotrophs depend on autotrophic production.*

"In most ecosystems, sunlight (or solar energy) is the initial source of energy absorbed by producers through the process of photosynthesis". In a typical terrestrial ecosystem, the producers, who are capable of such photosynthesis are the only organisms capable of utilizing the sun's energy and thus provide the basis for food to the entire ecosystem. For that reason, the greatest amount of biomass in the ecosystem must come from producers to be able to support higher organisms. When moving up to another trophic level, the higher levels have 1/10 of the biomass as the previous level of the pyramid.

8. *Describe how differences in climate cause Earth to be partitioned into major biomes.*

A biome is "a large geographic biotic community usually named after the dominant type of vegetation". Climatic factors such as temperature and precipitation determine which types of organisms are capable of surviving in a given area and also carve out the Earth's ecosystems into what are called biomes.

9. *What are three situations that might cause microclimates to develop within an ecosystem?*

A microclimate describes "the conditions found in a specific localized area ...that result in variations of ecosystems within a biome". Three situations that might cause a microclimate include: changes in elevation, soil type, and topography. Elevation effects the temperature of the microclimate whereas soil type and topography "contribute to the availability of moisture" in the microclimate. Since biomes are delineated by temperature and precipitation, these factors can exceptions to the typical biome properties within a particular area.

10. *Identify and describe the biotic and abiotic components of the biome of the region in which you live.*

Answers will vary based on region. Biotic components of an area refer to the living components of the ecosystem whereas the abiotic components refer to the non-living, yet still important, factors in an ecosystem. Use Table 5-1 and Figure 5-10 as references for determining biome type.

11. *Define the terms ecological succession and climax ecosystem. How do disturbances allow for ecological succession?*

Ecological succession is the gradual replacement of one biotic community of organisms with another. "Succession occurs because the physical environment may be gradually modified by the growth of the biotic community itself, such that the area becomes more favorable to another group of species and less favorable to the present occupants." The final stage of ecological succession is the climax ecosystem.

Disturbances, (e.g., fire, tornadoes, and hurricanes), can remove plants and animals from an area, returning the area to an earlier stage of succession. Fire can increase the quantity of light reaching the forest floor by reducing the density of the canopy. Fire can also be necessary the reproduction of some trees. For example, the fire pines do not release their seeds without fire, and the seeds need to germinate on bare soil. Patchiness results from having different areas of an ecosystem in different successional stages. Because each successional stage has a different array of species, a mosaic of successional stages creates an ecosystem with more species present; biodiversity is enhanced by a mosaic ecosystem structure.

12. *What role may fire play in ecological succession and how may fire be used in the management of certain ecosystems?*

Periodic fire will favor some species over others, just like any other abiotic limiting factor. Grassland and pine forests are ecosystems that depend upon fire. "Fire is being increasingly used as a tool in the management of" grasslands and pine forests. "In pine forests, if ground fires occur every few years, relatively little deadwood accumulates. With only small amounts of fuel, fires usually just burn along the ground, harming neither pines nor wildlife significantly. In forests where fires have not occurred for many decades, however, deadwood accumulates and if a fire does break out, it will almost certainly become disastrous.

13. *What is meant by ecosystem resilience? What can cause it to fail? How does this relate to environmental tipping points?*

"The ability of an ecosystem to return to normal functioning after a disturbance is resilience". Resilience mechanisms are "the processes of replenishment of nutrients, dispersion by surrounding plants and animals, rapid re-growth of plant cover and succession to a forest." Resilience can fail when soil is lost through deforestation, overgrazing, and other devastating factors.

14. *What is meant by stakeholders? How does ecosystem management involve stakeholders?*

Stakeholders "are people who have an interest in or may be impacted by a given approach to environmental management, including government decision makers". Both individuals who have a "stake" or interest in an environmental decision and those who will be impacted by the decision must be involved in making decisions about ecosystem management because both parties will be affected, either economically, physically, or both.

15. *Succinctly describe ecosystem management.*

"Ecosystem management comprises several main principles" in that "it looks at ecosystems on both small and large scales." Ecosystem management is dependent on good management that "preserves the range of possible landscapes in an ecosystem instead of allowing one type to take over the area".

16. *Can ecosystems be restored? What has to happen for that to work?*

Ecosystems can in fact be restored. The amount of work required to restore an ecosystem depends on the extent of disruption to the ecosystem. In the simplest case "restoration simply involves stopping the abuse" from human use or overuse. In other cases, extensive time and money must be invested into the ecosystem to return it to normal. Despite great efforts, however, some restoration efforts are unsuccessful. Success will include the following three factors: 1) "abiotic factors must have remained unaltered or, if not, can at least be returned to their original state, 2) viable populations of the species formerly inhabiting the ecosystem must still exist, and 3) the ecosystem must not have been upset by the introduction of one or more foreign species that cannot be eliminated and that may preclude the survival of reintroduced native species."

17. *How much of Earth's primary productivity is used or pre-empted by humans?*

Since humans are at the top of the biomass pyramid it can be expected that a very high percentage of Earth's primary productivity is used by humans and other top level organisms. However, because of their place in the ecosystem and tendency to treat the ecosystem in an un-sustainable fashion, humans use and preempt the Earth's primary productivity at unreasonably high rates—approximately 30% of the earth's total production.

18. *Examine the key messages from the Millennium Ecosystem Assessment's Governing Board, and evaluate how these points affect you now and will impact you and your children in the future.*

"At the heart of this assessment is a stark warning. Human activity is putting such a strain on the natural functions of Earth that the ability of the planet's ecosystems to sustain future generations can no longer be taken for granted." We are living off the future…. Human well-being apparently now depends on drawing down the ecosystem capital that provides the goods and services; agricultural soils erode, fish stocks decline, forests shrink, and pollution of land, water, and air increases. This situation is unsustainable."

It is very likely that the current generation of college students will see substantial changes in how we live our lives. The changes will either be ones we choose or ones that are forced upon us. If we choose to begin living in a more sustainable manner we and future generations will have more pleasant lives. We need to eliminate our wasteful lifestyles. The structure of our cities needs to change; transportation cannot be via the automobile, homes cannot be large stand-alone structures that are distant from other dwellings, and food needs to be locally grown. If we don't change how we live, mass starvation and death are likely to occur.

Thinking Environmentally: Possible Answers

1. *Write a scenario describing what would happen to an ecosystem or to the human system in the event of one of the following: (a) All producers are killed through loss of fertility of the soil or through toxic contamination or (b) decomposers and detritus feeders are eliminated. Support all of your statements with reasons drawn from your understanding of the way ecosystems function.*

If producers were killed in an ecosystem the entire ecosystem would suffer greatly because they provide energy in the form of food to the various consumers in the ecosystem. In very quick order the consumers in every trophic level would be unable to find adequate food sources for their survival and would perish.

If decomposers and detritus feeders were eliminated from an ecosystem, nutrient cycling would not happen at the rates necessary to replenish the soil and provide nutrients necessary for the producers to survive. This scenario would also eventually feed back to all of the consumers in the ecosystem as well.

Due to the fact all organisms in the ecosystem are closely tied together by way of the food web and predator-prey relationships, the loss of any type of organism will cause a great disturbance and an accumulation of negative events in the ecosystem.

2. *Look at the following description of a broad global region and describe what the biome name and main biota would be and how you know; 40 centimeters (16 inches) of precipitation a year, seasons, frozen much of the year, high winds.*

This type of biome would be described as tundra. Because of the relatively low amount of precipitation in the area and cold temperatures (causing freezing through most of the year), the main producers that would be able to survive in this biome would be "low-growing sedges, dwarf shrubs, lichens, mosses, and grasses". Consumers would include "lemmings, arctic hares, arctic foxes, lynx, caribou, insects, and migrant shorebirds".

3. *Consider the plants, animals, and other organisms present in a natural area near you, and then do the following: (a) Imagine how the area may have undergone ecological succession and (b) Analyze the*

54

population-balancing mechanisms that are operating among the various organisms. Choose one species, and predict what will happen to it if two or three other native species are removed from the area. Then predict what will happen to your chosen species if two or three foreign species are introduced into the area.

The answers to these questions will vary depending upon the area of the country. (a) Ecological succession may be caused by grass fires (near a road, next to picnic areas), erosion (construction sites, logging, agricultural fields), clearing of land (building construction, road building), or demolition of buildings. Once you have identified possible ecological succession causes, it will be possible to consider the plant and animal changes that may have taken place. For example, grasses, pine trees, or invasive species could be favored. (b) Population balance mechanisms that should be considered are territoriality, interspecies plant competition, missing predators, and grazing by herbivores. Most species will not be directly impacted if another species is removed or introduced. You will see direct impacts if the species removed are a food source, a competitor, a predator, and so forth. You will see direct impacts from an introduced species if the introduced species competes for the same food, eats or provides food for the species you are evaluating, or competes for such needs as nesting sites and territory.

4. *Consult the Web site www.ecotippinopoints.org, and read several of the success stories from that site. Compare the tipping points as presented, and explain the common properties of the tipping points.*

From the web site: "What is an Ecotipping Point? An 'ecotipping point' is a point in a linked eco-social system where a small action can catalyze major changes in the system's health".

"A tipping point is a lever that sets a system moving in a better direction or a worse one. An invasive species like water hyacinth may degrade a lake, by choking out native plants. But introducing a creature that feeds on the hyacinth may tip aquatic plants back into balance."

"Tipping points work by stimulating feedback loops. These are mutually reinforcing cycles of cause and effect. Plants and animals contain hundreds of biological feedback loops, keeping parameters like body temperature and blood sugar in healthy balance. Ecological feedback loops regulate plant and animal populations in an ecosystem, so they can continue working together as a whole."

"Through history, many human societies have worked in harmony with feedback loops, reaping nature's bounty while respecting nature's boundaries. But critical social changes—in technology, values, organization and institutions—can disrupt the interplay of these forces. Then, feedback loops may amplify the disruption, until an eco-social system slides from healthy function into devastating decline."

"Once tipped, a system can spiral downward with surprising speed. On the Great Plains in the 1930s, interlocking feedback loops of overgrazing, declining crop yields, wind erosion, and foreclosures of farmers' mortgages produced the eco-social collapse of the Dust Bowl. The good news is that, once a system is tipped the right way, the multiplier effect of feedback loops can speed its recovery. Nature does much of the work, instead of cumbersome technological fixes. As recovery gains momentum, it can spin off further helpful feedbacks."

"The ecotipping point's paradigm is like a lens. It helps us focus on the systemic causes behind environmental problems. It also helps focus on the core solutions behind environmental success stories, so that we can apply them to other problems."

Ecotipping points are not magic bullets to solve environmental problems overnight. What they can do is set eco-social systems moving in the right directions, so that nature—and human nature—can take over the work of healing themselves. Moreover, they're not visions of a utopian future. They're at work, even now.

5. *Explore how the human system can be modified into a sustainable ecosystem in balance with (i.e. preserving) other natural ecosystems without losing the other benefits of modern civilization.*

Although most humans in the developed world believe that living a sustainable life will require great sacrifice, simple lifestyle changes that do not lead to major decreases in our standard of living can lead to more sustainable living. When humans examine their over-use of such things as water, energy, land, and mineral resources, and keep the future in mind rather than looking to short term gains in living standard and profits, then the negative impact of humans on the Earth will be greatly reduced. Sustainable options for living are possible with planning and when given precedence over profit. If and when our people and particularly our leaders begin to re-focus our priorities and become more sustainable then we will be able to live more in balance with the earth while maintaining a modern civilization. The sooner this shift in attitude happens the more likely that goal will be possible.

CHAPTER 6
Wild Species and Biodiversity

Chapter Outline:

I. The Value of Wild Species and Biodiversity
    A. Biological Wealth
    B. Two Kinds of Value
        1. Instrumental Value
        2. Intrinsic Value
    C. Sources for Food and Raw Materials
        1. Wild Genes
        2. New Food Plants
        3. Woods and Other Raw Materials
        4. Banking Genes
    D. Sources for Medicine
    E. Recreational, Aesthetic, and Scientific Value
        1. A Cautionary Note
        2. The Loss of Instrumental Value
    F. Value for Their Own Sake
        1. Religious Support
        2. The Land Ethic
II. Biodiversity and its Decline
    A. How Many Species?
    B. The Decline of Biodiversity
        1. North America
        2. Global Outlook
    C. Reasons for the Decline
        1. Habitat Change
            i. Conversion
            ii. Fragmentation
            iii. Simplification
            iv. Intrusion
        2. Invasive Species
            i. Accidental Introductions
            ii. May I Introduce…
            iii. Over Time
            iv. Invasive Species and Trophic Levels
        3. Pollution
        4. Population
        5. Overexploitation
            i. Trade in Exotics
            ii. Greed
    D. Consequences of Losing Biodiversity
        1. Moving Forward
III. Saving Wild Species

    A. The Science of Conservation
    B. Policy and Political Structure
        1. Game Animals in the United States
           i. Turkey Boom
        2. Hunting and Conservation
        3. Backyard Menagerie
    C. Protecting Endangered Species
        1. Lacey Act
        2. Endangered Species Act
        3. Alternatives and Roadblocks
        4. Conflicting Values
        5. Future Legislation
    D. Seeing Success
        1. Birds of Prey
        2. Fly Away Home
        3. The Spotted Owl
IV. Protecting Biodiversity Internationally
    A. International Developments
        1. The Red List
        2. Cites
        3. Convention on Biological Diversity
        4. Critical Ecosystem Partnership Fund
    B. Stewardship Concerns
        1. Wisdom
        2. Values

Key Topics:

1. The Value of Wild Species and Biodiversity
2. Biodiversity and Its Decline
3. Saving Wild Species
4. Protecting Biodiversity Internationally

Instructional Goals:

1. Protecting wild species and their ecosystems must receive priority, if for nothing else, because of the ecosystem capital that they provide. It is difficult to come to a consensus about the extent of protection that is necessary.

2. Human interactions with wild species have reduced biodiversity in just a short period of time.

3. Stopping the loss of biodiversity requires wisdom, policy, and enforcement.

4. Cooperation between local, state, federal, and international authorities are necessary to protect international biodiversity.

Concepts and Connections:

Biodiversity can be connected to many issues. Alteration of habitats is a significant factor in the United States in the decline of many species. There is a great deal of controversy over U.S. songbird decline. This decline is linked to destruction of their winter habitat (mostly in developing countries) and breeding habitats (mostly in the United States). Pollution is one of the suspected explanations for declines in frog populations. While other explanations have been offered, a certain percentage of the amphibian decline is likely attributable to chemical exposure. Exotic species have caused the decline of many native species. A Shakespeare lover intentionally introduced starlings into the United States around the turn of the century. (He wanted all of the species found in Shakespeare's plays to be found in the United States.) As a result of the introduction of this exotic species, the population of several native bird species has declined. Ballast water is the source of many exotic aquatic species. Zebra mussels have caused Lake Michigan water users to spend substantial quantities of money clearing water intake pipes. Between exotic species and pollution, the ecosystem of Lake Michigan has been severely damaged.

Concepts in Context:

Speciation and extinction (Chapter 5) over time lead to biodiversity. Keystone species create habitats, occupy niches, and so forth that are important for the maintenance of an ecosystem (Chapters 3, 4 and 5). The removal of a keystone species can cause species loss and ecosystem collapse. Biodiversity of terrestrial ecosystems is ultimately dependent on soil and soil ecosystems (Chapter 11.) The agro ecosystem (Chapter 12) is ultimately dependent upon the biodiversity of wild lands for genetic stock. To obtain goods and services from an ecosystem (Chapter 7) over time, it is necessary that the ecosystem be healthy and diverse.

Biodiversity can be adversely impacted by the alteration of habitats. Pest management (Chapter 13) strategies that rely on eradication techniques can reduce biodiversity. Pollution (Chapters 19, 20, 21, and 22), global climate change (Chapter 18), and ozone depletion (Chapter 18) may reduce biodiversity.

Key Terms and Vocabulary:

Biota, biological wealth, biodiversity, instrumental value, intrinsic value, genetic bank, ecotourism, endemic species, HIPPO, habitat destruction, invasive species, pollution, population, overexploitation, edges, aquaculture, taxonomy, Animal Damage Control, Wildlife Services, Lacey Act, Endangered Species Act, Northwest Forest Plan, International Union for Conservation of Nature, Convention on Biological Diversity

Discussion, Activities, and Labs:

1. Ask students the following questions to help them distinguish between and understand the implications of intrinsic and instrumental value. Does intrinsic value extend to all, some, or no species? Does a species having intrinsic value preclude humans from utilizing it? What would be the advantages and disadvantages of deciding that intrinsic value precludes humans from utilizing a species? If species only have instrumental value, then do we have the right to eliminate them? If each species has a role in an ecosystem and humans are either directly or indirectly dependent upon ecosystems for survival, then would every species have instrumental value? Is there a balance between intrinsic and instrumental value? If so, what is the balance?

2. Create two or more food webs. One food web should be more diverse than the other food web but both should be complex. The number of species in each of the food webs should be multiples of six. The food webs will be easiest to manipulate if the links between species are easily changed and the species can be easily removed. Using string for the links and Velcro cloth species would facilitate the removal of links and species. Each species in the food web is assigned a random number. Divide the class into groups of three to four students.

Provide each group of students with at least two food webs. Using from one to six die, depending upon the number of species (6–36) in the food web, roll the dice to remove species from the food web. After removal of a species, the students should evaluate if the role of the removed species could be assumed by a remaining species. The dice are rolled again and the food web is restructured. The students should quickly observe that the more diverse food web is more stable. Have the students discuss the effect of species removal on the food web. Remind the students that who eats whom is only one of the essential species interactions.

3. Pick several areas with obviously different levels of diversity, (e.g., undisturbed area, landscaped area, agricultural field, campus arboretum, area near a campus building, or soccer field). Have the students go to selected areas and list the plant species observed. [You will have some variation in observations for the same area. This information could be used in a classroom discussion about the importance of detailed observation and the tools necessary to be able to observe, (i.e., prior knowledge that something could exist or a plan to guide your observations).] It is not necessary to know the species names for this exercise; it is only necessary to distinguish between species. Grasses can be listed as grass 1, grass 2, and so forth. Have the students discuss the differences between the areas. Which of the areas has greater diversity? Which area would be less affected by disturbances? Which area would be less affected by pest infestation?

Suggested Lecture Format:

I.   The Value of Wild Species and Biodiversity

Protecting wild species and their ecosystems must receive priority, if for nothing else, because of the ecosystem capital that they provide, but it is difficult to come to a consensus about the extent of protection that is necessary.

A.   Biological Wealth—The natural species of living things represent the earth's biological wealth "that makes up most of the ecosystem capital and sustains human life and economic activity with goods and services".

B.   Two Kinds of Value—Living species either have instrumental value or have intrinsic value. **See Discussion Topic #1.**
1.   Instrumental Value—The species "existence or use benefits some other entity"
2.   Intrinsic Value—The species "has value for its own sake; that is, it does not have to be useful to us to possess value."

C.   Sources for Food and Raw Materials—Natural selection ensures that food supplies will be well adapted to the native environment, but selective breeding and cultivars reduce genetic variation which puts our food supplies at high risk in the environment.
1.   Wild Genes—Bringing wild genes into a cultivar by breeding can restore some variation in our food supply.
2.   New Food Plants—New sources of food could become more important as current food sources become threatened. See the winged bean as an example in Figure 6-2.
3.   Woods and Other Raw Materials—Materials that we rely on that come from trees could be at risk in the near future.
4.   Banking Genes—Seed banks may ensure survival of our food in the future.

D.   Sources for Medicine—"The field of ethnobotany, the study of relationships between plants and people" is helping us to understand how important natural species can be for medicine and

60

healing. See the rosy periwinkle example in Figure 6-3 and Table 6-1 Modern Drugs from Traditional Medicines.

E. Recreational, Aesthetic, and Scientific Value—"The species in natural ecosystems also provide the foundation for numerous recreational and aesthetic interest, ranging from sport fishing and hunting to hiking, camping, bird-watching, photography, and more". See Figure 6-4 for examples.
1. A Cautionary Note—"The indigenous people in the areas where biodiversity is the highest may not be the ones to benefit from their resources."
2. The Loss of Instrumental Value—The Economic of Ecosystems and Biodiversity report detailed the effects of loss of biodiversity.

F. Value for Their Own Sake—"Environmental ethicists argue that the long-established existence of species means they have a right to continued existence" despite their instrumental value or lack thereof.
1. Religious Support—Most major religions demonstrate the intrinsic value of species
2. The Land Ethic—The essay by Aldo Leopold in 1949 stated that "A thing is right when it tends to preserve the integrity, stability, and beauty of the biotic community."

II. Biodiversity and its Decline
Human interaction with wild species has reduced biodiversity over a short period of time.

A. How Many Species?—"Almost 2 million species have been discovered and described and certainly, many more than that exist". See Table 6-2 for examples of known species from each domain and kingdom. **See Discussion topic #3.**

B. The Decline of Biodiversity—Biodiversity is declining in the United States and throughout the entire world. See Figure 6-5 for the state of U.S. species. And Figure 6-6 for species extinction rates.
1. North America—"At least 500 species native to the United States, including at least 100 vertebrates, are known to have gone extinct (or have gone missing and are believed to have gone extinct) since the early days of colonization."
2. Global Outlook—The loss of biodiversity is even more profound on a global scale. Twenty-three percent of mammal species and 12% of bird species are globally threatened, according to a 2008 study by the International Union for Conservation of Nature (IUCN).

C. Reasons for the Decline—"Current threats to biodiversity" include "habitat destruction, invasive species, pollution, population, and overexploitation".
1. Habitat Change—Changes in natural habitats can happen because of human conversion of ecosystems to different types of systems (conversion see Figure 6-7), because humans build in ecosystems and change them in small pockets at a time (fragmentation see Figure 6-8), because humans think they understand the ecosystem and its members but really don't understand how deeply human actions can affect the ecosystem (simplification), and because of the intrusion of human technology into natural ecosystems.
   i. Conversion—"Natural areas are converted to farms, housing subdivisions, shopping malls, marinas, and industrial centers."
   ii. Fragmentation—"Human-dominated landscapes…" "…consist of a mosaic of different land uses, resulting in small, often geometrically configured patches that frequently contrast highly with neighboring patches. Small fragments of habitat can

support only small numbers and populations of species, making them vulnerable to extermination."

    iii. Simplification—"Human use of habitats often simplifies them."

    iv. Intrusion—Telecommunication towers present a unique hazard to migrating birds. "Any solution to wild species' decline must include creative ways to lower the impact of human structures on other organisms."

2. Invasive Species—A species that is introduced to an area, whether accidentally or on purpose, can severely disrupt native species.

    i. Accidental Introductions—Many species are introduced accidentally such as the Sahara mustard, which most likely came from date palm shipments brought from the Middle East.

    ii. May I Introduce…—Many species were introduced with good intentions, but had devastating effects on native species.

    iii. Over Time—"The transplantation of species by humans has occurred throughout history, to the point where most people are unable to distinguish between the native and exotic species living in their lands." "One report calculates the annual cost of invasive species in the United States to be $137 billion."

    iv. Invasive Species and Trophic Levels— "Plants provide food for herbivores that in turn provide food for carnivores. Non-native plants, because they may have different resistance mechanisms, may be difficult for herbivores to eat and thus may keep energy and materials from passing up the food chain, even if a species has been in a new ecosystem for a long time."

3. Pollution—Pollution can lead to a loss of biodiversity.

4. Population—The increasing human population continually displaces other native species because of the amount of space and resources that we currently use.

5. Overexploitation—"The overharvest of a particular species is known as overexploitation".

    i. Trade in Exotics—The illegal trade of exotic species provides at least $12 billion a year, making it very profitable.

    ii. Greed—"The long-term prospect of extinction does not curtail the activities of exploiters because, to them, the prospect of a huge immediate profit outweighs it."

D. Consequences of Losing Biodiversity—Consequences include loss of goods, loss of keystone species, and loss of ecosystem stability and resistance to environmental pressures. **See Discussion topic #2.**

1. Moving Forward—Despite the alarming numbers there are some success stories.

III. Saving Wild Species

Stopping the loss of biodiversity requires wisdom, policy, and enforcement.

A. The Science of Conservation—Conservation biology focuses "on the protection of populations and species" and the field of taxonomy "is the cataloging of species and the naming of new ones". Both are necessary for moving conservation efforts forward.

B. Policy and Political Structure—"Public policies, and the agencies that make and support them, are necessary for the protection of species". Examples of such policy include game animals in the United States, hunting and conservation, and how to deal with nuisance animals who move into human spaces because of the loss of natural ecosystems (see Figures 6-14, 6-15, and 6-16).

1. Game Animals in the United States—Those animals that are hunted for sport, meat, or pelts

62

i. Turkey Boom—Turkeys were hunted to the point of extinction, protected, and then re-introduced into native areas as well as non-native areas.
2. Hunting and Conservation—"Using hunting and trapping fees as a source of revenue, state and wildlife managers enhance the habitats that support important game species."
3. Backyard Menagerie—Many animals are finding their way into human dominated environments because of the fragmentation of their habitats

C. Protecting Endangered Species—"Government policies that protect animals from overharvesting are essential to keep species from the brink of extinction".
1. Lacey Act—This act forbids "interstate commerce in illegally killed wildlife-and therefore makes it more difficult for hunters to sell their kill."
2. Endangered Species Act—This act was passed in 1973 and reauthorized in 1988. "The law specifies substantial fines for killing, trapping, uprooting, modifying significant habitat of, or engaging in commerce in the species or its parts. See Figure 6-17 for examples of endangered species and Table 6-3 for the Federal Listings of Threatened and Endangered U.S. Plant and Animal Species in 2008.
3. Alternatives and Roadblocks—Opposition to the Endangered Species Act from "development, timber, recreational, and mineral interests as well as other lobby groups" is rampant.
4. Conflicting Values—While some people feel that the ESA goes too far, others feel that it isn't going far enough to address the problem.
5. Future Legislation—"The (Endangered Species) Act is something of a last resort for wild species, but it embodies an encouraging attitude toward nature that has now become public policy."

D. Seeing Success—Success is possible for endangered species. See "Return of the Gray Wolf" in the Sustainability box.
1. Birds of Prey—Other successes include the peregrine falcon and other birds of prey (see Figure 6-18).
2. Fly Away Home—The whooping crane (see Figure 6-19) is another success story.
3. he Spotted Owl—The Northwest Forest Plan was worked out in 1994 in an attempt to save the spotted owl.

IV. Protecting Biodiversity Internationally
Cooperation between local, state, federal, and international authorities are necessary to protect international biodiversity.

A. International Developments—The International Union for the Conservation of Nature (IUCN) is an international union focused on protection of species.
1. The Red List—A list maintained by the IUCN of threatened species
2. Cites—Convention on International Trade in Endangered Species of Wild Fauna and Flora
3. Convention on Biological Diversity—"The Biodiversity Treaty, as the convention was called" "addresses the conservation of biodiversity, the sustainable use of biodiversity services, and the equitable sharing of the use of genetic resources found in a country".
4. Critical Ecosystem Partnership Fund—"Jointly sponsored by the World Bank, Conservation International, the government of Japan, the MacArthur Foundation, and the Global Environment Facility" provides grants for conservation activity in biodiversity.

B. Stewardship Concerns—"What we do about wild species and biodiversity reflects on our wisdom and our values."
   1. Wisdom—Wisdom is needed on the part of policy makers and enforcers regarding stewardship.
   2. Values—"Our values are demonstrated by our approach to wild species."

Review Questions: Possible Answers

1. *Define biological wealth and apply the concept to human use of that wealth.*
    The biota "and the ecosystems they form represent wealth—the biological wealth—that comprises most of the ecosystem capital that sustains human life and economic activity with goods and services. From this perspective, the biota found in each country represents a major component of the country's wealth." "Humans have always depended upon Earth's biological wealth for food and materials, and as animals, we have always exploited wild species for food." Humans depend upon ecosystems and the biota for food, clothing, housing, and all aspects of our lives.

2. *Compare instrumental value and intrinsic value as they relate to determining the worth of natural species. Where does Leopold's idea of the land ethic fit into these two categories?*
    There are two kinds of value: instrumental and intrinsic. Instrumental value is anthropocentric and can be categorized into three areas. These areas are sources for agriculture, forestry, aquaculture, and animal husbandry, sources for medicines, and recreational, aesthetic, and scientific value. Instrumental value means that a species has a specific function for humans. "Something has intrinsic value when it has value for its own sake; that is, it does not have to be useful to use to possess value." Some will argue that only humans have intrinsic value but others argue that every species has intrinsic value. The difference in the assignment of intrinsic value to species is the source of many conflicts. A species with instrumental value has a very clear worth to humans while the worth of a species with intrinsic value is less easily defined or quantified. According to Leopold and "The Land Ethic", "A thing is right when it tends to preserve the integrity, stability, and beauty of the biotic community. It is wrong when it tends otherwise". Leopold tends to focus on intrinsic values above instrumental.

3. *What are the four categories into which the human valuing of natural species can be divided? Give examples of each one.*
    "The value of natural species can be categorized as follows:

    *   Value as sources for food and raw materials"
        *   Wild genes
        *   New food plants
        *   Pest control: natural enemies, genes for increasing resistance
    *   "Value as sources for medicines and pharmaceuticals"
        *   "Vincristine from the rosy periwinkle to treat childhood leukemia"
        *   Vinblastine from the rosy periwinkle to treat Hodgkin's disease
        *   Venom from a Brazilian pit viper led to the development of the drug Capoten, used to control high blood pressure
        *   Paclitaxel, (and Taxol) an extract from the bark of the Pacific yew, has proven valuable for treating ovarian, breast, and small cell cancers.
        *   Table 10-1 has additional examples
    *   "Recreational, aesthetic, and scientific value"
        *   sport fishing and hunting to hiking, camping, bird-watching, photography
        *   Table 10-2 has additional examples of recreational value
        *   Ecotourism

64

- "Value for their own sake" (intrinsic value)
  - The "long established existence of species means they have a right to continued existence"

4. *What means are used to preserve game species, and what are some problems emerging from the adaptations of many game species to the humanized environment?*

   Game animals are preserved by using hunting quotas; hunting and trapping fees; monitoring of game populations with adjustments of quotas; excise tax on hunting, fishing, shooting, and boating equipment; and establishment of game preserves, parks, and other areas where hunting and fishing are prohibited.

   Some problems that have emerged from the adaptations of game species to the humanized environment are "1. The number of animals killed on roadways now far exceeds the number killed by hunters. 2. Many nuisance animals are thriving in highly urbanized areas, creating various health threats. Opossums, skunks, and deer are attracted to urban areas by opportunities for food, unsecured garbage cans, and pet food. 3. Some game animals have no predators except hunters and tend to reach population densities that push them into suburban habitats, where they cannot be hunted effectively. The white-tailed deer, for example, has become a pest to gardeners and fruit nurseries; it also poses a public health risk because it is often infested with ticks that carry Lyme disease. 4. In recent years, suburbanites have been increasingly attacked by cougars, bears, and alligators as urbanization encroaches on the wild. 5. Coyotes, which once roamed only in the Midwest and western states, are now found in every state and are increasing in numbers. A highly adaptable predator, the coyote will eat almost anything. 6. Suburban parks and lawns, college campuses, and golf courses have become home to exploding flocks of Canada geese."

5. *What is the Lacey Act, and how is it used to protect wild species?*
   "In 1900 Congress passed the Lacey Act, forbidding interstate commerce in illegally killed wildlife, making it more difficult for hunters to sell their kills. Since then, numerous wildlife refuges have been established to protect the birds' breeding habitats. Under the act, the U.S. Fish and Wildlife Service (FWS) can bring federal charges against anyone violating a number of wildlife laws."

6. *How does the Endangered Species Act preserve threatened and endangered species in the United States? Give some examples of how the act has been implemented.*
   The Endangered Species Act of 1973 (ESA) provides protection to endangered and threatened species. "When a species is officially recognized as being either endangered or threatened, the law specifies substantial fines for killing, trapping, uprooting (in the case of plants), modifying significant habitat of, or engaging in commerce in the species or its parts. The legislation forbidding commerce includes wildlife threatened with extinction anywhere in the world." Critical habitats must be targeted for preservation and management to aid the recovery of the species. The ability of ESA to manage land extends to privately held land. Without this authority, the ability to manage ecosystems for species recovery would be non-existent. ESA has been implemented by using the listing of a species whose survival is in doubt, protecting critical habitat for species whose numbers have dropped to critical levels and developing "recovery plans that are designed to allow listed species to survive and thrive."

7. *What are the most critical controversies surrounding the Endangered Species Act? What alternatives have been proposed?*
   Some claim that "ESA has been a failure because only 10 of the 1,300 listed species have recovered and been taken off the list. In response, proponents state that the two main causes of extinction—habitat loss and invasive exotic species—are on the increase. Other critics of the ESA believe that the act does not go far enough. A major shortcoming is that protection is not provided until a species is officially listed by the FWS as endangered or threatened and a recovery plan is established. Currently, the backlog on listing includes some 281 'candidate species,' all of which are acknowledged to be in need of listing. Another contentious issue is the establishment of critical habitat. Opponents believe that the critical habitat designation places unwanted burdens on property owners, and assert that the critical habitat finds have little merit in conserving species. By

65

restricting the desires of property owners to use their land because it contains an endangered species, the ESA, in the views of opponents, 'takes' the property in the constitutional sense of the term."

8. *What is biodiversity? What do scientists need to know to calculate it for a habitat?*

Biodiversity is the result of speciation and extinction occurring over time, and the result of these two processes has been the gradual increase in the number of species. No one knows how much biodiversity exists. Estimates range widely and the upper limit estimates keep rising. The current estimates of biodiversity range from 13.6 to 111.6 million species, but only 1.75 million species have been described. Groups especially rich in species are the flowering plants (270,000 species) and the insects (950,000 species), but even less diverse groups, such as birds or ferns, are rich with species that are unknown to most people."

9. *What do the letters in the acronym HIPPO stand for? What is an example of each?*

HIPPO stands for habitat destruction, invasive species, pollution, population, and overexploitation. An example of habitat destruction can be seen at the border between Haiti and the Dominican Republic (see Figure 6-7). Numerous examples of invasive species may be given. Examples described in this chapter include the brown tree snake, Saltcedar, and Brazilian pepper. Pollution, like that seen in the Mississippi River can lead to a loss of biodiversity. In this example, nutrient pollution leads to a "dead zone" in the Gulf of Mexico. The overpopulation of humans displaces wildlife. Overexploitation was seen in the example of the puffins which were overharvested until they were on the brink of extinction.

10. *Give several examples of ways habitat change can either harm species or aid them.*

Habitat change in the form of conversion, fragmentation, and intrusion can lead to the harm of species because of lack of land for native species to live on. Most habitat changes lead to the harm of a species.

11. *What is IUCN, CITES, and the Convention of Biological Diversity? How do their roles differ?*

IUCN (International Union for the Conservation of Nature, now the World Conservation Union) maintains a "Red List of Threatened Species." It does not actively engage in preserving species in the field but its findings are often the basis of conservation activities throughout the world, and it provides crucial leadership to the world community on issues involving biodiversity.CITES is the Convention on Trade in Endangered Species of Wild Fauna and Flora. "(I)t is an international agreement that focuses on trade in wildlife and wildlife parts." Limitations include that the various countries must agree to a complete ban on trade and the restrictive trade permits are complicated, applying to 30,000 species. "Although CITES provides some protection for species that might be involved in international trade, it is inadequate to address broader issues pertaining to the loss of biodiversity."The Convention on Biological Diversity "addresses three complementary objectives: (1) the conservation of biodiversity, (2) the sustainable use of biodiversity services, and (3) the equitable sharing of the use of genetic resources found in a country. Although the targets laid out in the Strategic Plan are achievable, and the tools for achieving them are largely in place, it will take an unprecedented and costly effort to reach success."12. *What are the major recommendations of the UN Global Diversity Assessment for the protection of biodiversity?*The four major recommendations include: "1) Reforming policies that often lead to declines in biodiversity, 2) Addressing the needs of people who live adjacent to or in high-biodiversity areas or whole livelihood is derived from exploiting wild species, 3) Practicing conservation at the landscape level, and 4) Promoting more research on biodiversity."

Thinking Environmentally: Possible Answers

1. Some people argue that each individual animal has an intrinsic right to survival. Should this right extend to plants and microorganisms? What about the Anopheles mosquito, which transmits malaria or tigers that sometimes kill people in India? What about bacteria that causes typhoid fever? Defend your position.
      Answers to this question will vary. Asking about the release of domesticated cats and dogs into the wild rather than euthanasia might be an additional interesting question to pose. Is it better for the cat or dog to be released to fend for itself, killing wild animals (one of the largest causes of death among song birds is predation by cats), and dying unpleasantly after a possible short life (cats and dogs will be eaten by coyotes, cats will be injured by raccoons, etc.)?

2. Choose an endangered or threatened animal or plant species, and use the Internet to research what is currently being done to preserve it. What dangers is your chosen species subject to? Figure 6-17 gives some examples of endangered and threatened animal species. Answers will vary based on the species that each student chooses.

3. *The Endangered Species Act is the most important legislation in the United States for the protection of species. However, there are critics who think it is too strict and those who think it is not strict enough. Investigate one example of the application of the law-for example, to gray wolves-and decide what you think ought to be done.*

      Answers will vary depending on what example of the application of the Endangered Species Act that the student chooses.

4. *Log on to Conservation Internationals' biodiversity hot spots Web page, and research one of the 34 hot spots . What is being done to protect biodiversity in this location?*

      Depending upon the hot spot chosen, the answer to this question will differ. Below are the Conservation Actions described for the North and Central America hotspots.

California Floristic Province:

      "A little under 110,000 km², or 37 percent of the total land area of the California Floristic Province (CFP), is" protected. The CFP contains several national parks, almost 50 wilderness areas, 16 national wildlife refuges, 107 state parks and over 50 areas managed by non-profit organizations (or non-governmental organizations–NGOs). The Sierra Club, The Nature Conservancy, and the Wilderness Society worked very hard to help create many of these protected areas.

      "The hotspot includes two of the oldest national parks established in the United States: Yosemite National Park and Sequoia National Park (which provides protection to the biodiversity in the southern Sierra Nevada) were created within days of each other in 1890. Other important national parks in the region include Redwood National Park, officially establish in 1968 (and expanded in 1978) and the 1,010-km² Channel Islands National Park, a series of islands off the coast of southern California that provide protection for nesting colonies of seabirds and breeding populations of seals and sea lions, as well as the island fox.

      "In the last several decades, California has spent more money on conservation and set aside more habitat for protection than any other state in the United States. Nonetheless, the situation in California, the wealthiest of the United States, serves as an important reminder that biodiversity loss and the lack of complete and adequate protection for unique and threatened ecosystems is not just a problem in developing countries."

Madrean Pin-Oak Woodland:

"Although some 27,000 km² (around six percent of the hotspot's land area) is under some form of protection, only 8,900 km² (two percent of the land area) are in protected areas in IUCN categories I to IV. Most of the endemic terrestrial vertebrate species in Mexico that are still unprotected are located on the southern slopes of the Sierra Madre del Sur and, to a lesser extent, on the western slopes of the Sierra Madre Occidental and the eastern slopes of the Sierra Madre Oriental, making this hotspot an important conservation priority.

"One of the most important protected areas in the hotspot is the 563-km² Monarch Butterfly Biosphere Reserve in Michoacán, which was decreed in 1986. Other Mexican protected areas include the 1,396-km² Sierra de Manantlán Biosphere Reserve in Jalisco, which protects very diverse pine-oak forests, with some 33 species of *Quercus*. The largest protected area in the hotspot, and one of the largest in Mexico, is the 1,774-km² Cumbres de Monterrey National Park in the Sierra Madre Oriental. In the Sierra Madre Occidental, the 48-km² Cumbres de Majalca National Park, the 58-km² Cascada de Basaseachic National Park and the 93-km² La Michilía Biosphere Reserve conserve notable stands of pine-oak formations. In Baja California, the 1,124-km² Sierra de la Laguna Biosphere Reserve was established in 1994 to protect an island of intact pine-oak vegetation.

"On the American side of the hotspot, Big Bend National Park in Texas covers 3,245 km². Most of the pine-oak woodlands in the Madrean Sky Islands of the United States are protected, although the majority are in U.S. Forest Service land. Nevertheless, several smaller, highly protected reserves also occur, some operated by private owners, such as The Nature Conservancy, and others designated as U.S. National Monuments or U.S. Wilderness Areas.

"Several conservation NGOs are working in the Madrean Pine-Oak Woodlands, including the Fondo Mexicano para la Conservación de la Naturaleza, which is working to enhance social participation to prevent fires in key areas. PRONATURA/PRONATURA NORESTE, which was established in 1997, works in the Sierra Madre Occidental and Sierra Madre Oriental to conserve and promote the sustainable use of natural resources. The Sierra Madre Alliance, a network of Mexican and international partners working in the Sierra Madre Occidental in Chihuahua, aims to preserve biodiversity and restore the functioning of forested ecosystems through local participation. In the United States, the Sky Island Alliance, formed in 1992, has worked with agencies in Mexico to create a Sky Islands Wildlands Network Conservation Plan to consider the needs of all stakeholders and formulate a framework for conservation in this region.

"An important private initiative has been the work of CEMEX to protect Madres del Carmen, in the northern part of Coahuila. Since 1999, the cement company has purchased, and effectively protected, 700 km² of land, including several new pieces that bring El Carmen to the U.S. border and make it contiguous with Big Bend National Park in Texas. As a result, the two protected areas now form a 20,000 km² conservation unit that includes some of the most important remaining tracts of the Chihuahuan Desert wilderness and significant portions of the Madrean Pine-Oak Woodlands Hotspot."

Caribbean Islands:

"About 30,000 km², or 13 percent of the land area of this hotspot, is officially protected, but many of these protected areas are far from pristine. Just over half of the protected land area, totaling a little over 16,000 km² is in IUCN categories I to IV, which afford greater protection. In general, there is a great need for much better management, monitoring, and enforcement of protected areas throughout the Caribbean. Cuba has about 15 percent of its land area in conservation units, including the 300-km² Zapata Swamp. Dominica has a little over 20 percent of its territory designated for protection, while the Dominican

Republic reports about 15 percent. However, many of these reserves lack formal management plans, and are too small to effectively conserve biodiversity. In other countries, protected areas are effectively non-existent, as is the case in Haiti and Grenada, which both have less than 1.7 percent of their area protected. In general, the Caribbean Islands emerge as top priority for the expansion of the global protected areas network.

"A wide variety of local organizations promote conservation efforts in the Caribbean. For example, Grupo Jaragua, a group of citizens and scientists in the Dominican Republic, helps support and manage Jaragua National Park, one of the largest land-and-sea parks in the hotspot. In Haiti, the Foundation for the Protection of Marine Biodiversity works with both fishers and the government to promote sustainable use of the country's living marine resources. A non-governmental organization, the Bahamas National Trust, manages the Bahamian national park system, which is being expanded to cover twenty percent of the country's territorial seas. On Bonaire, the National Parks Foundation actively manages the Bonaire Marine Park, which is widely recognized as one of the most effective marine reserves inside the hotspot. Its counterpart on St. Eustacius, an island with only 2,000 people, provides technical backstopping for programs ranging from sea turtle tagging and monitoring of the island's pristine reefs to the development of nature trails that reach the elfin forest at the island's volcanic summit.

"The prospects for biodiversity conservation in the Caribbean Islands have been enhanced by the development of partnerships between major industries, such as tourism, and the governmental and private organizations that are promoting conservation on the ground. The Protocol for Specially Protected Areas and Wildlife (SPAW), which came into force in 2000, was created at the initiative of the Caribbean countries to provide region-wide standards and mechanisms for harmonizing conservation efforts across the region."

Mesoamerica:

"About 13 percent, or 142,000 km², of the total land area of the Mesoamerica hotspot is currently under some form of protection, though only 64,000 km² (six percent) of this is in IUCN categories I to IV. In two countries, national percentages for protected land are more than twice the hotspot average: Belize (37 percent) and Costa Rica (31 percent). El Salvador has the lowest percentage of protected land area; approximately two percent of the country is under protective status.

"Many of the parks in Mesoamerica exist on paper only and need improved enforcement and management in order to effectively conserve biodiversity. The integrity of many protected areas is further threatened by communities that live in or around the parks and must poach for food or clear agricultural lands within park borders in order to meet their basic needs.

"In recent decades, there has been important progress in regional cooperation and dialogue toward the creation and expansion of the transnational Mesoamerican Biological Corridor, a regional initiative aimed at conserving biodiversity and ecosystems while at the same time promoting sustainable social and economic development. The initiative attempts to protect important areas for biodiversity and provide connectivity between these areas through biodiversity-friendly plantation forests, agroforestry systems, and private reserves, to allow for the dispersal of plants and animals. Mesoamerican countries have been eager to participate in the creation of the corridor because it provides a tangible goal in the face of daunting conservation priorities. Among the important protected areas that comprise this initiative are the Maya Biosphere Reserve in northern Guatemala, a 10,000-km² expanse of tropical forest; the Calakmul Biosphere Reserve in Campeche, Mexico, with 7,000 km²; the Montes Azules Biosphere Reserve in Chiapas, Mexico, covering 3,300 km²; the Rio Bravo protected area in Belize; La Amistad International

69

Park and Biosphere reserve in Costa Rica and Panama, the largest block of undisturbed cloud forest in Central America and a convergence point for 75 percent of all migratory birds in the Western Hemisphere; and Guanacaste Conservation Area in northwestern Costa Rica.

"One method for identifying priority areas for the expansion of protected areas systems is by identifying sites for species that face the greatest risk of global extinction. Globally threatened species are best protected through the conservation of sites in which they occur; these sites are referred to as "key biodiversity areas" (KBAs). KBAs are discrete biological units that contain one or more globally threatened or restricted-range species, and can potentially be managed for conservation as a single unit. In the Mesoamerica hotspot, Conservation International and partners have been working on KBA identification in the northern portion (Mexico east of the Isthmus of Tehuantepec, Belize and Guatemala), Costa Rica, and Panama, building off of the Important Bird Areas identified by BirdLife International partners in Mexico and Panama. The process will continue as the collaboration expands to include all the countries of the hotspot during the next year. The La Amistad International Park in Costa Rica and Panama, the only place in the world from which the salamander *Oedipina grandis* (CR) has been recorded, is an example of the potential for developing a regional network of transboundary protected areas. Here the Critical Ecosystem Partnership Fund is facilitating a regional approach to protecting Mesoamerica's biodiversity by supporting bi- and tri-national conservation initiatives. The Cerro El Pital between Honduras and El Salvador, a site protected only on the Honduran side of the border by the Cerro El Pital Biological Reserve, and the only place in the world where the frog *Bolitoglossa synoria* (CR) occurs, serves as another example of the potential for expanding the network of protected areas through transboundary conservation initiatives.

"Ecotourism has become an important sector in nearly every country in Mesoamerica, notably Costa Rica, which is probably the world's best-known example of the successful promotion of economic benefit from conservation. In 2000, Costa Rica earned about $1.25 billion from ecotourism, and it is estimated that 70 percent of the country's tourists visit natural protected areas.

"In addition, several national level institutions for biodiversity conservation, including INBIO in Costa Rica and CONABIO in Mexico, are successfully promoting greater awareness and sustainable use of biodiversity, while smaller local institutions, such as the Belize Zoo and Mexico's Miguel Alvarez del Toro Zoological Park, promote knowledge, pride, and conservation of native fauna among the citizens of Mesoamerica."

CHAPTER 7
The Use and Restoration of Ecosystems

Chapter Outline:

I. Ecosystem Capital
    A. Ecosystems as Natural Resources
        1. Valuing
            i.   Private Versus Public Lands
            ii.   Domesticated Nature
            iii.   Future Pressures

II. Conservation, Preservation, Restoration
    A. Conservation Versus Preservation
    B. Patterns of Human Use of Natural Ecosystems
        1. Consumptive Use
            i.   Bush Meat
        2. Productive Use
            i.   Tenure
        3. Maximum Sustainable Yield
            i.   Optimal Population
            ii.   Precautionary Principle
        4. Using the Commons
            i.   Tragedy of the Commons
            ii.   Limiting Freedom
            iii.   Maine Lobsters
            iv.   Public Policies
    C. Ecosystem Restoration
        1. Everglades Restoration
            i.   In Bondage
            ii.   Water Release
            iii.   Land Buyout
         2. Pending Restorations

III. Biomes and Ecosystems Under Pressure
    A. Forest Ecosystems
        1. Forest Resources Assessments
        2. Forests as Obstacles
            i.   Consequences
        3. Types of Forest Management
            i.   Clear-Cutting
            ii.   Other Methods
        4. Sustainable Forestry
        5. Tropical Forests

Key Topics:

1. Ecosystem Capital: Natural ecosystems have great economic value, as they provide goods and services vital to human well-being.

2. Conservation, Preservation, Restoration: Ecosystems are put to both consumptive and productive usesand occasionally need to be restored to a more healthy state.

3. Biomes and Ecosystems Under Pressure: Forest and ocean ecosystems are under major pressures, but there are sustainable ways to fill the demands.

4. Protected Lands: Public and private management of lands is key to keeping habitats both protected and productive.

Instructional Goals:

1. Natural ecosystems provide a number of goods and services to humans that cannot be replaced.

2. The concept of conservation implies the management and use of goods and resources in a way that the use does not adversely affect the viability of species or ecosystems to renew themselves. The concept of preservation implies that a species or ecosystem will not be used, irrespective of its possible utility to humans. When conservation and preservation either have not happened, or have not been successful, restoration of the ecosystem is necessary to return it to a natural state.

3. Management of ecosystems as sustainable resources requires knowledge that humans do not yet have.

4. Substantial progress has been made toward attaining the information necessary for humans to interact sustainably with the world's ecosystems.

Concepts and Connections:

Nearly everything can be connected to the material in this chapter. Our climate is dependent upon the movement of energy (heat) through the water cycle. Changes in the pattern of heat distribution produce changes in our weather—El Niño and La Niña. When unplanned flooding occurs, it is frequently due to changes in the ability of an ecosystem to assist in the cycling of water. Humans are dependent on soil for our food; soil building and erosion control are services provided by ecosystems. For many years it was common to hear that the solution to pollution is dilution. This statement came from the observation that nature provided waste treatment services if we did not overwhelm them. We can learn from nature how to maximize the benefits we can obtain from it. To do this we need to understand the world around us.

Concepts in Context:

Humans are completely dependent on the goods and services provided by nature. Nature maintains the nutrient cycles (Chapter 4), water cycle (Chapter 10), and ecosystem balance (Chapter 5). An ecosystem's carrying capacity (Chapter 5) for each species determines the quantity of resources we can use. Without biodiversity (Chapter 6) the goods and services would be limited. The variety of niches and habitats (Chapter 3) within an ecosystem (Chapter 5) provide humans with a wide array of species from which we obtain goods and services. The ability to grow food (Chapter 12) depends on soil (Chapter 11). The tools (pesticides) we use to protect our food resources (Chapter 13) primarily come from fossil fuels (Chapter 14). Additionally, fossil fuels have replaced human and animal energy in food production (Chapter 12). Alternative energy (Chapter 16) and nuclear power (Chapter 15) are dependent on ecosystem goods and services. Biotic potential and environmental resistance (Chapter 5) are important for understanding Maximum Sustained Yield. The maintenance of global climate is explained by the hydrologic cycle (Chapter 10).Air pollution (Chapter 19) and water pollution (Chapter 20) adversely impact the goods and services provided by nature. How we handle solid (Chapter 20) and hazardous (Chapter 22) waste can adversely impact the nature's ability to provide goods and services. Global climate change and ozone depletion (Chapter 18) can also have adverse impacts on the goods and services.

Key Terms and Vocabulary:

Forests and woodlands, grasslands and savannas, croplands, wetlands, desert lands and tundra, coastal ocean and bays, coral reefs, open ocean, natural goods, natural services, natural resources, ecosystem capital, renewable resource, conservation, preservation, consumptive use, maximum sustainable yield (MSY), carrying capacity, optimal population, total allowable catch (TAC), precautionary principle, common-pool resource, commons, restoration ecology, Comprehensive Everglades Restoration Plan (CERP), silviculture, sustained yield, sustainable forest management, fishery, catch shares, Magnuson-Stevens Fishery Conservation and Management Reauthorization Act, zooxanthellae, wilderness, national parks, national wildlife refuges, new forestry, ecosystem management, private land trust, easements

Discussion, Activities, and Labs:

1. Ask the class to list the material goods and services obtained from ecosystems. Ask the class to list one to five ways we use each of the material goods or services. Are there resources (goods) we use/need that do not come from nature? Are there ways that we can obtain clean water or air without resources (goods) obtained from nature?

2. Ask the students if they have gone to a National Park, Wildlife Refuge, National or State Forest, State Park, and so on. List where the students have been. Ask them to list what they liked and did not like about the place. Ask the class to list what benefit those who have never gone to a particular park, refuge, or forest might obtain from the existence of the park, refuge, or forest (goods and services).

3. Provide groups of five to six students with resources and services obtained from the environment. These can be pieces of paper indicating enough oil to fuel 10 cars for 50 years with each car having fuel efficiency equal to one bus, enough food to feed 20 people for 100 years, enough wood to build 30 houses, and so forth. Various quantities of resources should be given to each group. Have each group determine how many people can be supported, and for how long based upon the available resources. Ask the students to come up with 10 ideas about what can be done to increase the number of people or the length of time that the resources will last. (Fewer people and more efficient use of resources are the main categories for changing the length of resource availability.) Have each group designate a spokesperson and discuss the conclusions of each group as a class.

4. Pick the five most important items to your daily life, (car, stereo, computer, clothing, and food). For each of these items list the goods and services necessary for the existence of that item. Use the Internet and library resources to determine all the components of the item and to discover all the environmental goods and services necessary for each component of the item.

Suggested Lecture Format:

I. Ecosystem Capital
   Natural ecosystems provide a number of goods and services to humans that cannot be replaced.

A. Ecosystems as Natural Resources—"A natural area will receive protection only if the value a society assigns to services provided in its natural state is higher than the value the society assigns to converting it to a more direct human use." See Figure 7-1. **See also Discussion Topic #1 and #4.**

    1. Valuing—Although economics helps us to assign value to services, ecological values are difficult to assign a monetary value.

        i.   Private Versus Public Lands—Both privately and publicly owned lands can be used sustainably; whether or not they are is determined by the current human need for the land.

        ii.   Domesticated Nature—"What we call natural may only be an illusion because humankind has so converted and domesticated natural systems that it is difficult to find areas of the world without human impact."

        iii.   Future Pressures—Increases in the number of humans will undoubtedly put more pressure on ecosystems to provide their natural services.

II. Conservation, Preservation, Restoration

The concept of conservation implies the management and use of goods and resources in a way that the use does not adversely affect the viability of species or ecosystems to renew themselves. The concept of preservation implies that a species or ecosystem will not be used, irrespective of its possible utility to humans. When conservation and preservation either have not happened, or have not been successful, restoration of the ecosystem is necessary to return it to a natural state. **See Discussion Topic #3.**

    A. Conservation Versus Preservation—"Conservation of natural biotas and ecosystems does not imply *no* use by humans whatsoever rather, the aim of conservation is to *manage or regulate use* so that it does not exceed the capacity of the species or system to renew itself. The objective of preservation of species and ecosystems is to *ensure their continuity, regardless of their potential utility.*"

    B. Patterns of Human Use of Natural Ecosystems—Humans use natural ecosystems in two major ways (consumptive and productive).

        1. Consumptive Use—People use natural resources to provide for their needs.

        i.   Bush Meat—Wild game is harvested in many developing countries to provide for the nutrition of native people

        2. Productive Use—"The exploitation of ecosystem resources for economic gain."

        i.   Tenure-Tenure refers to the property rights over land or water. Four types of tenure include: 1) private ownership, 2) communal ownership, 3) state ownership 4) open access.

        3. Maximum Sustainable Yield—"The highest possible rate of use that the system can match with its own rate of replacement and maintenance." See Figure 7-6.

        i.   Optimal Population—"Theoretically the optimal population for harvesting MSY is just halfway to the carrying capacity."

        ii.   Precautionary Principle-When there is uncertainty about the maximum sustainable yield, it is best to err on the side of protection of the natural resource.

        4. Using the Commons—A commons refers to a resource that is owned by many people or that can be owned by none. A commons has open access for all users.

   i. Tragedy of the Commons—Common areas are susceptible to the Tragedy of the Commons. Since the resource is used by many but owned by none it becomes exploited easily. When users note that the resource is becoming overused no-one wants to withdraw their use and lose profits because they know that the others will most likely keep overusing the resource. See "The Turtle Island Commons" p.169.

   ii. Limiting Freedom—Private ownership and/or regulating access to the commons can possibly prevent the Tragedy of the Commons from occurring. See Table 7-2.

   iii. Maine Lobsters—In Maine an informal local set of rules amongst fishers has helped keep the state's lobster populations thriving.

   iv. Public Policies—When MSY, social, and economic factors are taken into account, "public policies can be established and enforced that protect natural resources effectively."

 C. Ecosystem Restoration—"The intent of ecosystem restoration is to repair the damage to specific lands and waters so that normal ecosystem integrity, resilience, and productivity return."

  1. Everglades Restoration—"The Comprehensive Everglades Restoration Plan (CERP) is expected to take 36 years and almost $11 billion to complete." See Figure 7-8.

   i. In Bondage—The everglades are currently bound on all sides by natural or man-made elements that make restoration difficult.

   ii. Water Release—By removing levees and canals "new water flowage is designed to restore the river of grass, thereby restoring the 2.4 million acres of Everglades."

   iii. Land Buyout—In some cases federal and state funds are used to purchase private property for the purpose of restoring ecosystems.

  2. Pending Restorations—Examples include: the California Bay Delta, Chesapeake Bay, Platte River Basin, the Upper Mississippi River System, the Galapagos Islands, the Illinois River, the Brazilian Atlantic forest, and Tampa Bay.

III. Biomes and Ecosystems Under Pressure

  Management of ecosystems as sustainable resources requires knowledge that humans do not yet have.

 A. Forest Ecosystems—Forests are the most productive ecosystems. "In spite of this value, the major threat to the world's forest is not simply their exploitation, but rather their total destruction."

  1. Forest Resources Assessments—The Global Forest Resources Assessment 2000. See Figure 7-9 and 7-10.

  2. Forests as Obstacles—Forests are being cleared at high rates because despite their productivity, they are very difficult for humans to use for food.

   i. Consequences—Clearing a forest has significant consequences for the land and people.

  3. Types of Forest Management—"The practice of forest management, usually with the objective of producing a specific crop (hardwood, pulp, softwood, wood chips, etc.), is called silviculture."

   i. Clear-Cutting—The process of "removing and entire stand at a time."

   ii. Other Methods—Selective cutting and shelter-wood cutting can be more sustainable that clear-cutting forests.

4. Sustainable Forestry—"Forests are to be managed as ecosystems, with the objectives of maintaining the biodiversity and integrity of the ecosystem, but also to meet the social, economic, cultural, and spiritual needs of present and future generations."

5. Tropical Forests—These forests are being removed at a very high rate and this is of great concern.
   i. Reasons for Removal—The major reason for tropical forest deforestation is their replacement with pastures for agriculture.
   ii. New Trends—Logging companies are taking advantage of the desperation of developing nations with rain forests.
   iii. Certification—"Certification makes it possible for consumers to choose wood products that   have been harvested sustainably."

B. Ocean Ecosystems—Oceans cover much of the earth and provide value economic and ecological services.

1. Marine Fisheries—"Fisheries provide employment for at least 200 million people and account for more than 15% of the total human consumption of protein." See Figure 7-13.
   i. The Catch—The global fish catch in addition to the production by aquaculture equals the total world production of fish for consumption each year.
   ii. The Limits—"The world fish catch may appear stable, but many species and areas are overfished." See Figure 7-14.
   iii. Georges Bank—When fishing intensity doubled, economically important fish declined drastically. See Figure 7-15.
   iv. Management Councils—"The Magnuson Act established eight regional management councils made up of government officials and industry representatives."
   v. Other Cod Fisheries—The Grand Banks experienced a similar crash of the cod population
   vi. Fisheries Law Reauthorized-In new legislation, called the Magnuson-Stevens Fishery Conservation and Management Reauthorization Act, the councils were required to set catch limits based on scientific evidence of the size and health of marine populations.
   vii. Other Issues-Banning shark finning, "dolphin-safe" tuna, reducing bycatch with Gulf shrimping, declining stocks of swordfish and tuna, and ground meal issues all need to be addressed.
   viii. Marine Reserves-"Marine Protected Areas (MPAs) are areas of the coasts and sometimes open oceans that have been closed to all commercial fishing and mineral mining."

2. International Whaling-Whales being overharvested in the open oceans led to the moratorium on commercial whaling. See Table 7-3.
   i. Whale Stakes-Japan, Iceland, and Norway have persisted in killing whales. See Figure 7-17.
   ii. Whale Watching-"Whale watching has become an important tourist enterprise in coastal areas." See Figure 7-18.

3. Coral Reefs-"Coral reefs are among the most diverse and biologically productive ecosystems in the world."

i. Global Threats-Coral bleaching and ocean acidification are major threats to the coral reef ecosystems. See Figure 7-19.

ii. Exploitation-Whether driven by consumptive or productive use, the reefs are being exploited and harmed by human use.

4. Mangroves-"have the unique ability to take root and grow in shallow marine sediments. There they protect the coasts from damage due to storms and erosion and form a rich refuge and nursery for many marine fish." "Between 1983 and the present, half of the world's 45 million acres of mangroves were cut down, with percentages ranging from 40% to nearly 80%."

IV. Protected Lands

Substantial progress has been made toward attaining the information necessary for humans to interact sustainably with the world's ecosystems.

A. Public and Private Lands in the United States—"The United States is unique among the countries of the world in having set aside a major proportion of its landmass for public ownership." See Figure 7-20 and 7-21. **See also Discussion Topic #2.**

1. Wilderness—Preserved lands with the greatest amount of protection.

2. National Parks and National Wildlife Refuges—Intended to protect areas of "great scenic or unique ecological significance, protect the wildlife species, and provide public access for recreation and other uses."

3. National Forests—740 million acres in the United States.

i. Multiple Use—"allowed for a combination of extracting resources (grazing, logging, and mining), using the forest for recreation, and protecting watersheds and wildlife."

ii. New Forestry—"Involves cutting trees less frequently, leaving wider buffer zones along streams to reduce erosion and protect fish habitats, leaving dead logs and debris in the forest to replenish the soil, and protecting broad landscapes."

iii. The Roadless Controversy—The Clinton administration produced a moratorium on building new logging roads which the Bush administration tried to replace and the Obama administration intends to uphold.

iv. Fires—"The years of 2006 and 2007 set new records for forest fires."

4. Protecting Nonfederal Lands—Voters in local areas decided to pay taxes to keep open spaces for parks.

i. Land Trusts—Private land trusts are "non-profit organizations that will accept either outright gifts of land or easements but retain ownership of the parcel."

B. Finals Thoughts—"Other areas that are in trouble include wetlands drained for agriculture and recreation, overgrazed rangelands, and rivers that are overdrawn for irrigation of water.

Review Questions: Possible Answers

1. *What were the problems in the Pacific Halibut fishery, and how were they resolved?*

The management strategy was to set an annual total allowable catch (TAC) and allow the fishing fleet to fish until the TAC was reached. In 1990 the fishing season was only 6 days, most of the fish caught had to be frozen, gear was lost or damaged, and crews were endangered when the weather was bad. Now "a management strategy called the individual quota system" is used. "Owners of fishing vessels . . . (are) allocated a percentage of the annual TAC based on the size of their vessel and their recent fishing performance." They can "decide when to fish within a season that last(s) as long as 8 months. The fishers saw an increase in their income and they could fish in better weather, and they lost less fishing gear. To everyone's surprise, fish stock improved."

2. *What are some goods and services provided by natural ecosystems?*
    See Figure 7-1. Some examples may include: food, water, erosion control, climate regulation, recreation, aesthetic value, timber, fuel, food and disease regulation, medicine, nutrient cycling, pest regulation, air quality regulation, education, and waste processing.

3. *Compare the concept of ecosystem capital with that of natural resources. What do the two reveal about values?*
    Ecosystem capital includes the goods and services produced by the species within an ecosystem and the interactions between the biotic and abiotic portions of ecosystems. Ecosystems, and biota in them, are expected to produce something of economic value. Within this context, natural resources are only those items in an ecosystem that have a monetary value and things with a monetary value are not a resource. Ecosystem capital does not require that a monetary value is known or exists. All that matters with ecosystem capital is that there is ecological value.

4. *Compare and contrast the terms conservation and preservation.*
    "Conservation of natural biotas and ecosystems does not—or at least should not—imply no use by humans whatsoever, although this may sometimes be temporarily expedient in a management program to allow a certain species to recover its numbers. Rather, the aim of conservation is to manage or regulate use so that it does not exceed the capacity of the species or system to renew itself. The objective of preservation of species and ecosystems is to ensure their continuity, regardless of their potential utility. Thus, a second-growth forest can be conserved (trees can be cut, but at a rate that allows the forest to recover), but an old-growth forest must be preserved (it must not be cut down at all)."

5. *Differentiate between consumptive use and productive use. Give examples of each.*
    "Productive (use) is the exploitation of ecosystem resources for economic gain. Thus products such as timber and fish (and now, bush meat) are harvested and sold for national or international markets." Consumptive use is "when people harvest natural resources in order to provide for their needs for food, shelter, tools, fuel, and clothing. Thus, people are hunting for game, fishing, or gathering fruits and nuts in order to meet their food needs, or else they are gathering natural products like firewood, forage for animals, or wood and palm leaves to construct shelters or to use as traditional medicines."

6. *What does maximum sustained yield mean? What factors complicate its application?*
    Maximum sustained yield (MSY) is the "highest possible rate of use that the system can match with its own rate of replacement or maintenance." The problem with implementing MSY is that we do not know the highest recruitment rate for a species with a specified ecosystem but we make decisions as if we do know. The optimal population size to obtain MSY is one half of the size that it would be at the carrying capacity. We do not know an ecosystem's carry capacity for various species. Additionally, the carrying capacity will vary from year to year. When the maximum sustained yield is exceeded, the availability of the resource declines.

7. *What is the tragedy of the commons? Give an example of a common pool resource, and describe ways of protecting such resources.*
    The tragedy of the commons is "where a resource is owned by many people in common or by no one" and the resource is used by each individual to maximize his/her benefit. Resource exploitation is expected when each individual maximizes his/her benefit without regard to the ecosystem's ability to sustain the level of use. Examples of a common pool resource are federal grasslands, coast and open-ocean fisheries, groundwater, nationally owned woodlands and forests, and the atmosphere. "One arrangement that can mitigate the tragedy is private ownership. Where private ownership is unworkable, the alternative is to regulate access to the

commons. Regulation should allow for (1) protection, so that the benefits derived from the commons can be sustained, (2) fairness in access rights, and (3) mutual consent of the regulated."

8. *When are restoration efforts needed? Describe efforts underway to restore the Everglades.*

Restoration efforts are needed "to repair damage to specific lands and waters so that normal ecosystem integrity, resilience, and productivity return. The ecological problems that can be ameliorated by restoration include those resulting from soil erosion, surface strip mining, draining wetlands, coastal damage, agricultural use, deforestation, overgrazing, desertification, and the eutrophication of lakes. "The plan calls for removing 240 miles of levees and canals and creating a system of reservoirs and underground wells to capture water for release during the dry season. The new flowage is designed to restore the river of grass, thereby restoring the 2.4 million acres of Everglades not to original state, but at least to a healthy system."

9. *Describe some of the findings of the most recent FAO Global Forest Resources Assessment. What are the key elements of sustainable forest management?*

"Major findings of the new assessment are as follows: 1. In 2005, the world's forest cover was 3.95 billion hectares (9.8 billion acre). 2. Deforestation continues to occur, primarily in the developing countries. 3. Throughout the world, the most important forest product is wood for industrial use; half of the forest lands are designated for 'production,' where the wood is harvested for pulp (paper source), lumber, and fuelwood. FRA 2005 reports that there have not been any drastic changes in forest production over the past 15 years, except for the steady increase in plantation forests. 4. Worldwide, about 9% of the forests are protected as national parks or reserves. An additional 65% of the world's forests have protection as one of their designated functions. 5. The role of forests in climate change was formally acknowledged in November 2001 at a meeting of the signers of the Kyoto Protocol in Marrakech, Morocco. The outcome of this accord is a much more thorough inventory of the role of forests as carbon stores, sources of carbon emissions, and carbon sinks. FRA 2005 estimates that forest ecosystems in 2005 contained 638 Gt (gigatons) of carbon, more than the amount of carbon as CO_2 in the atmosphere. Half of this carbon is in living and dead wood, and half in forest soils."

The key elements of sustainable forest management include: 1. Maintain adequate forest cover to support "the social, economic, and environmental dimensions of forestry", 2. Conserve biological diversity, 3. Protect forest health and vitality, 4. Manage productive functions of forest resources, 5. Protect functions of forest resources, 6. Address socioeconomic function, and 7. Provide the legal framework to support the other six elements.

10. *What is deforestation, and what factors are primarily responsible for deforestation of the tropics?*

"Deforestation is the removal of forest and replacement by another land use. Deforestation is caused by a number of factors, all of which come down to the fact that the countries involved are in need of greater economic development and have rapid population growth. The FRA 2000 study concluded that the current major cause of deforestation is conversion to pastures and agriculture."

11. *What is the global pattern of exploitation of fisheries? Compare the yield of capture fisheries with that of aquaculture.*

"The harvest has increased remarkably since 1950, when it was just 20 million metric tons. By 2003 it had reached 132 million metric tons. Aquaculture accounted for 41.9 million tons, or 32% of the world fish supplies that year. Based on the trends shown in the figure, the 'capture' fisheries leveled off in the 1990s, and the continued rise in fish production is due to aquaculture.

12. *Compare the objectives of the original Magnuson Act with those of the 2006 Magnuson-Stevens Fishery Conservation and Management Reauthorization Act.*

The original Magnuson Act extended the limits of jurisdiction over fisheries from 12 miles offshore to 200 miles offshore. It also "established eight regional management councils made up of government officials and industry representatives." In 2006 the reauthorization kept the regional councils but required them to "set catch limits based on sound scientific advice from the council's Scientific and Statistical Committee.

13. *What is the current status of the large whales? Discuss the controversy over continued whaling by some countries.*

In 1986 the International Whaling Commission instituted a moratorium on the hunting of all whale species to allow for recovery. "The moratorium has never been lifted; however, some limited whaling by Japan, Iceland, and Norway continues, as does harvesting by indigenous people in Alaska, the Russian Federation, and Greenland." Because these countries continue to kill whales despite the moratorium at levels higher than necessary for "science" and ignore the commission's authority, the controversy continues.

14. *How are coral reefs and mangroves being threatened, and how is this destruction linked to other environmental problems?*

Coral reefs are being threatened by bleaching (caused by increases in ocean temperature) and exploitation of reefs for fish, shellfish, and other sea life in addition to tropical fish harvesting. Mangroves are being threatened by logging, coastal land development, and the development of shrimp ponds. The destruction of coral reefs and mangroves are linked to global climate change and the overexploitation of resources.

15. *Compare the different levels of protection versus use for the different categories of federal lands in the United States.*

Wilderness: "Permanent protection of these undeveloped and unexploited areas so that natural ecological process can operate freely. Permanent structures, roads, motor vehicles, and other mechanized transport are prohibited. Timber harvesting is excluded. Some livestock grazing and mineral development are allowed where such use existed previously; hiking and other similar activities are also allowed."

National Parks and National Wildlife Refuges: "(T)he intent is to protect areas of great scenic or unique ecological significance, protect important wildlife species, and provide public access for recreation and other uses."

National Forests: Multiple activities are attempted, such as recreation, timber harvesting, mining, grazing, and protection of watersheds and wildlife.

16. *Describe the progression of management of our national forests during the last half century. What are two current issues, and how are they being resolved?*

Management of our forests began in the 1950s as a multiple use strategy, "which meant a combination of extracting resources (grazing, logging, and mining), using the forest for recreation, and protecting watersheds and wildlife. Although the intent was to achieve a balance among these uses, multiple use actually emphasized the extractive uses; that is, it was output oriented and served to justify the ongoing exploitation of public lands by private, often favored, interest groups."

"A forestry-management strategy was introduced in the late 1980s called New Forestry. This practice of forestry is directed more toward protecting the ecological health and diversity of forests than toward producing a maximum harvest of logs. The Forest Service began adopting some of these management principles in the

81

early 1990s, and they formed the core of what is now the official management paradigm of the Forest Service: ecosystem management. This paradigm has been adopted by all federal agencies managing public lands."

17. *How do land trusts work, and what roles do they play in preserving natural lands?*
A private land trust is "a non-profit organization that will accept either outright gifts of land or easements—arrangements in which the landowner gives up development rights into the future, but retains ownership of the parcel. The land trust may also purchase land to protect it from development."

"Land trusts are proving to be a vital link in the preservation of ecosystem. The land trusts are serving the common desires of landowners and rural dwellers to preserve the sense of place that links the present to the past. At the same time, the undeveloped land remains in its natural state, sustaining natural population and promising to do so into the future."

Thinking Environmentally: Possible Answers

1. *It is an accepted fact that both consumptive use and productive use of natural ecosystems are necessary for high-level human development. To what degree should consumptive use hold priority over productive use? Think about more than one resource (lumber, bush meat, etc.).*

Opinions of students, and therefore their answers, will vary. Although productive use of environmental resources is necessary to continue the level of economic profit that humans have gained from the environment in the past, the trend in the future will undoubtedly be towards consumptive use, especially as human population numbers increase.

2. *Consider the problem presented by Hardin of open access to the commons without regulation. To what degree should the freedom of use of these areas be limited by the authorities? Make use of Table 7-2 when you defend your position.*

Answers will vary. It is well established that common areas will be exploited and authorities need to regulate such areas.

3. *Consider the benefits and problems associated with coastal and open-ocean aquaculture. Is it a useful practice overall? Justify your answer.*
Coastal aquaculture provides food sources for humans without the bycatch that is possible in the open areas of the ocean. However, in order to make suitable spaces for such aquaculture mangroves are being converted. Such mangroves actually provide significantly more environmental and economic benefit to the area than the aquaculture. Also, because pollution levels are highest near the coast, contamination of the populations is common. In open-ocean aquaculture, on the other hand, pollution is not as much of a problem. The problem with open-ocean aquaculture is that production levels are very low.

4. *Kofi Annan stated that we are in need of a "new ethic of stewardship." What principles should this new ethic be built upon?*
As in the example of the Billion Tree Campaign, the most important principle for this "new ethic of stewardship" will be acting out of concern for other world citizens. When we consider not only our needs, but

82

those of the others around us and those of future generations we will make much more sustainable environmental decisions.

CHAPTER 8
The Human Population

Chapter Outline:

I.   Humans and Population Ecology
- A. *r*- or *K*-Strategists
- B. Revolutions
    1. Neolithic Revolution
    2. Industrial Revolution
    3. Medical Revolution
    4. The Green Revolution
    5. The Newest Revolution
- C. Do Humans Have a Carrying Capacity?

II. Population and Consumption: Different Worlds
- A. Rich Nations, Middle-Income Nations, Poor Nations
- B. Population Growth in Rich and Poor Nations
- C. Different Populations, Different Problems
    1. Impact of Wealth
    2. Enter Stewardship

III. Consequences of Population Growth and Affluence
- A. Countries with Rapid Growth
    1. Land Ownership Reform
    2. Intensifying Cultivation
    3. Opening Up New Lands
    4. Illicit Activities
    5. Migration Between Countries
    6. Migration to Cities
    7. Challenges to Governments
- B. Countries with Affluence

IV. Projective Future Populations
- A. Population Profiles
- B. Predicting Populations
    1. Population Projections for Developed Countries
        i.   Graying of the population
        ii. Less Graying Here
    2. Population Projections for Developing Countries
        i.   Burkina Faso
        ii. Growth Impacts
- C. Population Momentum
- D. The Demographic Transition
    1. Birth and Death Rates
        i.   Epidemiologic Transition
        ii. Fertility Transition

    2.   Phases of the Demographic Transition

Key Topics:

1. Humans and Population Ecology
2. Population and Consumption
3. Consequences of Population Growth and Affluence
4. Protecting Future Populations

Instructional Goals:

1. Humans are a part of nature and subject to its laws, but upon closer inspection, the global human population holds a special place in the biosphere. Changes in the relationship of humans to their environment have caused major environmental revolutions throughout time.

2. Different people, in different parts of the world, live greatly different lives and therefore have greatly different types of impact on the environment.

3. Both countries with rapid growth and countries with affluence have to deal with population issues and the environmental consequences of those issues.

4. Population projections for developing and developed countries vary greatly. Developing countries tend to have a large base of young people and a small aged population whereas developed countries tend to have a large population of aged individuals with a small base of young.

Concepts and Connections:

Human population dynamics will be a topic about which students will know some information. Some of the information will be incorrect. Problems created by population size are seen by most Americans as problems outside our country. We fail to recognize that some of our urban problems are similar to problems observed in developing countries—overcrowding, lack of sanitation, poor health care, crime, poverty, and high illiteracy rates.

Americans, and others living in the developed world, are connected to the environmental consequences of too many people in the developing world because of our actions. The purchase of illegal drugs or endangered wildlife is likely to lead to adverse environmental consequences in a developing country.

Connecting an individual's consumption pattern with the related environmental consequences helps to create an understanding that no country or individual is solely at fault for our current environmental dilemma. All the substances on the Earth are connected by cycles. Humans in different countries are also connected to each other. Immigration into the United States is discussed by some as the cause of our population problem. Immigration into the United States is a population problem only insofar as it may result in increased consumption rates due to the greater average consumption rate of Americans as compared to people in developing countries. Immigrants into the United States do not increase the world population numbers, and they quickly match U.S. reproductive rates.

Concepts in Context:

Population dynamics of non-human species (Chapter 5) can be related to human population dynamics. The primary difference between humans and nonhumans is the human ability to choose the number of offspring we have (Chapter 9).

The impact of human consumption rates can be related to many adverse environmental consequences. Air pollution (Chapter 19) in the United States has not decreased despite substantial technological improvements due to the increase in the average number of miles driven by Americans. Our fuel consumption rate also can be related to the possibility of global climate change (Chapter 18). The rate of production of ozone depleting chemicals is due to consumer demand in the developed nations (Chapter 18). Loss of biodiversity (Chapter 6) is a problem in the developed countries when wetlands are drained for farming or housing, forests are invaded by those attempting to escape the city, and so forth. Water pollution (Chapter 20) in the developed world is a result of both nutrient loading and the disposal of unwanted chemicals—the solution to pollution is dilution. In the developed world, large quantities of energy are used per person, and each of these energy sources has adverse environmental impacts (Chapters 14, 15, 16).

In developing countries, the impact of human population size can be related to many environmental problems. Soil erosion (Chapter 11) and loss of biodiversity (Chapter 6) due to people moving on to previously unfarmed lands are very severe in many developing countries. Air pollution (Chapter 19) in the cities of many developing countries exceeds internationally recognized standards. Between the use of outdated technology and financial inability to maintain them, many automobiles in the developing world are severe polluters. Water pollution (Chapter 20) is mainly a problem due to nutrient loading. The quantity of energy used per person in the developed world is small when compared to the quantity used per person in the developed world. The primary sources of energy, gathered wood and dung, result in increased soil erosion, diversion of nutrients from soil, air pollution, and substantial energy expenditures by the individuals doing the gathering.

Key Terms and Vocabulary:

demography, demographers, Paleolithic, Neolithic Revolution, Industrial Revolution, environmental revolution, developed countries, developing countries, total fertility rate, replacement-level fertility, footprint, longevity, population profile, age structure, life expectancy, longevity, population momentum, demographic transition, crude birth rate (CBR), crude death rate (CDR), Phase I, Phase II, Phase III, Phase IV

Discussion, Activities, and Labs:

1. Divide the class into groups of three to four students. Ask each group to list four resources that are needed for survival (food, water, shelter, fuel, or clothing). Next ask the students to list five things that might happen if the number of people in a family, a village, or a country, is increased but the quantity of resources remains constant. The goal is to have students think about how if the number of people is increased and the quantity of resources does not increase, then there are fewer resources per person. Poverty is the result of attempting to spread the same quantity of resources over more people.

2. Make a population profile from the members of the class. Ask each student two class sessions before the session on human population dynamics to indicate how many people in their family (grandparents, parents, siblings,

themselves, and children) are in each of the five-year age groups. Also ask for the sex of each individual. (The information would be most accurate if a form with the age brackets and sex of each individual is provided.) Assure the students that no information other than the five-year age bracket and sex are necessary. Provide the students with the information from the class and have groups of two to three students create a population profile of the class and the class members' families. Discuss the similarities and differences between the class-generated profile and the profile for the country.

3. Divide the students into groups of two to three. Using the population profile created by the class and the current birthrate for various countries (include both developed and developing), have the students determine the number of people who will be born in the next ten years. Will the population of the country increase, decrease, or remain the same?

4. Population momentum, the time period between when fertility rates equal replacement level and the number of births equal the number of deaths, is not typically understood by students. Using the population profile of the United States, starting from 1955 when the fertility rate was 3.7 through the drop to 1.75 in 1975 to our current fertility rate of 2.0, have the students determine when the population will stop growing. For this exercise, do not include immigration or emigration. The exercise works just as well if you have the students work with round numbers for ease of calculation.

Suggested Lecture Format:

I. Humans and Population Ecology

Humans are a part of nature and subject to its laws, but upon closer inspection, the global human population holds a special place in the biosphere. Changes in the relationship of humans to their environment have cause major environmental revolutions throughout time. See Figure 8-1. **See also Discussion Topic #1.**

A. *r*- or *K*Strategists—Although it seems that the global human population is growing on a J-curve, humans are *K*-strategists; *K*-strategists typically remain near carrying capacity.

B. Revolutions—"In the past there have been several large-scale upheavals in the way humans do things. These include the development of agriculture, the Industrial Revolution, modern medicine, the green agricultural revolution, and the current environmental revolution."
1. Neolithic Revolution—Once humans began to farm, they settled into permanent living areas, domesticated animals, developed technology, began to store food, reduced mortality all of which lead to an increase in population. See Figure 8-2.
2. Industrial Revolution—Technological improvements made possible by the use of fossil fuels allowed humans to do work that was never possible before. See Figure 8-3.
3. Medical Revolution—Before the 1800's, mortality rate was high because of the prevalence of diseases. The discovery of antibiotics, vaccinations, and improvements in sewage treatment and nutrition reduced mortality and allowed for population expansion.
4. The Green Revolution—"The development of chemical pesticides in World War II, along with an increase in irrigation and fertilizer use, dramatically increased crop yields. See Figure 8-4.
5. The Newest Revolution—New technologies like the Internet may lead to a real "green" revolution, and environmental revolution.

87

C. Do Humans Have a Carrying Capacity?—"Throughout history, humans have improved their survival rate, increased their populations, and increased their life span by doing some things other organisms cannot do (or cannot doon the scale we can)." However, we have recently hit limits, like a reduction in non-renewable resources that may finally be limiting to population growth.

II. Population and Consumption: Different Worlds
Different people, in different parts of the world, live greatly different lives and therefore have greatly different types of impact on the environment. See Figure 8-5.

    A. Rich Nations, Middle-Income Nations, Poor Nations—"The high income nations are commonly referred to as developed countries, whereas the middle- and low-income countries are often grouped together and referred to as developing countries. See Figure 8-6.

    B. Population Growth in Rich and Poor Nations—"Total fertility rates have dropped all over the world, but most dramatically in the high-income countries. In developing countries, fertility rates have come down considerably." See Figure 8-7 and Figure 8-8.

    C. Different Populations, Different Problems—According to the IPAT formula "environmental impact (I) equals population (P), multiplied by the level of technology of the society (T)."
      1. Impact of Wealth—Increasing the wealth of individual countries will not necessarily lead to the environmental sustainability of that country.
      2. Enter Stewardship—"Stewardly concern" and practice is necessary before sustainability can be achieved.

III. Consequences of Population Growth and Affluence
Both countries with rapid growth and countries with affluence have to deal with population issues. Many of the ways that we deal expanding populations have environmental consequences.

    A. Countries with Rapid Growth—When humans began to move from small and sustainable populations to larger populations with the help of modern medicine, humans had several options for how to deal with growth, all with environmental consequences.

      1. Land Ownership Reform—Group ownership of large plots of land (collectivization) and ownership by the wealthy few have historically been two ways that land has been owned. Re-organization of ownership can sometimes increase agricultural output.
      2. Intensifying Cultivation—"The introduction of more highly productive varieties of basic food grains in the Green Revolution has had a dramatic beneficial effect in supporting the growing populations." Environmental impact includes "a deterioration of soil, decreased productivity, and erosion."
      3. Opening Up New Lands—Opening up land for agriculture may mean conversion or fragmentation of other environmentally important types of habitats.
      4. Illicit Activities—"Anyone who doesn't have a way to grow sufficient food must gain enough income to buy it-and sometimes desperate people break the law to do this."

5. Migration Between Countries—Migration (immigration) to countries with more money or more available jobs may seem like a good idea but often can lead to prejudice and exploitation.
6. Migration to Cities—"Faced with the poverty and hardship of the countryside, many hundreds of millions of people in developing nations continue to migrate to cities in search of employment and a better life." See Figure 8-12.
7. Challenges to Governments—Basic services like education, housing, healthcare, and transportation in cities with high populations are falling behind or not available.

B. Countries with Affluence—"High individual consumption places enormous demands on the environment. The world's wealthiest 20% of people are responsible for 86% of all private consumption and 80% of world trade."

IV. Projective Future Populations
Population projections for developing and developed countries vary greatly. Developing countries tend to have a large base of young people and a small aged population whereas developed countries tend to have a large population of aged individuals with a small base of the young.

A. Population Profiles—"A population profile is a bar graph showing the number or proportion of people at each age for a given population." **See Discussion Topic #2.**

B. Predicting Populations—"The United Nations gives three different projections of future world populations. The medium scenario assumes that world fertility will drop from 2.55 children per woman to slightly above 2 children per woman by 2050." See Figure 8-13 and 8-14. **See also Discussion Topic #3.**

1. Population Projections for Developed Countries—Italy can be used as an example of population trends in a developed country. It is expected that the number of older people will increase while the number of younger people will decline. See Figure 8-15 and Figure 8-16.
   i. Graying of the population—Graying is a term that refers to the number of elderly people in a population is increasing.
   ii. Less Graying Here—The United States is graying, but has a more stable younger population than other developed countries because of total fertility rate and high immigration.
2. Population Projections for Developing Countries—"Fertility rates in developing countries are generally declining, but they are still well above replacement level." See Figure 8-19.
   i. Burkina Faso—With a total fertility rate of 6.3, the population profile for this country will be a pyramid with a wide base of young people for the foreseeable future.
   ii. Growth Impacts—To maintain standards of living, countries that are growing quickly, like Burkina Faso, will have to double their resources for the population in the next two decades which is unlikely to happen.

C. Population Momentum—"Refers to the effect of current age structure on future populations." See Figure 8-20. **See also Discussion Topic #4.**

89

D. The Demographic Transition—"As economic development occurs, human societies move from a primitive population stability to a modern population stability, in which low infant and childhood mortality are balanced by low birthrates." See Figure 8-21.

    1. Birth and Death Rates—The crude birthrate (CBR) and the crude death rate (CDR) "are the number of births and deaths, respectively, per thousand of the population per year. A zero-growth population is achieved if, and only if, the CBR and CDR are equal and there is no net migration."

       i. Epidemiologic Transition—A shift from death due to epidemics and other social conditions to deaths from cancer, cardiovascular, and other degenerative diseases accounts for a change in mortality factors.

      ii. Fertility Transition—"In the now-developed countries, birthrates have declined from a high of 40 to 50 per thousand to 9 to 12 per thousand."

    2. Phases of the Demographic Transition—There are four stages of demographic transition. "Developed countries have generally completed the demographic transition. Developing countries, by contrast are still in Phases II and III." See Figure 8-22.

Review Questions: Possible Answers

1. *In what ways is human population ecology similar to and different from that of other organisms? Why is it difficult to determine a carrying capacity for humans?"*

    Humans are part of the natural world, and human populations are subject to processes such as birth and death." Even though the Millennium Ecosystem Assessment recognizes humans as an 'integral part of ecosystems,' there are some differences between humans and other organisms that make our role in ecosystems different from that of others. One major reason humans are different from other populations is that we have a global population which acts like a whole unit. We are also unique in our ability to control our reproduction, "use fire, store food for longer times, and adapt our environment with technology so we can live in more places." It is difficult to determine a carrying capacity for humans because we have the ability to increase our carrying capacity in the short term with technological advances. It is also difficult to determine at what standard of living to judge carrying capacity since there are so many lifestyle levels throughout the global population.

2. *How has the global human population changed from pre-historic times to 1800? From 1800 to the present? What is projected over the next 50 years?*

    "From the dawn of human history until the beginning of the 1800s, population increased slowly and variably, with periodic setbacks. It was roughly 1830 before world population reached the 1 billion mark. By 1930, however, just 100 years later, the population had doubled to 2 billion. Barely 30 years later, in 1960, it reached 3 billion, and in only 15 more years, by 1975, it had climbed to 4 billion. Thus, the population doubled in just 45 years, from 1930 to 1975. Then 12 years later, in 1987, it crossed the 5 billion mark! In 1999, world population passed 6 billion, and it is currently growing at the rate of nearly 77 million people per year."

    "On the basis of current trends (which assumes a continued decline in fertility rates), the U.N. Population Division (UNPD) medium projection predicts that world population will pass the 7 billion mark in 2012, the 8

90

billion mark in 2024, and the 9 billion mark in 2047, and will reach 9.1 billion in 2050. At that point, world population will still be increasing by 34 million per year."

3   *How does the World Bank classify countries in terms of economic categories?*
    "1. High-income, highly developed, industrialized countries. This group (1.056 billion in 2007) includes the United States, Canada, Japan, Korea, Australia, New Zealand, the countries of western Europe and Scandinavia, Singapore, Taiwan, Israel, and several Arab states (2007gross national income per capita, $11,456 and above; average of $37,566). Anje in Sweden is in this group.

    2. Middle-income, moderately developed countries. This group (4.26 billion) includes mainly the countries of Latin America (Mexico, Central America, and South America), northern and southern Africa, China, Indonesia and other southeastern Asian countries, many Arab states, eastern Europe, and countries of the former U.S.S.R. It is further divided by the World Bank in to lower middle income and upper middle-income countries. (2007 gross national income per capita, $936 – $3,705 for the former category, $3,706–$11,455; for the latter). Indonesia, home to Atin and her family, is in the lower middle income group.

    3. Low-income, developing countries. This group (1.296 billion) comprises the countries of eastern, western, and central Africa, India and other countries of southern Asia, and a few former Soviet republics. (2007 gross national income per capita, less than $936; average of $578). Awa and her family in Burkina Faso are members of this group."

4. *What three factors are multiplied to give total environmental impact? Are developed nations exempt from environmental impact? Why or why not?*
    The three factors are population, affluence, and technology. Developed nations are not exempt from environmental impact because these countries have tremendous affluence and therefore a substantial consumption level. Stewardship is a modifier; "attention to wildlife conservation, pollution control, energy conservation and efficiency, and recycling may offset, to some extent, the negative impact of a consumer lifestyle."

5. *What are the environmental and social consequences of rapid population growth in rural developing countries? In urban areas?*
    There are six impacts from rapid growth on the populations of rural developing countries:
    (1) overcultivation, soil erosion, and depletion of fertility; (2) overfishing and depletion of marine stocks;
    (3) poaching of wildlife, drugs, corruption, and other illegal activities; (4) moving to cities, squalor, and disease;
    (5) migration and immigration pressures on developed countries; and (6) bringing new land into production through deforestation, draining wetlands, and irrigation. In urban areas, environmental and social impact include: overpopulation in small spaces, conversion and fragmentation of natural ecosystems, concentration of municipal solid waste and human waste, and concentration of pollution.

6   *Describe negative and positive impacts of affluence (high individual consumption) on the environment.*
    "The United States has the dubious distinction of leading the world in the consumption of many resources. We are a large country and we are affluent. We consume the largest share of 11 of 20 major commodities: aluminum, coffee, copper, corn, lead, oil, oilseeds, natural gas, rubber, tin, and zinc. We lead in per capita consumption of many other items, such as meat. The average American eats more than three times the global average of meat. We lead the world in paper consumption, too, at 725 lbs per person per year. All of the factors (and many more like them) contribute to the unusually high environmental impact each of us makes on the world." We "lead the world in production of many pollutants. For example, by using such large quantities of fossil fuel (coal, oil, and natural gas) to drive our cars, heat and cool our homes, and generate electricity, the United States is responsible for a large share of the carbon dioxide produced. As mentioned, with about 5% of the world's population, the United States generates 24% of the emissions of carbon dioxide that may be

91

changing global climate. Similarly, emissions of chlorofluorocarbons (CFCs) that have degraded the ozone layer, emissions of chemicals that cause acid rain, emissions of hazardous chemicals, and the production of nuclear wastes are all largely the by-products of affluent societies. Consumption, often driven by advertising, places enormous demands on the environment and the developing world. The world's wealthiest 20% is responsible for 86% of all private consumption and 80% of world trade. As a consequence, 11 of 15 major world fishers are either fully exploited or overexploited, and old-growth forests in southern South America are being clear-cut and turned into chips to make fax paper."

Despite the adverse effects of affluence, increasing the average wealth of a population can affect the environment positively. An affluent country such as ours provides such amenities as safe drinking water, sanitary sewage systems and sewage treatment, and the collection and disposal of refuse. Thus, many forms of pollution are held in check, and the environment improves with increasing affluence. In addition, if we can afford gas and electricity, we are not destroying our parks and woodlands for firewood. In short, we can afford conservation and management, better agricultural practices, and pollution control, thereby improving our environment.

7. *What information is given by a population profile?*

"A population profile is a bar graph showing the number of proportion of people (males and females separately) at each age for a given population."

8. *How do the population profiles and fertility rates of developed countries differ from those of developing countries?*

The population profile for a developed country tends to be fairly columnar. The number of individuals in any particular age group is neither smaller nor larger than the number of individuals in any other age group. In some developed countries the number of individuals in the younger age groups is less than the number of individuals in the older age groups. The fertility rate is low, either below or at replacement

The population profile for a developing country tends to be pyramidal. The number of individuals in the youngest age groups exceeds, by a large margin, the number of individuals in the oldest age groups. This is partly due to the low life expectancy in the developing countries (fewer people survive to old age, 65+) and partly due to the large number of children born per women. The fertility rate is at or above replacement. Some developing countries have very high fertility rates (but the rates are lower than they were).

9. *Compare future population projections, and their possible consequences, for developed and developing countries.*

Developed countries are expected to see a population profile with increasing numbers of older individuals. The profile will look something like an inverted pyramid. Developing countries will become more columnar with increasingly the same number of individuals in each age group.

10. *Discuss immigration issues pertaining to developed and developing countries. Which countries are sending the most immigrants and which are receiving the most?*

When people emigrate from less affluent countries (developing) to more affluent countries (developed) they adopt the lifestyle of their new home. This increases the environmental impact per person. Many people who immigrate to developed countries are the most educated individuals from the developing countries. This can be beneficial to the developed country but detrimental to the developing country.

11. *What is meant by population momentum and what is its cause?*

Population momentum is when a country's population continues to grow "even after the total fertility rate is reduced to the replacement level." "Population momentum occurs because such a small portion of the population is in the upper age groups (where most death occurs) and many children are entering their reproductive years. Even if these . . . (individuals) have only two children per woman, the number of births will far exceed the number of deaths."

92

12. *Define crude birthrate (CBR) and crude death rate (CDR). Describe how these rates are used to calculate the percent rate of growth and the doubling time of a population.*

"The crude birthrate (CBR) and crude death rate (CDR) are the number of births and deaths, respectively, per thousand of the population per year." To obtain the percent rate of growth one subtracts the number of deaths from the number of births and then divides by 10 to give the percent increase or decrease in population per year. To obtain the doubling time the percent rate of growth is divided by 70.

13. *What is meant by the demographic transition? Relate the epidemiologic transition and fertility transition (two elements of demographic transition) to its four phases.*

"The basic premise of the demographic transition is that there is a causal link between modernization and a decline in birth and death rates." There are four phases of the demographic transition, as seen in the developed world. Phase I is a stable population size due to high death rates and high birthrates. In Phase II, the crude death rate drops but crude birthrates remain unchanged, resulting in increased population size. When a drop in crude birthrates begins, due to a drop in fertility rate, Phase III of the demographic transition has been reached. The population size is still increasing in Phase III. Phase IV occurs when the number of births equals the number of deaths and there is no growth in population size. The epidemiologic transition is the change in mortality factors from epidemics (acute illnesses) to chronic conditions (cancer and cardiovascular disease). The fertility transition is the decline in birthrates from "a high of 40 to 50 per thousand to 8 to 12 per thousand." The fertility transition does not happen at the same time that the epidemiologic transition occurs; the fertility transition is delayed, as compared to the epidemiologic transition, by decades or more. This has resulted in the very large increase in human populations. The epidemiologic transition begins in Phase II, while the fertility transition begins during Phase III of the demographic transition.

14. *How do the current positions of the developed and developing nations differ in demographic transition?*

Developed countries are thought to be within Phase IV of the demographic transition process, while developing countries are within Phase III. Some developing countries are at the beginning of Phase III, while others are at the end of Phase III, transitioning to Phase IV.

Thinking Environmentally: Possible Answers

1. *Consider how humans are different from and similar to other species. In what ways does it seem obvious that population ecology principles apply to humans? Why do some people see humans as not subject to the law of limiting factors?*

Humans are similar to other species in that we are subject to the laws of the natural world. We are living creatures that are dependent on the earth's resources to survive. Because of this, ecological principles apply to humans and are difficult to escape. However, because of our unique cognition, humans are able to engineer their circumstances to some degree. While we may be able to extend the limits of ecological principles, we are still subject to them.

2. *List the parameters you think you would need to keep track of to make accurate predictions about future human population growth. For example, what conditions might drive mortality and fertility trends?*

Parameters necessary for projection future human population growth include birth rates, death rates, fertility rate, expected immigration rates. Some conditions that might drive mortality and fertility trends include projected disease trends, economic environment, and recent trends in fertility rate.

3. *Consider the population in Italy or Germany: very low birthrates, an aging population, and an eventual decline in overall numbers. What policies would you recommend to these countries, assuming their desire to achieve a sustainable society?*

   Policies for caring for the elderly will be important to such countries. Also, although world population rates are high, each country will need to have a younger base of individuals for society to function properly. Immigration can be encouraged to a certain extent but will not be the entire answer and negative attitudes towards immigrants will need to be carefully balanced with policy and communication. This is a difficult situation and will need to be addressed carefully and with great wisdom.

4. *Consider the populations of Sweden, Indonesia, and Burkina Faso. How could people in each of these countries help those in other countries to steward their resources better or to promote a sustainable future?*

   Individuals in Sweden have reached a level of development where the average citizen has a high standard of living, an education, and choices about their future. They could teach others about how to achieve education for everyone, including women, and how to delay reproduction as a result. The people in Indonesia could teach others about the importance of the network of family and friends for survival. Sharing resources is something that those in developed countries have lost as a result of our independent spirits. Shared resources can be more sustainable than independent resources. In addition to understanding the need for family and friends for survival, those in Burkina Faso are closer to the environment than any of the others and can teach others about the natural cycles of ecosystems and how to live within their means as the environment changes.

CHAPTER 9
Population and Development

Chapter Outline:

I. Reassessing the Demographic Transition
- A. Different Ways Forward
  1. Population Conferences
     - i. End of Debate
- B. Demographic Dividend
- C. Large and Small Families
  1. Conclusions
     - i. Vicious Cycle

II. Promoting Development
- A. Millennium Development Goals
  1. The Millennium Project and MDG Support Team
  2. Progress toward the MDGs
     - i. Extreme Poverty
     - ii. Goals Affecting Children
     - iii. Other Goals
     - iv. Country-Level Reports
     - v. Paying for It
- B. World Agencies at Work
  1. What is the World Bank?
  2. Bad Bank, Good Bank
     - i. Bad Bank
     - ii. Good Bank
     - iii. Environmental Strategy
  3. Other UN Agencies
     - i. Should We Keep the UN?
- C. The Debt Crisis
  1. i. A Disaster
  2. Debt Cancellation
     - i. Zambia
- D. Development Aid
  1. Official Development Assistance
  2. Migration and Remittances
  3. Aid from the United States
  4. Global Financial Crisis

III. A New Direction: Social Modernization
- A. Improving Education
- B. Improving Health

1. Life Expectancy
2. Two Worlds
3. Reproductive Health
4. AIDS
   C. Family Planning
      1. Unmet Need
      2. Abortion
         i. How Many?
      3. Family-Planning Agencies
         i. The Global Gag Rule
   D. Employment and Income
      1. Grameen Bank
      2. More Microlending
   E. Resource Management
   F. Putting It All Together
      1. Globalization

Key Topics:

1. Reassessing the Demographic Transition
2. Promoting Development
3. A New Direction: Social Modernization

Instructional Goals:

1. There are many factors influencing family size. Knowing these factors and how they are interrelated can provide solutions to excessive population growth rates.

2. Economic development has been the traditional mode for promoting decreased fertility rates. Development focused on large-scale projects does not necessarily change the living conditions of the poorest individuals who have the highest fertility rates.

3. Development focused on improving access to education, family planning, and health care and enhancement of the management of resources are potentially effective means of reducing fertility rates.

Concepts and Connections:

Population and economic development issues can be related to innumerable events reported in the daily newspaper. Free trade agreements are claimed by many environmentalists to have a negative impact on the environment. This concern, and other possible consequences of free trade, has become part of the public debate. Free trade agreements are a result of the belief that reductions in trade barriers will reduce the impediments for development. Many believe the economic development that results from free trade will reduce fertility rates.

Discussion of the reasons why people choose to have children and choose to have a particular number of children can be related to other decisions we make about resource consumption. We choose to consume resources depending upon how expensive we perceive those resources are. It is assumed in a developed country that the basic

96

items needed to raise a child are considerable, whereas it is assumed by people living in a developing country that the basic items needed to raise a child are minimal. Children in a developed country are expensive, while gasoline is inexpensive. In a developing country, children are inexpensive but gasoline is expensive.

Concepts in Context:

Relating the reasons why people have children to the demographic transition (Chapter 8) observed in developed countries could help students see how the overall development of a country does not necessarily cause a decline in fertility rates. The relationships between the reasons people choose to have children and the biological underpinnings for population growth—biotic potential and recruitment (Chapter 4)—could be useful. Childhood and infant mortality, which affect recruitment, are important in the perception of the need to have a large family.

The relationship between population size and human impacts on ecosystems (Chapters 3, 4, and 5), soil erosion (Chapter 11), and biodiversity loss (Chapter 6) can be a focus of a class discussion. The production and distribution of food (Chapter 12) have a clear relationship with the number of people in the world, and our ability to grow more food will influence how many people can be supported and the ways we protect our food resources (Chapter 13). The resources use per person and the total number of people on the planet influence the resources we can obtain from ecosystems (Chapter 7), the quantity and types of energy needed (Chapters 15, 16, and 17), the quality of our air (Chapter 19) and water (Chapter 15), the quantity and types of wastes produced (Chapter 21 and 18), and the overall health of people and the environment (Chapter 17).

Key Terms and Vocabulary:

Dependency ratio, $1.25 per day, Millennium Project, MDG Support Team, World Bank, remittances, acquired immune deficiency syndrome (AIDS), microlending

Discussion, Activities, and Labs:

1. Divide students into groups of two to three. Ask the students to discuss who will benefit and who will pay the cost if the World Bank funds the building of a series of large dams in India. The dams will displace a number of indigenous people. These people will be relocated to a city. The amount of agricultural land that will be taken out of production due to flooding will not equal the amount of land that can be put into agricultural production when the irrigation potential from the dam is tapped. Ask the students to list the beneficiaries and those who will absorb the social costs of the dam. What are the benefits? What are the costs? Is the building of these dams likely to change the balance in the birth and death rates of the indigenous people? Why?

2. Because there are no correct or incorrect answers to the following questions, indicate to the students that you wish for them to seriously consider the questions, but you will be evaluating the answers based only on the seriousness of the response. Ask each student to indicate how many children they would like to have and why. Ask each student the age at which they would like to have their first child and why. Collect this information at least one lecture before this one so you can look at the responses and summarize them for the class.

Suggested Lecture Format:

I.   Reassessing the Demographic Transition

There are many factors influencing family size. Knowing these factors and how they are interrelated can provide solutions to excessive population growth rates.

A.   Different Ways Forward—Two basic theories about how developing countries will move through their demographic transitions: either they will move forward with economic development or with family planning technologies. See Figures 9-2 and 9-3.
1.   Population Conferences—The two basic theories were represented at conferences in Bucharest, Romania, and in Mexico City in the 70's and 80's.
   i.   End of Debate—At the population conference in Cairo in 1994 "the ideological split between developed and developing countries was a thing of the past—all agreed that population growth must be dealt with in order to make progress in reducing poverty and promoting economic development."

B.   Demographic Dividend—As a country goes through a demographic transition there is a brief window of opportunity when the younger and older classes of individuals are small compared to the working age group. If a country takes advantage of this window then it can shift towards development by making "the necessary investments in health, education, and economic opportunities to take full advantage of the demographic window." See Figure 9-4.

C.   Large and Small Families—Those in developing countries who have not entered the demographic transition tend to have larger families. Although this does not make sense to those of us in developed countries, there are clearly defined reasons for this phenomenon. See p. 225-226 for examples. See also Figures 9-5 and 9-7.
1.   Conclusions—"With industrialization and development, however, come conditions conducive to having small families."
   i.   Vicious Cycle—High fertility and poverty leads to consistent and difficult to escape environmental degradation. See Figure 9-8.

II. Promoting Development

Economic development has been the traditional mode for promoting decreased fertility rates. Development focused on large-scale projects does not necessarily change the living conditions of the poorest individuals who have the highest fertility rates.

A.   Millennium Development Goals—"In 1997, representatives from the United Nations, the World Bank, and the Organization for Economic Co-Operation and Development met to formulate a set of goals for international development that would reduce the extreme poverty in many countries and its carious impacts on human well-being."
1.   The Millennium Project and MDG Support Team—"The Millennium Project was given the mandate to develop a coordinated action plan that other agencies and organizations can consult as they address the MDGs." See Figure 9-2 for the MDGs.

2. Progress toward the MDGs—The Millennium Development Goals Report of 2008 summarizes the progress towards the goals. See Figure 9-9.
    i. Extreme Poverty—The goal to reduce the number of people globally living at extreme poverty levels has almost been met.
    ii. Goals Affecting Children—Although education for children is progressing well, childhood mortality rates are still high and difficult to combat.
    iii. Other Goals—Several other important goals are currently being met while others still require greater effort to achieve.
    iv. Country-Level Reports—"Global and regional reports are important in providing a general picture of progress being made toward the MDGs, but the real action is in the individual countries."
    v. Paying for It—"Both developing countries and donor countries will have to commit major new outlays of funds if the MDGs are to be met."

B. World Agencies at Work—"The World Bank functions as a special agency under the UN umbrella, owned by the countries that provide its funds."
    1. What is the World Bank?—"The World Bank is actually five closely associated agencies. The most prominent ones are the International Bank for Reconstruction and Development (IBRD) and the International Development Association (IDA)." Each has a particular specialty and focus.
    2. Bad Bank, Good Bank—While much progress has been made because of the World Bank's contributions, critics have also complained that it may be exacerbating the cycle of poverty in some cases. **See Discussion Topic #1.**
        i. Bad Bank—Some projects, like one in India that displaced farmers to build and environmentally destructive electrical facility, have continued the cycle of poverty.
        ii. Good Bank—The World Bank helped to develop the MDGs and now requires documentation from all countries receiving IDA loans.
        iii. Environmental Strategy—In 2002 the World Bank adopted a new strategy "to promote environmental improvements as a fundamental element of development and poverty reduction strategies and actions."
    3. Other UN Agencies—The UNDP, the FAO, and the WHO are other important agencies.
        i. Should We Keep the UN?—Although countries like the United States may not benefit greatly from the benefits of the UN and its agencies, it is still critically important for the rest of the world.

C. The Debt Crisis—Lending to developing countries typically involves interest which can accumulate and become difficult for developing countries to pay back. See Figure 9-10.
    1. A Disaster—"In order to keep up even partial interest payments, poor countries often do one or more of the following": Focus on cash crops, adopt austerity measures, or exploit natural resources.
    2. Debt Cancellation—With the help of the CGAP and the HIPC "by 2008, 33 countries had received debt relief totaling $105 billion, leaving a remaining debt of $9 billion in those countries."

i. Zambia—"Before the HIPC, (Zambia's) debt was $7.1 billion. Through HIPC, (it's) total was reduced to $500 million."

D. Development Aid—Aid is the type of assistance that does not have to be paid back.
1. Official Development Assistance—The best records of aid come from the ODA. See Figure 9-11.
2. Migration and Remittances—When migrant workers send money home to family in the form of remittances it accounts for more money than international aid.
3. Aid from the United States—"When remittances and private capital investments are added to these (ODA), the total economic contributions from the United States to developing countries amount to $235 billion which is actually 1.35% of our 2007 GNI. See Table 9-3.
4. Global Financial Crisis—The U.S. housing bubble burst in 2007 causing a severe recession which had global impact.

III. A New Direction: Social Modernization

Development focused on improving access to education, family planning, and health care and enhancement of the management of resources are potentially effective means of reducing fertility rates.

A. Improving Education—Focusing on educating women and children goes a long way towards reducing poverty and eventually controlling population.

B. Improving Health—"The basics of good nutrition and hygiene-steps such as boiling water to avoid the spread of disease and properly treating infections and common ailments such as diarrhea" are the most important health issues worldwide.
1. Life Expectancy—"One universal indicator of health is human life expectancy."
2. Two Worlds—"The discrepancy between the most developed and least developed countries can be seen quite clearly in the distribution of deaths by main causes." See Figure 9-13.
3. Reproductive Health—Focus on prenatal care, safe childbirth and postnatal care, contraception, prevention of STDs, abortion services, prevention of infertility, and elimination of violence against women are required to help improve the health of women and children.
4. AIDS-"One of the greatest challenges to health care in the developing countries is the sexually transmitted disease known as acquired immune deficiency syndrome (AIDS)."

C. Family Planning—"The stated policy of family-planning agencies is to enable people to plan their own family size—that is, to have children only if and when they want them." **See Discussion Topic #2.**
1. Unmet Need—"Women who are not currently using contraceptives, but who want to postpone or prevent childbearing, are said to have an unmet need."
2. Abortion—If family-planning services were universally available and people availed themselves of these services, there would be far fewer unwanted pregnancies and, hence, fewer abortions.
i. How Many?—"According to the Who, 219 million women become pregnant each year. Of these, 46 million (21%) resort to abortion." See Figure 9-14.

100

3. Family-Planning Agencies—Political policies about family planning agencies have flip-flopped based on who is in office.
    i. The Global Gag Rule—"The gag rule prohibits any U.S. government aid from being given to foreign family-planning agencies if they provide abortions, counsel women about abortion if they are dealing with an unwanted pregnancy, or advocate for abortion law reforms in their own country."

D. Employment and Income—Those who want to start a business in a developing country often need small loans to start. These people are typically too much of a credit risk to get a loan or they need loans too small for commercial banks to consider.
    1. Grameen Bank—This bank engaged in microlending-small, short term loans to individuals.
    2. More Microlending—"The unqualified success of microlending in stimulating economic activity and enhancing the incomes of people within poor communities has been so remarkable that the Grameen concept has been adopted in more than 40 countries around the world, including the United States."

E. Resource Management—Common pool resources are an important source of income to the poor, but these resources, because they are a common, must be managed to sustain the poor.

F. Putting It All Together—"Each of the five components of social modernization—education, health, family planning, employment and income, and resource management—depends on and supports the other components."
    1. Globalization—"The accelerating interconnectedness of human activities, ideas, and cultures".

Review Questions: Possible Answers

1. *What have been the two basic schools of thought regarding the demographic transition? How were these reflected in the three most recent global population conferences?*
    "From early on, there were two basic conflicting schools of thought regarding the demographic transition: 1. We need to concentrate on population policies and family-planning technologies to bring down birthrates. 2. If we concentrate on development, population growth will slow down 'automatically,' as it did in the developed countries." In the first two conferences, the developed countries (including the U.S.) were emphasizing family planning while the developing countries were arguing that "development was the best contraceptive." These "sides were somewhat reversed" at the third conference. The U.S. was opposed to family planning, while the other developed countries were advocating family planning. The developing countries were asking for assistance in the area of family planning.

2. *Discuss the five specific factors that influence the number of children a poor couple may desire.*
    Security in one's old age: In many countries the only means the elderly have to support themselves are their children. Only in developed countries with social security, welfare, retirement plans, and nursing homes is it not the norm to see parents supported by their children.

    Infant and childhood mortality: High infant mortality rate is associated with high birthrate. If you expect that a number of your children will die, you expect to have a larger number of children.

Helping hands: In a developing country, children are economic assets. At a very young age they begin to contribute to the family's financial well being. In a developed country, children are an economic liability. It is not until the children reach adulthood or beyond that they become economically independent.

Importance of education: If education is seen as important, a child is more of an economic liability. The longer a child is in school, the longer it takes for each child to gain economic independence or contribute to the family's economic well-being. When a child is in school, he/she is not contributing to the family income and it costs money to support the child (food, clothing, shelter, school supplies, etc.).

Status of women: If education is limited to only men, the decrease in fertility rates is less than if women have the opportunity to become educated. If for no other reason, being in school provides a socially acceptable alternative to motherhood. The same can be said for access to careers. If a woman has socially acceptable options other than motherhood, then a large percentage of women will delay child bearing. The more years that elapse between the age at which a child could be conceived and when the first child is conceived, the fewer children will be born.

Availability of contraceptives: The ability to obtain contraceptives when they are desired will decrease fertility rates. Studies show that women are interested in increasing the spacing between children or limiting the number of children, but access to contraceptives in many countries and in rural areas is limited.

3. *What are the MDGs? Where did they come from? Cite an example of one goal and the target used to measure progress in attaining it.*
   MDG = Millennium Development Goals. The following is verbatim from Table 6-2:

   - Goal 1: Eradicate extreme poverty and hungerTarget 1: Reduce by half the proportion of people whose income is less than $1 per day

   - Target 2: Reduce by half the proportion of people who suffer from hunger
   - Goal 2: Achieve universal primary educationTarget 3: Ensure that all children, boys and girls alike, are enrolled in primary school

   - Goal 3: Promote gender equity and empower womenTarget 4: Eliminate gender disparities in primary and secondary education

   - Goal 4: Reduce child mortality Target 5: Reduce mortality rates by two-thirds for all infants and children under 5

   - Goal 5: Improve maternal health Target 6: Reduce maternal mortality rates by three-quarters

   - Goal 6: Combat HIV/AIDS, malaria, and other diseases Target 7: Have halted by 2015 and begun to reverse the spread of HIV/AIDS

   - Target 8: Have halted by 2015 and begun to reverse the incidence of malaria and other major diseases
   - Goal 7: Ensure environmental stability Target 9: Integrate the principles of sustainability into country policies and programs, and reverse the loss of environmental resources

- Target 10: Reduce by half the proportion of people without sustainable access to safe drinking water and basic sanitation
- Target 11: Achieve a significant improvement in the lives of at least 100 million slum dwellers by 2020
- Goal 8: Forge a global partnership for development Target 12: Develop a trading system that is open, rule based, and nondiscriminatory—one that is committed to sustainable development, good governance, and a reduction in poverty

- Target 13: With Official Development Assistance (ODA), address the special needs of the least-developed countries (including the elimination of tariffs and quotas for their exports and an increase in programs for debt relief)
- Target 14: Deal with the debt problems of all developing countries by taking measures that will make debt sustainable in the long run
- Target 15: In cooperation with the private sector, make the benefits of new technologies available, especially information and communications technologies

4. *What are two major agencies that promote development in poor nations, and how do they carry out their work?*
The major agencies that promote development are the World Band and the ODA. The World Bank lends to governments in need with interest while the Official Development Aid (ODA) gives aid that is not expected to be paid back. "More important is the work of various U.N. and private organizations that directly provide assistance and funnel aid to developing countries."

5. *What is meant by the debt crisis of the developing world? What is being done to help resolve this crisis?*
Debt crisis: Borrowers become overwhelmed by interest payments. Theoretically, development projects were intended to generate additional revenues that would be sufficient for the recipient to pay back the loan with interest. Interest payments have result in a "net flow to the creditor countries." This did not occur and the "debt situation continues to be an economic, social, and ecological crisis for many developing countries." "...the concept of fostering the development of poor countries through massive loans for large-scale projects—whatever the advantages in enhancing gross national products—has not broken the cycle of excess population, poverty, and environmental degradation."

"The World Bank is addressing the problems of debt and poverty directly through two new initiatives: the Consultative Group to Assist the Poorest (CGAP) and the Heavily Indebted Poor Countries (HIPC) initiative. CGAP is designed to increase access to financial services for very poor households though what is called 'microfinancing.' The HIPC initiative addresses the dept problem of 42 of the poorest developing countries— amounting to $190 billion in 2000—by providing direct debt relief to a level deemed sustainable."

6. *What is development aid, and how does it measure up against the need for such aid?*
Development aid is money from the donor countries. "The total amount in 2004 was $78.6 billion, the highest level ever and part of an encouraging trend following a decade of declining aid in the 1990s. Not all the current $78.6 billion ODA (Office of Development Assistance) goes to basic human needs; much goes to debt cancellation and emergency assistance (e.g., the Asian tsunami disaster). The best estimates of the Millennium Project suggest that the costs of meeting the MDGs (donor's share) in all countries in 2006 would be $121 billion! Add to this the other estimated ODA outlays, and the total rises to $135 billion for ODA. This represents a $37.5 billion shortfall, in light of the projected $97.5 billion ODA for 2006 based on public commitments of the donor countries."

7. *What are the five interdependent components that must be addressed to bring about social modernization?*

"Social modernization does not require the economic trappings of a developed country. Instead, what is needed are efforts made on behalf of the poor, with particular emphasis on the following: (1) education, especially improving literacy and education of girls and women equally with boys and men; (2) improving health—especially lowering infant mortality; (3) making family planning accessible; (4) enhancing income through employment opportunities; (5) improving resource management (reversing environmental degradation)."

8. *Define family planning, and explain why it is critically important to all other aspects of development.*

Family planning is the ability of "people to plan their own family size—that is, to have children only if and when they want them." Additionally, family-planning services include counseling and education on sexually transmitted diseases and contraceptives, "on the best possible pre- and postnatal health for mother and children," "to avoid high-risk pregnancies," and "providing contraceptive materials or treatments after people have been properly instructed about all alternatives."

Family planning is critical for lowering fertility rates. "Those countries which have implemented effective family-planning programs have experienced the most rapid decline in fertility. Encouraging and implementing family planning is the first and most important step a country can take to improve its chances of developing economically."

9. *What is meant by an unmet need? What is the Global Gag Rule?*

"Women who are not currently using contraception, but who want to postpone or prevent childbearing, are said to have an unmet need."

"The gag rule prohibits any U.S. government aid from being given to foreign family-planning agencies if they provide abortions, counsel women about abortion if they are dealing with an unwanted pregnancy, or advocate for abortion law reforms in their own country."

10. *What is microlending? How does it work?*

Microloans are small, short-term loans. "They provide such basic things as seed and fertilizer for a peasant farmer to start growing tomatoes, some pans for a baker to start baking bread, supply of yarn for a weaver, some tools for an auto mechanic, and so on." Loans are secured "by having the recipients form credit associations—groups of several people who agreed to be responsible for each other's loans."

11. *What is the significance of globalization for economic and social development in the developing countries?*

Connecting the global economy is important for both the economic and social development of developing countries. It can, however, be damaging to the environment and culture of a country.

Thinking Environmentally: Possible Answers

1. *Is the world population below, at, or above the optimum? Defend your answer by pointing out things that may improve and things that may worsen as the population increases.*

Answers to this question will vary. No one knows if the world's population is below, at, or above the optimum. All that is important is that improvements are included along with the way things have worsened.

2. *Suppose you are the head of an island nation with a poor, growing population and the natural resources of the island are being degraded. What kinds of policies would you initiate, and what help would you ask for to try to provide a better, sustainable future for your nation's people?*

Answers to this question will vary. The important points are that all actions need to result in the population living within the resources available. The policies suggested will probably include methods to limit population growth, methods to conserve resources, and methods to decrease each individual's impact on the natural resources of the island.

3. *List and discuss the benefits and harms of writing off debts owed by developing nations.*

Benefits of writing off debts: Money would not be transferred from the developing countries to the developed countries. There will be less of a focus on growing cash crops for export, the pressure to exploit natural resources will be reduced, and funds for schools, health care, police protection, and so on will no longer need to be eliminated to pay off the debts.

Harms of writing off debts: Those that diverted money from the original loans will have succeeded in keeping the money. (This money was stolen from the public coffers.)

4. *Imagine you are an official in a third-world country working to deal with an epidemic such as AIDS. Do you emphasize prevention or treatment? What priority does this take over other government tasks?*

Answers to this question will vary. Both prevention and treatment are necessary to conquer AIDS. This disease is important worldwide and governments should focus the necessary resources on this problem.

5. *Do you believe contraceptives should be made available free of charge by governments, since this would have the potential to curb population growth and/or abortion rates? Defend your answer.*

Answers to this question will vary based on student beliefs and experience.

CHAPTER 10
Water: Hydrologic Cycle and Human Use

Chapter Outline:

I.   Water: A Vital Resource
II. Hydrologic Cycle: Natural Cycle, Human Impacts
    A. Evaporation, Condensation, and Purification
    B. Precipitation
        1. Convection Currents
        2. Rain Shadow
    C. Groundwater
        1. Recharge
        2. Underground Purification
    D. Loops, Pools, and Fluxes in the Cycle
    E. Human Impacts on the Hydrologic Cycle
        1. Changes to the Surface of the Earth
        2. Climate Change
        3. Atmospheric Pollution
III. Water: A Resource to Manage, a Threat to Control
    A. Sources
        i. Technologies
    B. Surface Waters
        1. Dams and the Environment
            i. Dam Impacts
            ii. Dams Gone
        2. Impacts on Estuaries
        3. Floods
        4. Groundwater Levels
        5. Falling Water Tables
            i.   Diminishing Surface Water
            ii. Land Subsidence
            iii. Saltwater Intrusion
IV. Water Stewardship: Supply and Public Policy
    A. More Dams to Capture Runoff
        1. Three Gorges Dam
        2. Wild Rivers
    B. Tapping More Groundwater
    C. Desalting Saltwater
        1. Tampa Bay Lead the Way (in the United States)
    D. Using Less Water
        1. Agriculture
            i. Drip, Drip
            ii. Treadle Pumps

Key Topics:

1. Water: A Vital Resource
2. Hydrologic Cycle: Natural Cycle, Human Impacts
3. Water: A Resource to Manage
4. Water Stewardship: Supply and Public Policy

Instructional Goals:

1. Water is the basis of life. The water cycle moves water around and removes impurities.

2. Humans can adversely impact water purity and cycling by changing the surface of the earth, introducing pollutants, and removing water rapidly from different sources.

3. Increasing the availability of water and decreasing the risk of water pollution will involve changing our view of water and developing mechanisms to encourage stewardship.

4. Water is more essential than any other resource. It has been the basis for disputes and wars in the past, and future wars will occur unless we find a sustainable and equitable way to steward this resource.

Concepts and Connections:

Obvious connections can be made between lost biodiversity and habitat destruction and changes to aquatic ecosystems. The less obvious connection between changes in the water cycle and the surface of the earth and habitat destruction can also be made. The non-obvious link between habitat changes and the disruption of the water cycle can be used to explain the subtleties of many environmental problems. For example, destroying a habitat can result in greater runoff and less water infiltration. If less water infiltrates the soil, then groundwater quantities can be reduced. Because groundwater supplies water for springs, seeps, and so forth, the ecosystems created by the springs, seeps, and so forth will be damaged if the groundwater source is diminished.

When humans extract too much water from any portion of the water cycle, there are a variety of consequences. The mining of water can lead to land subsidence, saltwater intrusion, loss of riparian habitat, loss of aquatic habitat, degradation of estuaries, and loss of wetlands.

Changing where or when precipitation occurs will cause environmental changes. Increased carbon dioxide levels (and other greenhouse gases) are predicted to alter ecosystems due to changes in when and where precipitation occurs. Increasing irrigation in an area can increase the amount of evaporation and causes changes in relative humidity or rainfall patterns. Decreasing the ability of water to infiltrate soil by removing plants (erosion, deforestation, overgrazing, and ove-rcultivation) can decrease the rate of evapotranspiration and evaporation for soil, causing a decrease in the relative humidity and changes in rainfall patterns. Those who study *Sequoia sempervirens* (coast redwoods) note that the quantity of evapotranspiration by the trees creates a high humidity level. Removing the trees decreases humidity, which is one of the limiting factors for coast redwoods.

The risk of floods is directly linked to land use. In urban and suburban areas, paving increases the quantity of water reaching streams. Additionally, the water arrives at the streams much more quickly. In agricultural areas, removal of plants increases the quantity of water reaching streams and therefore the quantity of sediments carried to the stream increases. Decisions to straighten streams, remove streamside vegetation, and pave stream banks all increase the risk of flooding.

Concepts in Context:

Water is an integral part of any ecosystem. It is an abiotic factor (Chapter 3), creates habitats and niches (Chapter 3), is a limiting factor (Chapter 3), is a molecule that is cycled like carbon, phosphorus, and nitrogen (Chapter 4), is important for the cycling of nutrients and flow of energy (chapter 5), can create disturbances (Chapter 5) that increase diversity (Chapter 7), and can be important as a non-equilibrium factor (Chapter 5). The cycling of water uses energy and must comply with the Laws of Thermodynamics (Chapter 5).

Water is a major limiting factor for human population growth (Chapter 8). The unequal distribution of water around the planet influences how people live and has been a major factor in determining the level of development and food availability (Chapter 12). Water and soil (Chapter 11) are integrally linked with food availability (Chapter 12). The oceans (Chapter 7) and food resources (Chapter 12) are linked to human survival and population growth (Chapters 8 and 9).

Water may be polluted (Chapter 20). Solid (Chapter 21) and hazardous (Chapter 22) waste if not handled properly can pollute both surface and groundwater. Air pollution (Chapter 19) has long been known to pollute precipitation, and precipitation can carry pollutants long distances. The legal use of pesticides on farmland and in urban/suburban areas has been known to pollute surface and groundwater (Chapter 13).

Key Terms and Vocabulary:

Fresh water, water vapor, humidity, relative humidity, condensation, aerosols, purification, Hadley cell, rain shadow, infiltration-runoff ratio, watershed, surface waters, evapotranspiration, percolation, gravitational water, groundwater, water table, aquifers, recharge area, seep, spring, nonconsumptive, consumptive, land subsidence, sinkhole, saltwater intrusion, desalination, gray water

Discussion, Activities, and Labs:

1. Divide the students into groups of three to four. Ask them to list all the resources they can think of necessary to deliver clean water to their homes. To get them started ask them the source of their water and how the water gets from that source to their faucet. Ask the students if they are willing to drink water directly from the local

stream. If not, why not. If the water comes from the local streams, what is done so that people are willing to drink it?

2. Land subsidence can be simulated. Have the students fill a balloon with as much water as possible. (Air can be used but this does not provide the same visual or intuitive clues that water provides.) Clamp the balloon with a device that can be clamped and unclamped as desired. Using a box with a slit cut in one side to accommodate the stem of the balloon, place the balloon at the bottom of the box with the opening of the balloon and the clamp on the outside of the box. Fill the box with soil, packing the soil firmly but being careful to not break the balloon. (Lining the box with a plastic bag will reduce the mess.) Mark the soil level on the box. Release the water from the balloon into a beaker. The soil surface should drop so that the volume of water released is now occupied by the soil.

3. Have the students keep a record of all the water they consume in two days. Tell the students to find on the Internet or in the library the average quantity of water used to flush a toilet, to take a shower, and to do other activities that directly consume water. Have each student estimate the quantity of direct water used per day. After the students have collected this information, ask the students if they included non-direct water consumption such as water used to boil pasta, water used to make coffee, and water used to grow grain, cattle, and vegetables. Ask them to research how much water is used for these non-direct uses. Include in their research the quantity of water used for landscaping (making our environment look pleasant) and for pleasure (for example, golf courses). Ask the students to think about what they would be willing to do to reduce the amount of water they use directly and the amount of water that is used indirectly in their name.

Suggested Lecture Format:

I.   Water: A Vital Resource
        Water is the basis of life. The water cycle moves water around and removes impurities. **See Discussion Topic #1.** See also Figure 10-1.

II.   Hydrologic Cycle: Natural Cycle, Human Impacts
        Humans can adversely impact water purity and cycling by changing the surface of the earth, introducing pollutants, and removing water rapidly from different sources. See Figure 10-3 and Table 10-1.

        A.   Evaporation, Condensation, and Purification—As water enters its different phases (water vapor, liquid water, and ice) it moves through different sections of the earth and the atmosphere and is purified naturally. See Figure 10-4.

        B.   Precipitation—"Two factors—global convection currents and rain shadow—may cause more or less continuously rising or falling air currents over particular regions, with major effects on" precipitation. See Figure 10-5.
             1.   Convection Currents—"Global convection currents occur because the sun heats Earth most intensely over and near the equator." See Figure 10-6.
             2.   Rain Shadow—"The dry region down-wind of a mountain range is referred to as a rain shadow. The severest deserts in the world are caused by the rain-shadow effect." See Figure 10-7.

109

C. Groundwater—Gravitational water accumulates, "filling all the spaces above the impervious layer. This accumulated water is called groundwater.
   1. Recharge—"The recharge area—the area where water enters an aquifer—may be many miles away from where the water leaves the aquifer."
   2. Underground Purification—"As water percolates through the soil, debris and bacteria from the surface are generally filtered out. Thus, groundwater is generally high-quality fresh water that is safe for drinking."

D. Loops, Pools, and Fluxes in the Cycle—"In the hydrologic cycle, there are substantial exchanges of water amongst the land, the atmosphere, and the oceans; such exchanges are the cycle's 'fluxes'".

E. Human Impacts on the Hydrologic Cycle—Humans induce changes in the water cycle in one of four ways: by changing the earth's surface, by changing Earth's climate, by adding atmospheric pollution, and by withdrawing water for use. See Table 10-2 and Figure 10-10.
   1. Changes to the Surface of the Earth—When humans change the surface of the earth by building structures and removing native ecosystems and adding man-made surfaces, the water cycle must shift.
   2. Climate Change—"A warmer climate means more evaporation from land surfaces, plants, and water bodies because evaporation increases exponentially with temperature.
   3. Atmospheric Pollution—The more aerosol particles there are in the atmosphere from human pollution, the greater the tendency for clouds to form and suppress rainfall.

III. Water: A Resource to Manage, a Threat to Control
Increasing the availability of water and decreasing the risk of water pollution will involve changing our view of water and developing mechanisms to encourage stewardship.

A. Sources—"About 37% of domestic water comes from groundwater sources and 63% from surface waters in the United States."
   1. Technologies—Municipalities, reservoirs, treatment plants are all used in developed countries to ensure the delivery of safe and clean water. See Figure 10-12 and Figure 10-13.

B. Surface Waters—Dams are used to control surface waters for human use.
   1. Dams and the Environment—"To trap and control flowing rivers, more than 45,000 large dams have been built around the world. The large dams have an enormous direct social impact, leading to the displacement of at least 40 million people world-wide and preventing access by local people to the goods and services of the now-buried ecosystems."
      i. Dam Impacts—Examples of ecological impacts of dams include: loss of valuable freshwater habitats, deprivation of ecosystem water, loss of water to wildlife, draining of wetlands, loss of wildlife, and effects on spawning fish. See Figure 10-14 and Figure 10-15.
      ii. Dams Gone—Because of the awareness of the damage done by dams, many have recently been dismantled.

2. Impacts on Estuaries—"When river waters are diverted on their way to the sea, serious impacts are seen in estuaries—bays and rivers in which fresh water from a river mixes with seawater."
3. Floods—Flooding has increased because of deforestation and cultivation removing important "sponges" in the form of forests.
4. Groundwater Levels—Removal of non-renewable groundwater that came from the melting of ice long ago is not being balanced by recharge. See Figure 10-16.
5. Falling Water Tables—"The simplest indication that groundwater withdrawals are exceeding recharge is a falling water table, a situation that is common throughout the world."
    i. Diminishing Surface Water—"When water tables drop, wetlands dry up…springs and seeps dry up as well."
    ii. Land Subsidence—"Over the ages, groundwater has leached cavities in the ground. Where these spaces are filled with water, the water helps support the overlying rock and soil. As the water table drops, however, this support is lost. There may be a gradual settling of the land." **See Discussion Topic #2.** See also Figure 10-17.
    iii. Saltwater Intrusion—"In coastal regions, springs of outflowing groundwater may lie under the ocean. As long as a high water table maintains a sufficient head of pressure in the aquifer, fresh water will flow into the ocean. However, lowering the water table or removing groundwater at a rapid rate may reduce the pressure in the aquifer, permitting salt water to flow back into the aquifer and hence into wells." See Figure 10-18.

IV. Water Stewardship: Supply and Public Policy
Water is more essential than any other resource. It has been the basis for disputes and wars in the past, and future wars will occur unless we find a sustainable and equitable way to steward this resource. **See Discussion Topic #3.**

A. More Dams to Capture Runoff—"Some 260 new dams become operational each year around the world."
    1. Three Gorges Dam—Built across China's Yellow River, this dam has relocated untold numbers of people but has helped China to industrialize, bringing power to its people. See Figure 10-19.
    2. Wild Rivers—"Protection has been accorded to some rivers with the passage of the Wild and Scenic Rivers Act of 1968."

B. Tapping More Groundwater—"In many areas, groundwater use exceeds aquifer recharge, leading to shortages as the water table drops below pump levels." In addition, pollution makes groundwater an unlikely "new" sustainable source of water in the future.

C. Desalting Saltwater—"With increasing water shortages and most of the world's population living near coasts, there is a growing trend toward desalination (desalting) of seawater for domestic use." Unfortunately the cost of desalination is 2 to 4 times what most people in the U.S. are used to paying for water. See Figure 10-20.

1. Tampa Bay Lead the Way (in the United States)—The first desalinization plant in the U.S. is in Tampa Bay, FL. It provides drinking water to the area for approximately $2.50 per 1000 gallons. Globally, the countries of the Middle East are leading the way in desalinization.

D. Using Less Water—We need to move towards the attitude in the U.S. of "how much water is available and how can we best use it?"
   1. Agriculture—"Agriculture is far and away the largest consumer of fresh water-some 40% of the world's food is grown using irrigated soils."
      i. Drip, Drip—A "water-saving method is the drip irrigation system, a network of plastic pipe with pinholes that literally drip water at the base of each plant." See Figure 10-21.
      ii. Treadle Pumps—These water pumps work like a step exercise machine and allows local farmers to irrigate small plots of land. See Figure 10-22.
   2. Municipal Systems—As supply of water is dwindling, water saving methods like low flow faucets and shower heads and water-displacement devices in toilets are being installed.
      i. A Flush World—In 1997 "it became illegal to sell 6-gallon commodes. In their place is the new wonder of the flush world: the 1.6 gallon toilet." See Figure 10-23.
      ii. Gray Water—"the slightly dirtied water from sinks, showers, bathtubs, and laundry tubs is collected in a holding tank and used for such things as flushing toilets, watering lawns, and washing cars."

E. Making Food Production and Use More Efficient—"A great deal of water goes into the manufacturing of food. One pound of wheat, for example, takes about 1000 pounds of water to grow."

F. Public Policy Challenges—"It takes public policy to strike a sustainable balance between competing water needs, and this is often sadly lacking."
   1. Water Wars—With water shortages, areas that compete for the same water sources are getting into "water wars" or conflicts over the sharing of water.
   2. National Water Policy—"Many countries have addressed their water resources and water needs with a national policy; not so in the United States."
      i. Key Issues—In the United States we need to address the following issues at the national level: 1) Water efficiency promotion, 2) Reduction or elimination of water subsidies, 3) Pollution must be regulated and fined, 4) Watershed management is necessary, 5) Regulation of dam operations, 6) International development aid for the water crisis, and 7) Research and monitoring of water must take place
   3. International Action—"The World Commission on Water for the 21st Century sponsors the World Water Forum, which convened for the fifth time in 2009. The findings of the forum relate directly to solving the great water-related needs of the earth, especially in the developing countries."

Review Questions: Possible Answers

1. What are the lessons to be learned from the Aral Sea story?

The diversion of water can be an environmental and economic disaster. Doing something without thinking through the consequences can be disastrous. The fishing industry dependent upon the Aral Sea has been destroyed; the health of residents in the area has been adversely impacted (increased cancer and infant mortality rates, increased respiratory irritation); the local climate has changed; many species have gone extinct.

2. *Give examples of the infrastructure that has been fashioned to manage water resources. What are the challenges related to developing countries?*
    The infrastructure includes dams, reservoirs, aqueducts, canals, intake and outflow pipes, water and sewage treatment plants, water storage facilities, and the piping from and to homes and businesses. All of these industrialized techniques cost money and cause displacement and ecological damage which can be difficult to absorb in developing countries.

3. *What are the two processes that result in natural water purification? State the difference between them. Distinguish between green water and blue water.*
    Water rises to the atmosphere through evaporation and returns to the earth's surface after condensation through precipitation. This process purifies water because only water evaporates. All impurities are left behind during the process of evaporation. After condensation of the evaporated water, only water is present. Water will remain clean as it returns to the earth's surface as long as it does not fall through an area with air pollution. Green water is "water in the soil and in organisms that eventually ends up as water vapor—the main source of water for natural ecosystems and rain-fed agriculture." Blue water is "renewable surface water runoff and groundwater recharge—the focus of management and the main source of water for human withdrawals."

4. *Describe how a Hadley cell works, and explain how Earth's rotation creates the trade winds.*
    Hadley cell: "Dry air absorbs moisture as it descends. Moist air releases moisture as it ascends. Global convection currents occur because the sun heats Earth most intensely over and near the equator, where rays of sunlight are almost perpendicular to Earth's surface. As the air at the equator is heated, it expands, rises, and cools; condensation and precipitation occur. Rising air over the equator is just half of the convection current, however. The air must come down again, too. Pushed from beneath by more rising air, it literally 'spills over' to the north and south of the equator and descends over subtropical regions, resulting in subtropical deserts. . . ." Earth's rotation deflects the vertical and horizontal path created by the Hadley cell, thus creating trade winds.

5. *Why do different regions receive different amounts of precipitation?*
    Different amounts of precipitation in different regions are caused by the Hadley cells—wet in the tropics and dry in the subtropics and by mountains. "Air is deflected upward, causing cooling and high precipitation on the windward side of the range. As the air crosses the range and descends on the other side, it becomes warmer and increases its capacity to pick up moisture. Hence, deserts occur on the leeward sides of mountain ranges."

6. *Define precipitation, infiltration, runoff, capillary water, transpiration, evapotranspiration, percolation, gravitational water, groundwater, water table, aquifer, recharge area, seep, and spring.*
    Precipitation: any form of water (snow, sleet, hail, rain) that falls from the atmosphere;
    Infiltration: water that soaks into the ground;
    Runoff: water the runs off the surface—a blue water flow;
    Capillary water: water that "returns to the atmosphere either by way of evaporation from the soil or by transpiration through plants";
    Transpiration: the green flow of water through plants;
    Evapotranspiration: "the combination of evaporation and transpiration";
    Percolation: water that infiltrates into the ground and trickles through the pores or cracks;
    Gravitational water: "water that is not held in the soil" and moves downward "under the pull of gravity";
    Groundwater: the accumulated water from gravitational water that has "encountered an impervious layer of rock or dense clay";

113

Water table: the upper surface of groundwater;

Aquifer: "layers of porous material through which groundwater moves";

Recharge area: "the area where water enters an aquifer";

Seep: a natural exit from groundwater where the "water flows out over a relative wide area";

Spring: "water exits the ground as a significant flow from a relatively small opening."

7. *Use the terms defined in Question 6 to give a full description of the hydrologic cycle, including each of its three loops—namely, the evapotranspiration, surface runoff, and groundwater loops. What is the water quality (purity) at different points in the cycle? Explain the reasons for the differences.*

   Water evaporates from surface water when it is heated and condenses when it cools. Water is pure at this point because only water molecules evaporate. When enough water condenses, precipitation occurs. As precipitation moves through the atmosphere it may pick up water soluble pollutants but it may also be fairly pure if not many water soluble compounds are encountered. When precipitation reaches the ground some of the water infiltrates the soil and some runs off to streams, lakes, and the oceans. This water will pick up solutes from the soil. The water that soaks into the ground may either be capillary water or gravitational water. Gravitational water will percolate through the ground and collect as groundwater in an aquifer and may be released to the surface through seeps and springs. The height of the water table will determine if springs or seeps are flowing or dry. The recharge area for an aquifer may be over a fairly large surface of land. Capillary water will be picked up by plants or evaporate from the soil. Water is transpired through plants, and evapotranspiration is the process by with water is evaporated and transpired from plants.

   "There are three principal loops in the cycle: (1) In the evapotranspiration loop (consisting of green water), the water evaporates and is returned by precipitation. On land, this water, the main source for natural ecosystems and rain-fed agriculture, is held as capillary water and then returns to the atmosphere by way of evapotranspiration. (2) In the surface runoff loop (containing blue water), the water runs across the ground surface and becomes part of the surface water system. (3) In the groundwater loop (also containing blue water), the water infiltrates, percolates down to join the groundwater, and then moves through aquifers, finally exiting through seeps, springs, or wells, where it rejoins the surface water."

8. *How does changing the earth's surface (for example, by deforestation) change the pathway of water? How does it affect streams and rivers? Humans? Natural ecology?*

   Deforestation, assuming all the trees are removed, would eliminate the portion of the water cycle that involves evapotranspiration of water through the trees. This is likely to decrease the amount of water in the ecosystem because the water that would have been absorbed by the trees will now run off to the streams and rivers. This is likely to increase erosion and the quantity of nutrients in the streams and rivers in the short run. In the longer term, the area would become drier. The water that would have been evaporated from the trees is no longer available to contribute to the humidity, and the precipitation in the area will be reduced. Any organism that was dependent on particular levels of precipitation would be stressed or eliminated and not available for human use. The amount of water available for human use would be reduced.

9. *Explain how climate change and atmospheric pollution can affect the hydrologic cycle.*

   "A warmer climate means more evaporation from land surfaces, plants, and water bodies, because evaporation increases exponentially with temperature. A wetter atmosphere means more and, frequently, heavier precipitation and more flood events. Aerosol particles form nuclei for condensation. The more such particles there are, the greater is the tendency for clouds to form. Anthropogenic aerosols are on the increase, primarily in the form of sulfates (from sulfur dioxide in coal), carbon (as soot), and dust. They form a brownish haze that is associated with industrial areas, tropical burning, and dust storms." The "most significant impact"

114

of aerosol particles "is on the hydrologic cycle. The unique size spectrum of the anthropogenic aerosols causes them actually to suppress rainfall where they occur in abundance, even though they encourage cloud formation. As they do so, the atmospheric cleansing that would normally clear the aerosols is suppressed, and they remain in the atmosphere longer than usual. With suppressed rainfall come drier conditions, so more dust and smoke (and more aerosols) are the result."

10. *What are the three major uses of water? What are the major sources of water to match these uses?*

The three major uses of water are agricultural (80%), industry (20%), and direct human use (10%). The sources of water for agriculture, industry, and domestic use are surface and groundwater. Agricultural use is considered consumptive use while industrial and domestic uses are considered nonconsumptive.

11. *How do dams facilitate the control of surface waters? What kinds of impacts do they have?*

Dams can limit the flow of water, reducing the risk of flooding below the dam and provide reliable domestic and agricultural water supplies during the months with less precipitation, flat water recreation and hydroelectric power. Dams "have been built to run mills (now an obsolete usage), control floods, and provide water for municipal and agricultural use."

"Dams have enormous ecological impacts. When a river is dammed, valuable freshwater habitats, such as waterfalls, rapids, and prime fish runs, are lost. When the river's flow is diverted to cities or croplands, the waterway below the diversion is deprived of that much water. The impact on fish and other aquatic organisms is obvious, but the ecological ramifications go far beyond the river. Wildlife that depends on the water or on food chains involving aquatic organisms is also adversely affected. Wetlands occupying floodplains along many rivers, no longer nourished by occasional overflows, dry up, resulting in frequent die-offs of waterfowl and other wildlife that depended on those habitats. Fish such as salmon, which swim from the ocean far upriver to spawn, are seriously affected by the reduced water level and have problems getting around the dam."

12. *Distinguish between renewable and nonrenewable groundwater resources. What are the consequences of overdrawing these two kinds of groundwater?*

A nonrenewable groundwater resource is one "with a recharge rate of centuries or more." A renewable groundwater resource "is replenished by the percolation of precipitation water, so it is vulnerable to variations in precipitation."

The consequences of overdrawing groundwater include falling water tables, less surface water (e.g., wetlands, seeps, and springs dry up when water tables fall, thus decreasing water to streams), land subsidence, and salt water intrusion.

13. *What are the four options for meeting existing water scarcity needs and growing demands?*

The four options for meeting existing water scarcity needs and growing demands are "(1) capture more of the runoff water, (2) gain better access to existing groundwater aquifers, (3) desalt seawater, and (4) conserve present supplies by using less water."

14. *Describe how water demands might be reduced in agriculture, industry, and households.*

Agriculture can use less water by using (1) a "surge flow method, in which computers control the periodic release of water" or (2) drip irrigation systems. Industry and homes can use less water by using toilets that require less water, putting in xeriscaping, replacing leaking faucets, replacing faucets with low-flow alternatives, and using water displacement devices. Gray water (from sinks, showers, bathtubs, and laundry) can be used for irrigation."

15. *What is the status of water policy in the United States? Cite some key issues that should be addressed by any new initiatives to establish a national water policy.*

115

There are seven key issues: "1. Water efficiency must be promoted as the primary strategy for meeting future water needs. 2. Water subsidies need to be reduced or eliminated. 3. Polluters must be charged according to their effluents. 4. Watershed management must be integrated into the pricing of water. 5. Water authorities must regulate dam operations so that river flow is maintained in a way that simulates natural flow regimes. The United States must respond to the global water crisis with adequate levels of international development aid. 6. The United States must take action to reduce the emissions of greenhouse gases that are bringing on global climate change. 7. Much more research and monitoring are needed to provide the basic data for making informed policy decisions."

Thinking Environmentally: Possible Answers

1. *Imagine that you are a water molecule, and describe your travels through the many places you have been and might go in the future as you make your way around the hydrologic cycle time after time. Include travels through organisms.*

    I evaporate from surface water when it is heated and then I condense as I cool off. When enough other water molecules condense around me, I fall from the sky as precipitation. I reach the ground and I might infiltrate the soil or I run off into a stream, lake, or ocean. If I have soaked into the ground, I may end up as capillary water or gravitational water. If I'm gravitational water, I will percolate through the ground and collect as groundwater in an aquifer. I then may be released to the surface through a seep or a spring. If I'm capillary water, I will be picked up by a plant. I'll move up through the plant's roots through its stem and will transpire through a pore (stomata) in the leaves. I might be incorporated into glucose. I could also be drunk by an animal if I am a molecule in surface water or by a human if I'm pumped from groundwater. If am consumed by an animal I will move through the organism and become sweat, tears, or spit or I could be excreted via urine.

2. *Suppose some commercial interests want to create a large new development on what is presently wetland. Describe a debate between those representing the commercial interests and those representing environmentalists who are concerned about the environmental and economic costs of development. Work toward negotiating a compromise.*

    Most communities have some type of development occurring. It could be very informative to send the students to a city, county, or township planning meeting. Most local governments have a planning office. A small group of students could interview a knowledgeable person in the planning office.

    Each side should present economic benefits—the benefits from development and the benefits derived from a wetland. The ability to create a wetland should be discussed—how likely are we to replicate existing wetlands? Alternatives such as moving the development should be discussed.

3. *Describe how many of your everyday activities, including your demands for food and other materials, add pollution to the water cycle or alter it in other ways. How can you be more stewardly with your water consumption?*

    Everyday activities add pollution to water—food production can result in pollution from fertilizer and pesticide runoff along with erosion of soil into streams. Driving a car can result in water pollution from the oil and gasoline from cars. The oil slick on the road that is visible after a rainstorm is from cars as they are driven daily. The air pollutants from automobiles, if they are not destroyed in the atmosphere, end up in water, (for

116

example, acid rain). Virtually all consumer goods can result in water pollution because water is used in most manufacturing processes. Even computers have an impact because of the solvents, which are used in production, have polluted the groundwater beneath some of the manufacturing facilities.

We alter water cycles by consumptive uses such as food production, watering the landscaping around our homes and businesses, and so forth. Water provided for drinking water, washing, flushing toilets, and so on is being diverted from the ecosystem.

We can all be more stewardly by reducing our water consumption—take shorter showers, take showers rather than baths, turn off the water when shaving or brushing teeth, run full loads of laundry, buy water-saving appliances, install drip irrigation, and keep water in the refrigerator rather than letting the water run to cool it.

4. *An increasing number of people are moving to the arid southwestern United States, even though water supplies are already being overdrawn. If you were the governor of one of the states in this region, what policies would you advocate to address this situation?*

Strict requirements for low flow showerhead and faucets in addition to the latest toilet technology would be required in homes. Also, all new homes built should incorporate holding tanks for the use of gray water. Municipalities that collect gray water should use it for watering in government facilities and properties. Xeriscaping and drip irrigation should be mandatory. Possibly the use of desalination facilities might be incorporated into municipalities.

5. *Suppose some commercial interests want to develop a golf course on what is presently forested land next to a reservoir used for city water. Describe the impacts this development might have on water quality in the reservoir.*

The impact from a golf course could include contamination from nitrates and phosphates (fertilizers), pesticides, and sediments from erosion. Increased flow of sediments into the reservoir could influence the taste, color, and odor of the drinking water. The nitrates and phosphates could increase the growth of algae and other organisms, lowering the level of dissolved oxygen in the reservoir. Any fish or benthic organisms in the reservoir would be adversely impacted. The pesticides could include hormonally active agents or other compounds that are related to adverse human impacts.

CHAPTER 11
Soil: The Foundation for Land Ecosystems

Chapter Outline:

I. Soil and Plants
   A. Soil Characteristics
      1. Soil Texture
      2. Proportions
      3. Properties
      4. Soil Profiles
         i. Subsurface Layers
      5. Soil Classification
         i. Mollisols
         ii. Oxisols
         iii. Alfisols
         iv. Aridisols
   B. Soil and Plant Growth
      1. Mineral Nutrients and Nutrient-Holding Capacity
         i. Leaching
         ii. Fertilizer
      2. Water and Water-Holding Capacity
         i. Three Soil Attributes
      3. Aeration
      4. Relative Acidity (pH)
   5. Salt and Water Uptake
   C. The Soil Community
      1. Organisms and Organic Matter in the Soil
         i. Humus
         ii. Soil Structure and Topsoil
         iii. Interactions
   D. Soil Enrichment or Mineralization
II. Soil Degradation
   A. Erosion
      1. Splash, Sheet, and Gully Erosion
      2. Desert Pavement and Cryptogamic Crusts
   B. Drylands and Desertification
   C. Causing and Correcting Erosion
      1. Overcultivation
         i. No-Till
         ii. Fertilizer
         iii. NRCS
      2. Overgrazing
         i. Public Lands
      3. Deforestation
      4. The Other End of the Erosion Problem
   D. Irrigation and Salinization
III. Soil Conservation

A. Helping Individual Landholders
   1. The Keita Project
   2. Two Paradigms
B. Public Policy and Soils
   1. Subsidies
   2. Sustainable Agriculture
   3. Farm Legislation
   4. Conservation Programs

Key Topics:

1. Soil and Plants
2. Soil Degradation
3. Soil Conservation

Instructional Goals:

1. There are a number of factors that influence soil characteristics. The water- and nutrient-holding capacity of soil, along with its aeration, workability, salinity, and pH, influence the survivorship of plants.

2. Soil is an ecosystem. All terrestrial ecosystems are dependent upon soil ecosystems for survival. The division between soil and terrestrial ecosystems is artificial and only useful so we can study the components of each ecosystem.

3. A number of processes, (e.g., overcultivation, overgrazing, deforestation, and salinization), remove plants from soil. Once plants have been removed from soil, erosion and desertification may result. Erosion is the movement of soil by wind or water. Desertification results from the loss of soil structure and the inability of the land to hold water.

Concepts and Connections:

Students will become familiar with soil and the dependence of plants (with the exception of bromeliads) on soil for survival. Students know there is a connection between good soil and plant survival. An obvious link can be made between soil characteristics and plant health by asking the students if we could farm on beaches. Indicating to students that the low organic matter content of sand is the primary reason for the lack of plant growth on beaches will quickly make intuitive sense.

Our dependence on healthy soil is an obvious and important connection to make while discussing soils and soil ecosystems. Agricultural and natural terrestrial ecosystems have a fundamental dependence upon soil. Humans would not have food or any of the goods and services provided by terrestrial ecosystems if soil did not exist.

Decisions about land use will influence soil health. Urbanization, overgrazing, overcultivation, deforestation, and desertification all affect our ability to obtain goods and services from soil.

Concepts in Context:

All the ecosystem concepts (Chapters 3–5) are applicable to the material in this chapter on soils and soil ecosystems. Soil ecosystems are fundamental units of sustainability (Chapter 3). Soils and the organisms contained in soils interact with the organisms above the ground. Without soil, food production would be adversely impacted (Chapter 12). The diversity (Chapter 6) found in soil ecosystems is tremendous and is very dependent upon the type of ecosystem found above ground (Chapter 3). Without soil organisms, detritus feeders and decomposers (Chapter 4), there would be no above ground ecosystem because these organisms are essential for the cycling of nutrients (Chapter 3). Succession (Chapter 5) is dependent upon the creation or prior existence of soil.

The goods and services (Chapter 7) obtained from soil will be adversely impacted by a number of activities. Air pollution, in the form of acid rain, adversely impacts the availability of nutrients and toxic compounds in soil. The deposition of hazardous materials (Chapter 22) or solid waste (Chapter 21) on soil adversely impacts the soil ecosystem. The mining of resources, especially surface mining, disrupts soil ecosystems.

Key Terms and Vocabulary:

soil, parent material, sand, silt, clay, soil texture, loam, workability, horizons, soil profile, O horizon, humus, A horizon, topsoil, E horizon, eluviations, B horizon, subsoil, C horizon, soil fertility, nutrient-holding capacity, fertilizer, organic fertilizer, inorganic fertilizers, transpiration, water-holding capacity, evaporative water loss, soil aeration, compaction, composting, castings, soil structure, splash erosion, sheet erosion, gully erosion, desert pavement, cryptogamic crust, TerrAfrica, no-till agriculture, low-till farming, contour strip cropping, shelterbelts, U.S. Natural Resource Conservation Service, Conservation Stewardship Program, sediments, flood irrigation, center-pivot irrigation, salinization, Sustainable Agriculture Research and Education (SARE), Federal Agricultural Improvement and Reform Act (FAIR), Farm Security and Rural Investment Act, Conservation Reserve Program (CRP), Wildlife Habitat Incentives Program (WHIP), Environmental Quality Initiatives Program (EQIP), Conservation Security Program (CSP), Conservation Stewardship Program

Discussion, Activities, and Labs:

1. Ask the students if they have seen erosion and if so, to describe what they have seen. If they cannot describe a situation, ask if they have seen soil being moved by water when it is raining. They may not have observed gullies but it is likely that they have seen soil being moved onto pavement. Ask the students to speculate about why the soil does not stay in place. If they are not sure, ask where they have tended to see erosion. What does the area look like? Construction sites are common locations. Areas around campus where there are slopes and little or no vegetation are also good locations for erosion.

2. It is possible to simulate differences in erosion rates by using flats of bedding plants (baby's tears works well), flats with soil but no plants, and spray bottles that have fairly large droplets. Ask the students to devise tests to determine if erosion is more or less likely when a flat does or does not have plants. Conditions that will increase the erosion rate are: (1) propping the flat at a 10-degree angle or more, (2) using a spray bottle with a fairly heavy spray, and (3) wetting the soil so that it is moist before beginning to spray the water.

3. The rates of erosion by soil type can be tested. Repeat the above experiment using flats containing mainly clay, mainly silt, mainly sand, and mainly loam. Determine which soil type will hold the most water and which soil type will erode most easily.

4. Soil is alive. A way to bring this home to students is to ask them what happens when the soil becomes saturated. Ask what happens when land is flooded. Anything that lives underground that cannot move and needs oxygen dies. Most students have seen this when earthworms move onto sidewalks after rain has saturated the soil.

5. Collect several different kinds of soil, including sand, clay, silt, and compost. Divide the class into groups of two to three students and provide them with a container of soil. Have the students look at the various kinds of soils and create a classification system for them. (Have them define and justify the classification system.) If

you have dissecting microscopes, have the students look at the soil under the microscope to help them see the components. After looking at the soil, have the students test the water-holding capacity of the different soil types. Discuss, as a class, the various observations and the classification systems developed by the groups. Discuss which of the soil types might support the greatest diversity of plant life.

6. Have the students go to different locations to collect different kinds of soil. About a liter of soil should be collected from each location. Each location from which soil is obtained should be described. If the student can obtain compost, tell them that this would be acceptable. Have each student compare the various kinds of soils he/she collected and describe the soils. Similarities and differences in the soil should be noted. If there are different numbers or kinds of soil organisms present in the soil, this should be noted. Using the descriptions of the locations from which the soil were obtained, have each student hypothesize as to why the soil may (or may not) look different. Is one location more or less likely to support a healthy soil ecosystem?

Suggested Lecture Format:

I. Soil and Plants
There are a number of factors that influence soil characteristics. The water- and nutrient-holding capacity of soil, along with its aeration, workability, salinity, and pH, influence the survivorship of plants.

    A. Soil Characteristics—"Many years of study of soils have resulted in a system of classification of soil profiles and soil structure and taxonomy of soil types from all over the world."
       1. Soil Texture—The materials making up soil are segregated by size. See Figure 11-3.
       2. Proportions—"The sand, silt, and clay particles constitute the mineral portion of soil." The proportion of each determines the soil texture. See Table 11-1.
       3. Properties—Several properties determine soil texture and determine the extent of infiltration, nutrient, and water-holding capacity, as well as aeration.
       4. Soil Profiles—"The processes of soil formation create a vertical gradient of layers that are often (but not always) quite distinct. These horizontal layers are known as horizons."
          i. Subsurface Layers—The O horizon, the A horizon, the E horizon, the B horizon, and the C horizon all contain distinct materials. See Figure 11-4.
       5. Soil Classification—"To give some order to this diversity (of soils), soil scientists have created a taxonomy, or classification system, of soils." **See Discussion Topic #5.**
          i. Mollisols—"are fertile, dark soils found in temperate grassland biomes. They are the world's best agricultural soils."
          ii. Oxisols—"These are soils of the tropical and subtropical rain forests. They have a layer of iron and aluminum oxides in the B horizon and have little O horizon, due to the rapid decomposition of plant matter."
          iii. Alfisols—"are widespread, moderately weathered forest soils. Although not deep, they have well-developed O, A, E, and B horizons."
          iv. Aridisols—"These are the very widespread soils of the drylands and deserts."

    B. Soil and Plant Growth—"Soil fertility—the soil's ability to support plant growth—often refers specifically to the presence of proper amounts of nutrients, but it also includes the soil's ability to meet all the other needs of plants." **See Discussion Topic #6.**
       1. Mineral Nutrients and Nutrient—Holding Capacity—Mineral nutrients become available to plant roots through weathering, leaching, and fertilizing. **See Discussion Topic #3.**
          i. Leaching—"Nutrients may literally be washed from the soil as water moves through it."

121

   ii. Fertilizer—"Fertilizer is a material that contains one or more of the necessary nutrients. Fertilizer may be organic or inorganic."

  2. Water and Water—Holding Capacity—The ability of soil to hold water is important to the health of plants because plants are constantly using water through the process of transpiration. See Figure 11-6.

   i. Three Soil Attributes—Infiltration, water-holding capacity, and evaporative water loss are the three critical attributes of soil. See Figure 11-7.

  3. Aeration—Plants need oxygen and overwatering and compaction reduces the ability of plants to "breathe". **See Discussion Topic #4.**

  4. Relative Acidity (pH)—"Different plants are adapted to different pH ranges."

  5. Salt and Water Uptake—"A buildup of salts in the soil makes it impossible for the roots of a plant to take in water."

 C. The Soil Community—"The poorest attribute (of soil) is the limiting factor."

  1. Organisms and Organic Matter in the Soil—"The dead leaves, roots, and other detritus accumulated on and in the soil support a complex food web, including numerous species of bacteria, fungi, protozoans, mites, insects, millipedes, spiders, centipedes, earthworms, snails, slugs, moles, and other burrowing animals." See Figure 11-8 and Figure 11-9.

   i. Humus—"each organism leaves a certain portion undigested…this residue of partly decomposed organic matter is humus." See Figure 11-10.

   ii. Soil Structure and Topsoil—"Whereas soil texture describes the size of soil particles, soil structure refers to their arrangement."

   iii. Interactions—The interactions between the roots of some plants and fungi are important.

 D. Soil Enrichment or Mineralization—"The maintenance of topsoil depends on additions of detritus in sufficient quantity to balance losses." See Figure 11-13.

II. Soil Degradation

Soil is an ecosystem. All terrestrial ecosystems are dependent upon soil ecosystems for survival. The division between soil and terrestrial ecosystems is artificial and only useful so we can study the components of each ecosystem.

 A. Erosion—"erosion is the process of soil and humus particles being picked up and carried away by water or wind." **See Discussion Topic #1.**

  1. Splash, Sheet, and Gully Erosion—Splash erosion is when raindrops break up the topsoil. Sheet erosion is when water runs off and carries fine soil particles with it. Finally, gully erosion is when soil gathers into gullies as a result of large amounts of water carrying it elsewhere.

  2. Desert Pavement and Cryptogamic Crusts—During erosion, "the lighter particles of humus and clay are the first to be carried away, while rocks, stones, and coarse sand remain behind. Consequently, as erosion removes the finer materials, the remaining soil becomes progressively coarser." **See Discussion Topic #2.** See also Figure 11-16.

 B. Drylands and Desertification—"Desertification is a permanent reduction in the productivity of arid, semiarid, and seasonally dry areas. Dryland ecosystems cover 41% of Earth's land area."

 C. Causing and Correcting Erosion—"The three major practices that expose soil to erosion and lead to soil degradation are overcultivation, overgrazing, and deforestation."

1. Overcultivation—The process of farming can leave soil bare for long periods of time, causing erosion. Also, using the same crop year after year can strip the soil of nutrients.
    i. No-Till—By leaving the field untilled after harvest, existing plant structures left over through the winter season can help to hold soil in place and prevent erosion.
    ii. Fertilizer—"What is required is for growers to understand the different roles played by organic material and inorganic nutrients and then to use each as necessary."
    iii. NRCS—"Through a nationwide network of regional offices, the NRCS provides information to farmers or other interested persons regarding soil and water conservation practices."
2. Overgrazing—When overgrazing occurs, "grass production fails to keep up with consumption, (and) the land becomes barren. Wind and water erosion follows, and soils become degraded."
    i. Public Lands—The Tragedy of the Commons often occurs on grasslands.
3. Deforestation—Forests are highly effective ecosystems and the removal of trees has a major impact on soil ecosystems as well as the living ecosystems in the forest.
4. The Other End of the Erosion Problem—"Eroding soil, called sediments, is carried into streams and rivers, clogging channels and intensifying flooding."

D. Irrigation and Salinization—"Supplying water to croplands by artificial means" can sometimes cause increased salt deposits on irrigated soils suppressing plant growth. See Figure 11-21.

III. Soil Conservation
A number of processes, (e.g., overcultivation, overgrazing, deforestation, and salinization), remove plants from soil. Once plants have been removed from soil, erosion and desertification may result. Erosion is the movement of soil by wind or water. Desertification results from the loss of soil structure and the inability of the land to hold water.

A. Helping Individual Landholders—"In the developing world, as well as the developed world, it is the individual landholders, farmers, and herders, who hold the key to sustainable soil stewardship."
    1. The Keita Project—"The project targeted the serious degradation brought on by overpopulation and the effects of soil and wind erosion. Some 41 dams were established to catch water from the monsoonal summer rains, more than 18 million trees were planted, and countless rock dams were constructed to stop rainwater sheet erosion and provide soil and moisture for crops." See Figure 11-22.
    2. Two Paradigms—"Dryland soils are resilient and desertification is not the inevitable outcome of human occupation."

B. Public Policy and Soils—Two levels of responsibility exist for soil ecosystems: the landowner and public policy makers.
    1. Subsidies—"In recent years, farm policy has emphasized maintaining farm income and support of farm commodities."
    2. Sustainable Agriculture—"The goals of sustainable agriculture are to 1) maintain a productive topsoil, 2) keep food safe and wholesome, 3) reduce the use of chemical fertilizers and pesticides, and 4) keep farms economically viable."
    3. Farm Legislation—Legislation includes the 2002 Farm Security and Rural Investment Act and the Food Conservation and Energy Act of 2008.

4. Conservation Programs—Legislations includes the Conservation Reserve Program, the Wildlife Habitat Incentive Program, the Environmental Quality Incentives Program, The Conservation Security Program, and the Conservation Stewardship Program.

Review Questions: Possible Answers

1. Compare the land use decisions and their consequences in Guatemala and Kalmukia, as found in the opening story.

In Guatemala local farmers decided to employ environmentally sustainable farming methods to care for their soil and increase crop outputs. The success caught on and spread to other farms in the area. In Kalmukia, historically farmers cared for their soil by rotating crops and being very careful not to disturb topsoil unnecessarily. However, several communist practices forced unsustainable practices in regards to farming and soil that led to a devastating desertification of the area.

2. Name and describe the properties of the three main components of soil texture.

Soil texture can be differentiated by the proportion of sand, silt, and clay. If sand predominates, the soil is called sandy and the particles size ranges from 2.0 to 0.02 mm. If silt predominates, then the soil is called silty and the particles range from 0.02 to 0.002 mm. If clay predominates, the soil is called clayey and the particles are less than 0.002 mm. If the soil is roughly 40% sand, 40% silt, and 20% clay, the soil is called loam. The three properties are "larger particles have larger spaces separating them than smaller particles have," "smaller particles have more surface area relative to their volume than larger particles have," and "nutrient ions and water molecules tend to cling to surfaces."

3. What are the different layers, or horizons, that compose the soil profile? What makes each one distinct from the others?

A typical soil profile consists of the O horizon, consisting of dead organic matter; the A horizon (top soil), consisting of a mixture of the mineral soil from below with the humus from above; the E horizon, consisting of a layer from which the minerals have been leached; the B horizon (subsoil), consisting of the layer to which to minerals leach from and A and E horizons; and the C horizon, consisting of the parent mineral material. The differences between each layer can sometimes be minor, but the size of particles is the main determinant.

4. Name and describe the four major soil orders listed in this chapter. Where are they mainly found?

The four major soil orders in this chapter are Mollisols, Oxisols, Alfisols, and Aridisols.
Mollisols are "fertile, dark soils found in temperate grassland biomes." Oxisols "are soils of the tropical and subtropical rain forests." Alfisols "are widespread, moderately weathered forest soils." Aridisols "are the very widespread soils of drylands and deserts."

5. What are the main things that plant roots must obtain from the soil? Name and describe a process (natural or unnatural) that can keep plants from obtaining the amounts of each of these things they need for survival.

The main things that plant roots must obtain are "optimal amounts of mineral nutrients, water, and air. The pH and salinity of the soil are also critically important."

Erosion—"the process of soil and humus particles being picked up and carried away by water or wind."

Desertification—"the formation and expansion of degraded areas of soil and vegetation cover in arid, semiarid, and seasonally dry areas, caused by climatic variations and human activities."

Overcultivation—leaving the land bare between agricultural crops; continually planting and not leaving fallow; plowing repeatedly resulting in compaction.

Overgrazing—too many animals grazing in too little space.

Deforestation—removal of trees in such a way that soil is exposed and erosion occurs.

6. *Describe, in terms of both content and physical structure, the soil environment that will best fulfill the needs of plants.*

"To support a good crop, the soil must (1) have a good supply of nutrients and a good nutrient-holding capacity; (2) allow infiltration, have a good water-holding capacity, and resist evaporative water loss; (3) have a porous structure that permits good aeration; (4) have a pH near neutral; and (5) have a low salt content. Moreover, these attributes must be sustained."

7. *State and define the relationships among humus, detritus, and soil organisms. Describe the role each of these factors plays in creating a soil favorable to plants.*

Detritus is the food source for decomposers and detritus feeders. These organisms consume the detritus for energy and nutrients and release carbon dioxide, water, and minerals into the soil. The undigested portion of detritus excreted by the soil organisms is called humus. As minerals go through the guts of detritus feeders, (e.g., worms), the minerals adhere to the humus. The clumps of humus create the structure of soil. The soil structure is the arrangement of soil particles. Humus improves a soil's ability to hold water and nutrients, and increases its workability and aeration, while improving the ability of water to infiltrate the soil.

8. *What is meant by mineralization? What causes it? What are its consequences for soil?*

The "loss of humus and the consequent collapse of topsoil is referred to as the mineralization of the soil, because what is left is just the gritty mineral content—sand, silt, and clay—devoid of humus." The loss of topsoil would mean "the mutually supportive relationship between plants and soil" is broken. When mineralization occurs the soil is no longer able to support plants.

9. *What are some problems with the sweeping claims made about soil erosion and soil degradation? How have these claims been challenged?*

"The National Resource Inventory reports erosion rates on an annual basis. For 2001, they amounted to about 1.8 billion tons of eroded material. Much erosion is judged to be 'excessive,' originating from 101 million acres of cropland deemed vulnerable." These claims are made by "map-reading, aerial photography, and the judicious use of 'universal soil loss equation' and 'wind erosion equation.' As a result, the figures that are obtained are estimates rather than measurements." UCLA geographer Stanley W. Trimble studied the Coon Creek Basin in Wisconsin. "He found rates of erosion that were high in the late 19th century, went even higher in the 1920s and 1930s, and then began to decline as farmers adopted conservation practices. Most remarkable, the rates from the 1970s to the 1990s were only 6% of their peak rates."

10. *What is the impact of water and wind on bare soil? Define and describe the process of erosion in detail.*

Erosion is "the process of soil and humus particles being picked up and carried away by water or wind." "When soil is left bare and unprotected, however, it is easily eroded. Water erosion starts with what is called splash erosion as the impact of falling raindrops breaks up the clumpy structure of the topsoil. The dislodged particles wash into spaces between other aggregates, clogging the pores and thereby decreasing infiltration and aeration. The decreased infiltration results in more water running off and carrying away the fine particles from the surface, a phenomenon called sheet erosion. As further runoff occurs, the water converges into rivulets and streams, which have greater volume, velocity, and energy, and hence greater capacity to pick up and remove soil. The result is the erosion of gullies, or gully erosion." Wind is able to pick up and carry away soil and humus particles from bare soil. Wind erosion will remove the finer particles from soil, leaving the larger grains and stones. The "remaining soil become progressively coarser—sandy, stony, and, finally, rocky. Such coarse soils frequently reflect past or ongoing erosion."

11. *What is meant by desertification? Describe how the process of erosion leads to a loss of water-holding capacity and, hence to desertification.*

    Desertification "refers to the formation and expansion of degraded areas of soil and vegetation cover in arid, semiarid, and seasonally dry areas, caused by climatic variations and human activities. Erosion results in the loss of water-holding capacity." Water-holding capacity is determined by plant cover, humus, and the vegetative or litter mat; these things will slow the movement of water and allow for infiltration. Erosion removes topsoil and humus. When these are removed the ability to hold water is reduced and desertification results.

12. *What are drylands? Where are they found, and how important are they for human habitation and agriculture?*

    Drylands are arid, semiarid, and seasonally dry ecosystems. "Dryland ecosystems cover over one-third of Earth's land area. They are defined by precipitation, not temperature. Beyond the relatively uninhabited deserts, much of the land receives only 10 to 30 inches (25–75 cm) of rainfall a year, a minimal amount to support rangeland or non-irrigated cropland. These lands, occupying some 5.2 billion hectares, are home to more than 2 billion people and are found on every continent except Antarctica."

13. *What are the three major cultural practices that expose soil to the weather?*

    Overcultivation, overgrazing, and deforestation.

14. *What is meant by salinization, and what are its consequences? How does salinization result from irrigation?*

    "Salinization is the accumulation of salts in and on the soil to the point where plant growth is suppressed. Salinization occurs because even the freshest irrigation water contains at least 200 to 500 ppm (0.02 to 0.05%) of dissolved salts. Adding water to dryland soils also dissolves the high concentrations of soluble minerals that are often present in those soils. As the applied water leaves by evaporation or transpiration, the salts remain behind and gradually accumulate as a precipitate. Because it happens in drylands, salinization is considered a form of desertification, since it renders the land less productive or even useless." Salt is a limiting factor for plants—when salt levels are too high the plants die, leaving the land bare and vulnerable to erosion.

15. *What are the two levels at which soil conservation must be practiced? Give an example of what is being done at each level.*

    "Soil conservation must be practiced at two levels. The most important is the level of the individual landholder. The second level is the level of public policy." Farmers will find that protecting soil and reducing erosion will result in greater farm productivity over the long run, replacing subsidies with sustainable agriculture. "The goals of sustainable agriculture are to (1) maintain a productive topsoil, (2) keep food safe and wholesome, (3) reduce the use of chemical fertilizers and pesticides, and last, but far from least, (4) keep farms economically viable." The Conservation Reserve Program has been established to remove highly erodible cropland from production. "Farmers are required to develop and implement soil-conservation programs in order to remain eligible for price supports and other benefits provided by the government." The "Wetlands Reserve Program pays farmers to set aside and restore wetlands on their property."

Thinking Environmentally: Possible Answers

1. *Why is soil considered to be a detritus-based ecosystem? Describe how the aboveground portion and the belowground portion of an ecosystem act as two interrelated, interdependent communities.*

    Soil is a detritus-based ecosystem because the source of energy for the ecosystem is detritus. The aboveground portion of an ecosystem provides the detritus (energy and nutrients) for the belowground ecosystem, and the belowground ecosystem breaks down the detritus into a form that can be taken up by plants in the aboveground portion. Each ecosystem is dependent upon the other.

126

2. *Suppose you have uncovered an excellent new technique for keeping dryland soils moist and fertile. How would you get your message to the subsistence farmers?*

Answers will vary. Demonstration projects by the Peace Corps, the U.N. agencies, and nonprofit development agencies would be useful to show subsistence farmers the new techniques. Introducing the techniques into schools would also be a method to deliver the information.

3. *Critique the following argument: Erosion is always with us; mountains are formed and then erode, and rivers erode canyons. You can't ever eliminate soil erosion, so it is foolish to ask farmers to do so.*

It is true that erosion is always with us and that it cannot be eliminated. The goal is to not increase the rate of soil erosion by human activities. Farmers and everyone else interested in maintaining our ability to produce food should be concerned about maintaining soil fertility. Erosion decreases fertility. Our goal should be to decrease rates of erosion to "background." This would result in a sustainable ecosystem that will be able to continue to provide goods and resources to the current, and future, human population.

4. *The current system of management of grazing lands by the BLM is clearly unsustainable. What would you suggest in the way of public policy to make it sustainable?*

While a simple increase in fee per cattle has not worked in the past, stricter requirements for the use of space could be employed which mimic the recommendations for private land owners. For example, the use of more sustainable practices like burning woody plants, the use grasses that hold water better, and management of the movement of herds to prevent overgrazing could all help prevent the tragedy of the commons on public lands.

CHAPTER 12
The Production and Distribution of Food

Chapter Outline:

I. Crops and Animals: Major Patterns of Food Production
    A. The Development of Modern Industrialized Agriculture
        1. The Transformation of Traditional Agriculture
            i. Infrastucture
            ii. Machinery
            iii. Land Under Cultivation
            iv. Fertilizers and Pesticides
            v. Irrigation
            vi. High-Yielding Varieties of Plants
    B. The Green Revolution
        i. Nobel Effort
        ii. Panacea
        iii. Impacts
    C. Subsistence Agriculture in the Developing World
        i. Problems in Africa
        ii. Successes
    D. Animal Farming and Its Consequences
        1. CAFOs
            i. Rain Forest Crunched
            ii. Climate Change
            iii. Good Cow
    E. Biofuels and Food Production
        i. Consequences
        1. Future Prospects
            i. Global Picture
            ii. Less Meat and Biofuels
II. From Green Revolution to Gene Revolution
    A. The Promise
        i. Marker-Assisted Breeding
    B. The Problems
        1. Environmental Concerns
        2. Safety Issues
        3. Access in the Developing World
    C. The Policies
        1. Cartagena Protocol
        2. Precautionary Principle
III. Food Distribution and Trade
    A. Patterns in Food Trade
        1. Grain on the Move
    B. The Global Food Crisis
    C. Food Security

      1. Family Level
      2. National Level
      3. Global Level
      4. Other Needs
IV. Hunger, Malnutrition, and Famine
    A. Malnutrition Versus Hunger
    B. Extent of Consequences of Hunger
      1. Where?
      2. Consequences
    C. Root Cause of Hunger
    D. Famine
      1. Drought
      2. Warning Systems
      3. Conflict
    E. Hunger Hot Spots
    F. Food Aid
      1. When Aid Doesn't Help
      2. When It Does
    G. Closing Thoughts on Hunger

Key Topics:

1. Crops and Animals: Major Patterns of Food Production
2. From Green Revolution to Gene Revolution
3. Food Distribution and Trade
4. Hunger, Malnutrition, and Famine

Instructional Goals:

1. Since the Neolithic Revolution and the introduction of agriculture in human culture, the relationship of humans to food has been changing.

2. With the ability of researchers to produce genetically modified varieties of food, the world can potentially produce more food for its increasing population with greater efficiency.

3. While in the past, countries were responsible for producing their own food, the movement since the Industrial Revolution has been towards trading food between nations.

4. Despite our improvements in growing and producing food, the proportion of hungry, malnourished, and undernourished people in the world is still significant due to poverty, drought, and conflict.

Concepts and Connections:

    Hunger, food production, and population size are clearly linked. We see these same links in animal populations. Students may be familiar with the boom–bust cycle of lemmings. Discussing the bust portion of the cycle can prompt the students to think about the ethical dilemma that would be caused by overshooting Earth's carrying capacity for humans.

Students may know something about the Green Revolution. Whether the students have previous knowledge of the Green Revolution or not, it is possible to connect our past efforts to improve crops' quality with our current efforts to genetically modify crops. While the goals are similar and it can be argued that recombinant DNA does not fundamentally differ from traditional plant breeding, there are ethical and safety concerns.

Almost every ecological problem we face impacts agriculture. Erosion, air pollution, water pollution, water availability, soil fertility, population growth, biodiversity, deforestation, global warming, and ozone depletion all impact agriculture. The interconnectedness of everything cannot be avoided when discussing our ability to have enough food to feed the people of the world.

Concepts in Context:

Food productivity is dependent upon soil (Chapter 11) and water (Chapter 10) availability. Phosphorus and nitrogen, whose cycles were discussed in Chapter 4, are limiting factors (Chapter 3) in agricultural systems. When too much of these limiting factors is added to the soils, water pollution (Chapter 20) results. The problem of Physteria in Chesapeake Bay can be related to excess nutrients from agricultural production (Chapters 12 and 20).

Agricultural and forest productivity in parts of the world is adversely impacted by air pollution (Chapter 19). Global warming (Chapter 18) will alter rainfall and temperature patterns, changing where food is grown. Agriculture is severely impacted by how we obtain our energy. Currently, most modern agriculture is fueled by fossil fuels (Chapter 14). Proposals have been made to produce energy by growing crops to burn (Chapter 16); bio-fuel production could impact our ability to feed people.

The Green Revolution is an excellent example of the First and Second Laws of Thermodynamics (Chapter 4). There is only so much energy that plants can capture from the sun. The captured energy is partitioned between the roots, vegetative material (leaves and stems), and seeds. Because plants with high seed output were selected, the plants had less extensive root systems and shorter stalks. The result was a need to irrigate (Chapter 10), fertilize, and use herbicides (Chapter 13).

Biodiversity (Chapter 6) is adversely affected by the clearing of land for agricultural use. Geneticists, evolutionary biologists, and food experts are concerned about the genetic diversity of food crops (Chapter 5). Agricultural ecosystems are simplified ecosystems and are vulnerable to pests (Chapter 13) and other ecological imbalances (Chapters 3, 4, and 5).

Key Terms and Vocabulary:

Conservation Reserve Program, Green Revolution, subsistence farmers, Doubly Green Revolution, Cartagena Protocol on Biosafety, precautionary principle, food security, family, nation, global community, malnutrition, undernourishment, overnourishment

Discussion, Activities, and Labs:

1. Divide the class into groups of three to four students per group. Have each group list five reasons why food aid might be economically, socially, or environmentally a good idea and five reasons why food aid might be economically, socially, or environmentally a poor idea. Ask each group to propose to stop or continue food aid. What are the most persuasive reasons to support the chosen position?

2. Divide the class into groups of three to four students per group. Have each group list the characteristics of a sustainable agricultural system. Next, have each group list the characteristics of conventional agriculture and subsistence (slash and burn) agriculture. Discuss why conventional and subsistence agriculture are not sustainable. (Why have farms become monocultures? Why do you see wide spread erosion where subsistence agriculture is practiced? What needs to be done to achieve sustainable agriculture?)

3. Have students discuss, within the context of the precautionary principle, the consequences of making decisions and the errors that would be possible. Include in the discussion the acceptability of these errors. Are we willing to accept the consequences of introducing genetically modified organisms if these organisms modify ecosystems? Speed resistance development? Cause allergic reactions in children and adults? Cause greater income inequity?

4. Send each student to the grocery store. In the produce section (especially during the winter) it should be possible to find many items that have been imported from a developing country. Have each student find as many produce labels as they can and list the items and their country of origination. For all the produce without a label identifying the country of origin, have the student list these produce items. (This list could be quite long.) Then have the students do an Internet or library search to determine what crops are grown in their state. (The state Agriculture Department should be a good source for this information.) In most parts of the country during the winter, very little produce will be local. Using the list from the grocery store and the list from the Agriculture Department, the students should be able to see how dependent we are on international trade and trade between states. Have the students discuss the impact of the movement of food around the world. The environmental, energy, political, economic, and nutritional impacts of food transport should be considered.

Suggested Lecture Format:

I. Crops and Animals: Major Patterns of Food Production
Since the Neolithic Revolution and the introduction of agriculture in human culture, the relationship of humans to food has been changing.

    A. The Development of Modern Industrialized Agriculture—Traditional farmers rotated crops regularly, grew a variety of crops, and used animal waste to fertilize the soil.

        1. The Transformation of Traditional Agriculture—"The Industrial Revolution transformed agriculture so profoundly that today, in the United States, some 3 million farmers and farm workers produce enough food for all the nation's needs, plus a substantial amount for trade on world markets." **See Discussion Topic #2.**

           i. Infrastructure—"The transformation of agriculture was greatly facilitated by developing a supporting infrastructure."

           ii. Machinery—"Machinery has enabled farmers to cultivate far more land than ever. However, the shift from animal labor to machinery has created a dependency on fossil fuel energy."

           iii. Land Under Cultivation—"Essentially all of the good cropland in the United States is now under cultivation or held in short-term reserve."

           iv. Fertilizers and Pesticides—"When chemical fertilizers first became available for use, however, farmers discovered that they could achieve even greater yields."

           v. Irrigation—Irrigation is important and still expanding, but is unsustainable because groundwater resources are being depleted.

vi. High-Yielding Varieties of Plants—"As new (genetically modified) variations of traditional crops) were grown in the developed countries and then introduced throughout the world, production soared, and the Green Revolution was born."

B. The Green Revolution—"The same technologies that gave rise to the agricultural revolution in the industrialized countries were eventually introduced into the developing world. There, they gave birth to the remarkable increases in crop production called the Green Revolution."
   i. Nobel Effort—"The Green Revolution has probably done more than any other single scientific or other achievement to prevent hunger and malnutrition."
   ii. Panacea—"The Green Revolution is not a panacea for all of the world's food-population difficulties."
   iii. Impacts—A recent study concluded that the Green Revolution has benefited many of the developing countries but "agricultural production in sub-Saharan Africa has lagged behind that of the rest of the developing world."

C. Subsistence Agriculture in the Developing World—"Subsistence farmers live on small parcels of land that provide them with the food for their households and, it is hoped, a small cash crop."
   i. Problems in Africa—Subsistence farming in some developing countries is not adequate to support growing populations in a water restricted area."
   ii. Successes—Slash and burn agriculture has led to some success in parts of the world.

D. Animal Farming and Its Consequences—With an increased demand for meat from developing countries, animal husbandry has occupied what would otherwise be cropland.
   1. CAFOs—"The crowded factory farms are perfect conditions for diseases to incubate and spread among the animals and from animals to humans."
      i. Rain Forest Crunched—"In Latin America, more than 58 million acres of tropical rain forests have been converted to cattle pasture."
      ii. Climate Change—Increased carbon in the atmosphere because of deforestation for the purpose of animal husbandry in addition to methane gases as a by-product of the digestion of animals has led to many environmental problems.
      iii. Good Cow—"The well-being of millions in the developing world is tied directly to the animals they raise, and the impact of these animals on the environment is often sustainable."

E. Biofuels and Food Production—"The most basic cause of climate change is the burning of fossil fuels, which has driven atmospheric CO_2 (a greenhouse gas) more than 35% above preindustrial levels. One of the important ways to mitigate climate change is to burn biofuels."
   i. Consequences—Critics of biofuels argue that using corn for biofuels is taking food away from those who need it and driving up the cost of food because of increased demand for corn.
   1. Future Prospects—"Grain production has kept up with the population increase, and meat production has greatly outpaced it over the last 35 years."
      i. Global Picture—"It turns out that the great differences in grain yields among regions have less to do with the genetic strains used and more to do with the weather."
      ii. Less Meat and Biofuels—The Doubly Green Revolution is "a revolution that is even more productive than the first Green Revolution and even more 'green' in terms of conserving natural resources and the environment.

II. From Green Revolution to Gene Revolution

With the ability of researchers to produce genetically modified varieties of food, the world can potentially produce more food for its increasing population with greater efficiency.

A. The Promise—"Among the important environmental benefits of bioengineered crops are reduction in the use of pesticide because the crops are already resistant to pests, less erosion because of no-till cropping is facilitated by the use of herbicide-resistant crops, and less environmental damage associated with bringing more land into production because of existing agricultural lands will produce more food."

   i. Marker-Assisted Breeding—"…identifies desirable traits in crop plants or their wild ancestors and locates the genes with DNA sequencing. Next, plants with the desired gene are crossbred with a modern crop breeding line."

B. The Problems—"Concerns about genetic engineering technology involve three considerations: environmental problems, food safety, and access to the new techniques."

   1. Environmental Concerns—Pests, being living organisms, tend to adapt to the genetic changes in crops over time for their own survival. Additionally, there is concern that genetically modified species may impact other related organisms in the ecosystem negatively.

   2. Safety Issues—"Food safety issues arise because transgenic crops contain proteins from different organisms and might trigger allergic response in people who consume food."

   3. Access in the Developing World—"Farmers in developing countries are less able to afford the higher costs of the new seeds, which must be paid up from each year."

C. The Policies—"Biotechnology and its applications to food crops do not exist in a regulatory vacuum."

   1. Cartagena Protocol—"Those skeptical of the claims of biotech companies about the safety of their products wanted proof that the genetically modified organisms were safe before they were allowed into their countries."

   2. Precautionary Principle—"where there are threats of serious or irreversible damage, lack of scientific certainty should not be used as a reason for failing to take measures to prevent potential damage." **See Discussion Topic #3.**

III. Food Distribution and Trade

While in the past, countries were responsible for producing their own food, the movement since the Industrial Revolution has been towards trading food between nations. **See Discussion Topic #4.**

A. Patterns in Food Trade—Whether a developed or developing country, exporting foodstuffs are an important economic factor.

   1. Grain on the Move—"At no time in recent history has the world grain supply run out."

B. The Global Food Crisis—"Between 2006 and 2008, the prices of food commodities on the world market rose precipitously…triggering food riots and emergency measures in many countries."

C. Food Security—Food security is "assured access for every person to enough nutritious food to sustain an active and healthy life."

   1. Family Level—"The most important level of responsibility (for food security) is the family."

   2. National Level—Whether developed or developing, each country has a responsibility to provide food security for its people."

133

3. Global Level—"The WTO is the body that governs international trade. Meeting every few years, the WTO brings together developed and developing member countries for negotiations and policy decisions."
4. Other Needs—"One of the most important (initiative) is relieving the debt crisis in developing countries...Another factor in meeting global nutrition needs is the trade imbalance between the industrial and developing countries."

IV. Hunger, Malnutrition, and Famine
Despite our improvements in growing and producing food, the proportion of hungry, malnourished, and undernourished people in the world is still significant due to poverty, drought, and conflict.

   A. Malnutrition Versus Hunger—"Hunger is the general term referring to a lack of basic food required to provide energy and to meet nutritional needs. Malnutrition is the lack of essential nutrients, such as specific amino acids, vitamins, and minerals, and undernourishment is the lack of adequate food energy."

   B. Extent of Consequences of Hunger—"On the basis of surveys of available food in the society, with accessibility to food factored in, the FAO estimated in mid 2009 that 1 billion people in the developing world and an additional 15 million in the rest of the world are underfed and undernourished."
      1. Where?—"The most severely affected are India, Bangladesh, Pakistan, and China."
      2. Consequences—"Hunger can prevent normal growth in children, leaving them thin, stunted, and often mentally and physically impaired."

   C. Root Cause of Hunger—"In the view of most observers, the root cause of hunger is poverty."

   D. Famine—"A famine is a severe shortage of food accompanied by a significant increase in the death rate. Two factors—drought and conflict—have been immediate causes."
      1. Drought—Extended periods without adequate rainfall can lead to the devastation of crops and foodstuffs.
      2. Warning Systems—The Global Information and Early Warning System and the Famine Early Warning System Network focus on watching for signs of drought to help prevent famine.
      3. Conflict—"At least 15 countries in Sub-Saharan Africa have experienced food emergencies in recent years because of internal conflicts and their effects on neighboring countries."

   E. Hunger Hot Spots—"Much of Africa has experienced long-term and severe droughts as well as widespread civil conflict. Erratic weather patterns and a general warming trend thought by some scientists to be the outcome of global climate change have caused crop harvests to oscillate between average and poor."

   F. Food Aid—"The World Food Program (WFP) of the United Nations coordinates global food aid, receiving donations from the United States, Japan, and the countries of the European Union. In addition, many nations conduct their own programs of bilateral food aid to needy countries." **See Discussion Topic #1.**
      1. When Aid Doesn't Help—"The donation of food, while well intended, often aggravates the very condition that it is meant to alleviate."
      2. When It Does—"Some aid does go to 'development projects', benefiting poor people in countries where food security is at risk and regions where malnutrition is severe."

134

G. Closing Thoughts on Hunger—"Given the current groundswell of concern about the environment and the global attention to the Millennium Development Goals, there may never be a better time to turn things around and take more seriously our responsibilities as stewards of the planet and as our brother's (and sisters') keepers.

Review Questions: Possible Answers

1. Describe the major components of the agricultural revolution. What are the environmental costs of each?

The major components of the agricultural revolution are infrastructure, machinery, fertilizers and pesticides, irrigation, and the discovery of high yield plants. With infrastructure comes buildings and technology which can have environmental consequences. Similarly, machinery increases efficiency in farming, but can also add greenhouse emissions to the atmosphere and cause soil compaction and other destruction. Fertilizers and pesticides have also increased production but have environmentally devastating impacts because of resistance, contamination of water, and eutrophication. Irrigation has allowed areas that were previously not farmable to be farmed, but has depleted ground water resources significantly. Finally high yield plants, like those that are genetically modified have known and unknown environmental impacts. Possible allergic reactions in food-sensitive individuals and loss of wild type species have been speculated upon.

2. What is the Green Revolution? What have been its limitations and its gains?

The Green Revolution was the implementation of the technologies (described in Question 1) developed in the industrialized world to increase agricultural productivity. The Green Revolution was dependent on the development of crop varieties that would produce more food. This led to selecting plants that partitioned the energy captured from the sun differently than normal. Plants with less root material, less vegetative material, and more seed material were chosen for breeding. This selection process resulted in the need to increase herbicide use—weeds would compete more effectively for sunlight. These new plants also had an increased need for fertilizer and irrigation because the root system was less extensive.

3. Describe subsistence agriculture, and discuss its relationship to sustainability.

Subsistence agriculture is farming done typically on small parcels of land that provide the farmer and his/her family with food for the household and possibly a small cash crop. This type of "farming is labor intensive and lacks practically all of the inputs of industrialized agriculture. Also, it is often practiced on marginally productive land." Subsistence farming is sustainable when the land being cultivated is not marginal farmland supporting too many people. When animals are combined with subsistence farming, sustainability can be enhanced and is more likely to be sustainable "than the beef ranches and hog pens of the developed world."

4. How do sustainable animal farming and industrial-style animal farming affect the environment on different scales?

"Industrial-style animal farming can affect the environment in a host of non-sustainable ways. Because so much of the plant crop is fed to animals, all the problems of industrialized agriculture apply to animal farming. In addition, rangelands are susceptible to overgrazing, either because of mismanagement of prime grazing land or because the land on which the animals graze is marginal dry grassland, used in that manner because the better lands have been converted to producing crops. Another serious problem is the management of animal manure. Close to 1.3 billion tons of animal waste is produced each year in the United States, some of which leaks into surface waters and contributes to die-offs of fish, contamination with pathogens, and a proliferation of algae." Land in the tropics has been converted to grazing land; much of this land is not suitable for long-term grazing. Climate change is also influenced by cattle production. The digestive process of cows is anaerobic; "cows and other ruminant animals annually eliminate some 100 million tons of methane, another greenhouse gas, through belching and flatulence. The anaerobic decomposition of manure leads to an additional 30 million tons of methane per year. All this methane released by livestock makes up about 3% of the gases causing global warming."

135

Sustainable animal farming is more easily done on small rural farms with pastoral herds as seen in the developing world. The soil can be enhanced if the animals are well managed. The nutrition of women and small children is especially enhanced.

5. *What are biofuels, and what are their impacts on food production?*

Biofuels are made from ethanol and oils derived from agricultural crops. Although they have been decreasing the need for fossil fuels while still providing energy resources, because they are based on agricultural crops, growing crops for the purpose of fuel takes land and resources away from growing food for consumption.

6. *What are our viable options for increasing food production in the future?*

"There are two prospects for increasing food production: (1) Continue to increase crop yields and (2) Grow food crops on land that is now used for feedstock or cash crops."

"The global trends in food production look rather rosy. Food production is keeping up with (and surpassing, for meat production) population growth. In particular, rising incomes in the developing world have stimulated the rapid rise in meat consumption. The real concern, then, is whether these trends can continue. Looking ahead to 2020, we will be able to feed the additional 1.5 billion people and also make significant progress on meeting the MDG (Millennium Development Goal) of reducing by half existing hunger and malnutrition. The prospects for developing countries to meet the rise in demand for grains are not good. Net grain imports by developing countries will likely double by 2020, but only those countries making significant progress in economic development will be able to afford the imports. Poorer countries may be left behind. Because poorer countries are where much of the malnutrition and hunger already occur, the prospects for a great reduction in these conditions are not good."

7. *What are the major advantages and problems associated with using biotechnology in food production?*

The promise of genetically modified crops has been, like the Green Revolution to increase food production. "Among other aims, the objectives of genomics (genetically modified food) are (1) to incorporate resistance to diseases and pests that attach important tropical plants, (2) to increase tolerance to environmental conditions, such as drought and high salt levels, which stress most plants, (3) to improve the nutritional value of commonly eaten crops (like the work with golden rice), and (4) to produce pharmaceutical products in ordinary plants ("pharma" crops). "Among the important environmental benefits of bioengineered crops are reductions in the use of pesticides, because the crops are already resistant to pests; less erosion, because no till cropping is facilitated by the use of herbicide resistant crops; and less environmental damage associated with bringing more land into production, because the existing agricultural lands will produce more food."

"Concerns about genetic engineering technology involve three considerations: environmental problems, food safety, and access to the new techniques. A major environmental concern focuses on the pest-resistant properties of the transgenic crops. With such broad exposure to the toxin or some other resistance incorporated into the plant, it is possible that the pest will develop its own resistance to the toxin more rapidly and thus render it ineffective as an independent pesticide. Another concern is the ecological impact of the crops. For example, pollen from Bt corn (resistant to the corn borer) disperses in the wind and can spread to adjacent natural areas where beneficial insects may pick it up and be killed by the toxin. A third environmental concern arises because genes for herbicide resistance or for tolerance to drought and other environmental conditions can also spread by pollen to wild relatives of crop plants, possibly creating new or 'super' weeds. Food safety issues arise because transgenic crops contain proteins from different organisms and might trigger an unexpected allergic response in people who consume the food. The problems concerning access to the new technologies related to the developing world. For the first few years, almost all genetically modified organisms were developed by large agricultural-industrial firms, with profit as the primary motive. Accordingly, farmers have been forbidden by contract from simply propagating the seeds themselves and must purchase seeds annually. Farmers in the developing countries are far less able to afford the higher costs of the new seeds, which must be paid up front each year."

8. *Describe the patterns in grain trade between different world regions over the last 70 years. How does the food crisis of 2007-2008 relate to these patterns?*

Over the past 70 years countries have shifted from being self-sustaining in food production towards trading foodstuffs with each other. "A number of factors conspired to create the situation where supply was unable to keep up with demand: 1) higher production costs due to the rising cost of petroleum and fertilizer, 2) as we have seen already, the diversion of corn and other commodities to the production of biofuels, 3) a strong demand for higher-quality diets in the emerging economies of Asia, 4) weather-related shortfalls of harvests in key exporting countries and, 5) a background of declining carryover stocks of many commodities."

9. *Describe the three levels of responsibility for meeting food needs. At each level, list several ways food security can be improved.*

There are "three major levels of responsibility for food security: the family, the nation, and the global community." Food security at the family level can be improved by "(1) official policies, represented by a variety of welfare measures, such as the Food Stamp Program and the Supplemental Security Income program; and (2) voluntary aid through hunger-relief organizations." Increasing the ability of individuals to produce their own food would also increase food security at a family level. Food security at the national level can be improved, increasing the ability of a country to be food self-sufficient. Food aid from the global community also helps countries have some level of food security. Global food security would be improved if problems such as the trade imbalance and human exploitation were addressed.

10. *Define hunger, malnutrition, and undernourishment. What is the extent of these problems in the world? What is their root cause?*

"Hunger is the general term referring to the lack of basic food required for energy and for meeting nutritional needs such that the individual is able to lead a normal, healthy life. Malnutrition is the lack of essential nutrients, such as specific amino acids, vitamins, and minerals, and undernourishment is the lack of adequate food energy (usually measured in calories)."

"In 2004, the FAO published an update showing that 852 million are still suffering from hunger."

11. *Discuss the causes of famine and severe hunger, and name the geographical areas most threatened by it.*

"Two factors—drought and conflict—have been immediate causes of famines in recent years." In recent years, the Sahel region of Africa has been the site of two major famines caused by drought. The countries of Ethiopia, Eritrea, Somalia, Rwanda, Sudan, Mozambique, Angola, and Congo have experienced famine in the 1990s due to conflict. North Korea has also experienced famine recently due to drought and the failure of centrally planned agriculture.

12. *How is relief for famine and severe hunger accomplished? Why does food aid sometimes aggravate poverty and hunger?*

Food "aid is vital in saving lives where famines occur." Food aid is "a buffer against famine." Food aid may sometimes aggravate poverty and hunger by undercutting the local farming economy and result in more people being dependent upon food aid.

Thinking Environmentally: Possible Answers

1. *Imagine that you have been sent as a Peace Corp volunteer to a poor African nation experiencing widespread hunger. Design a strategy for assessing the needs of the people and for contacting appropriate sources for help.*

It would be necessary to determine the kind of food that is consumed by the population—it would be a waste of effort and so on to bring in food that the population does not know how to prepare or consume. Once the kind of food is known, contacting the FAO and Famine Early Warning System Network would be the next step. Once the immediate food problem has been addressed it would be time to plan how to avoid the problem in the future.

2. *Log on to www.mypyramid.gov and compare your diet with that recommended by the USDA program. Use the meal tracking worksheet to record your food intake over a two- to three-day period. Which nutrients are lacking? Which are in excess? What changes in your diet would reconcile these differences?*

A typical American diet (including vegetarian) will have more protein than considered nutritionally necessary. It is also likely that some vitamins and minerals will be too low, especially calcium for women. The caloric intake is likely to be higher than necessary to maintain an ideal body weight. This later issue is become a larger and larger problem within the college-age group.

Because keeping a food diary can influence dietary decisions, it could be useful to discuss this effect on the results of the students' evaluation of their diets. Most individuals will change what they eat because they don't want to write down that they have eaten something that nutritionists would say they shouldn't eat. For example, a person might typically eat a large pizza or a gallon of ice cream by him/herself but won't eat these things if someone is going to know about it.

3. *Use the Web to evaluate the work of FEWS (www.fews.net) and the GIEWS (http://geoweb.fao.org/). How do these organizations function in bringing aid to people with the greatest need?*

These organizations provide information about where food emergencies are happening in the world along with information about where emergency food aid might be needed in the near and more distant future. By providing information about food emergencies, aid can be directed to where it is needed the most.

CHAPTER 13
Pests and Pest Control

Chapter Outline:

I. The Need for Pest Control
- A. The Importance of Pest Control
- B. Different Philosophies of Pest Control

II. Chemical Treatment: Promises and Problems
- A. Development of Chemical Pesticides and Their Successes
  - 1. The DDT Story
    - i. In War...
    - ii. And in Peace...
- B. Problems Stemming from Chemical Pesticide Use
  - 1. Development of Resistance by Pests
    - i. Evolution at Work
    - ii. The Last Roundup©
  - 2. Resurgences and Secondary-Pest Outbreaks
    - i. Treadmill
  - 3. Adverse Human Health Effects
    - i. Acute Effects
    - ii. Chronic Effects
    - iii. Endocrine Disruptors
  - 4. Adverse Environmental Effects
    - i. DDT, Continued
    - ii. Up the Chain
    - iii. Silent Spring
  - 5. Nonpersistent Pesticides: Are They the Answer?
    - i. Toxicity
    - ii. Bird Kill

III. Alternative Pest Control Methods
- A. Cultural Control
  - 1. Control of Pests Affecting Crops, Gardens, and Lawns
    - i. Crops
    - ii. Border Patrol
- B. Cultural Control of Pests Affecting Humans
- C. Control by Natural Enemies
  - 1. Protect the Natives
  - 2. Import Aliens as a Last Resort
- D. Genetic Control
  - 1. Control with Chemical Barriers
  - 2. Control with Physical Barriers
  - 3. Control with Sterile Males
  - 4. Strategies Using Biotechnology
    - i. Roundup© Again
    - ii. Not So Fast...

Key Topics:

1. The Need for Pest Control
2. Chemical Treatment: Promises and Problems
3. Alternative Pest Control Methods
4. Socioeconomic Issues in Pesticide Use
5. Pesticides and Policy

Instructional Goals:

1. With new farming practices in place, food production has increased dramatically, and with it, the need for pest control has increased dramatically in the past 50-60 years. Pest control has taken on two basic forms: chemical treatment or integrated pest management.

2. Use of chemical pesticides, including DDT have simultaneously allowed for higher food production and for increased pest resistance, human health conditions, and effects on the broader environment. Recently, we have focused on the use of synthetic organic chemical pesticides with little resolution to our long standing issues with pesticides.

3. Ecological control of pests is a way of using natural factors to control pests in such a way that is not harmful to humans and allows for sustainable agriculture.

4. Agriculture is moving away from pesticides and towards integrated pest management and organically grown food as consumer concern over pesticides increases.

5. Policies have been put in place that address the effect of pesticides on human health, the need for proper training for those who work with pesticides, and the need to keep food free of pesticide residues.

Concepts and Connections:

This chapter on pesticides can be used to teach evolution. Pesticide resistance (and antibiotic resistance) is an excellent example of natural selection. The exposure of an insect to an insecticide results in the selection of the most resistant individuals. Those individuals are the most reproductively fit. The population of insects begins, within a very few generations, to consist mainly of individuals who are resistant to the insecticide.

The relationship between pesticides and human health is typically of great interest to students. The new Food Quality Protection Act (FQPA), with its emphasis on "a reasonable certainty of no harm" and special populations (children), would be an interesting lecture focus. There is a tremendous amount of information about FQPA on the EPA's web site. Discussion about the special status of children, the grouping of like chemicals for evaluation of total exposure, and the inclusion of all exposure routes provide an interesting format for the intersection of science and policy.

The National Organic Program (information on the USDA web site) oversees the federal organic standards for food production. The National Organic Standards Board is a 15-member board of individuals from the organic industry (producers, processors, and retailers), consumers, environmentalists, and academics. This Board determines which materials can be placed on the National List and, therefore, used in organic production and processing. The implementation of national organic standards can be an interesting study of the combination of science and public opinion in public policy. For example, there is no scientific reason (at least that we know of) for chickens to have access to outdoors but the organic rule requires this because people prefer to know that the chicken that produce their eggs or that they eat have been able to go outside.

Another way to discuss the intersection of science and policy would be to discuss the differences in decision outcomes when using risk-based policy making versus the precautionary principle. The inclusion of special populations, as discussed above, could be an additional variable in a discussion on how a person's world view influences policy making.

A discussion of the connections between organic agriculture, integrated pest management, and sustainable ecosystems would help students understand more clearly how modern agriculture is nonsustainable. The impact of pesticides on soil ecology can be linked in interesting ways to sustainability. A discussion about the link between developing a sustainable agricultural system and feeding the people of the world would relate social issues to scientific issues.

Concepts in Context:

The use of pesticides can be related to human health (Chapter 17), especially the new FQPA with its emphasis on "a reasonable certainty of no harm" and special populations (children). Traditional pesticide use in agriculture can be related to sustainability and the ecological principles (Chapters 3, 4, and 5). Ecological pest management is dependent upon ecological principles. Pesticide resistance (and antibiotic resistance) is an excellent example of natural selection. Human population size and feeding people (Chapters 8 and 12) are directly related to the organisms with which we compete for food.

Water pollution (Chapter 20), hazardous waste (Chapter 22), soil contamination (Chapter 11), and the use of fossil fuels (Chapter 14) can all relate to pesticide use and production. Biodiversity (Chapter 6) and the ecosystem goods and services (Chapter 7) are useful in the discussion of ecological pest management.

Economic impacts (Chapter 2) from pest damage are directly related to our use of pesticides and our ability to use integrated pest management or increase the quantity of organically grown food. Changing how we view our food, no longer needing it to be blemish free, is important for the building of sustainable communities and lifestyles (Chapter 23). Regulation of pesticides may be influenced by changes in how we make policy decisions. The current discussion of the precautionary principle (Chapter 17) could influence which pesticides are approved for use and where these pesticides may be used.

Key Terms and Vocabulary:

pest, agricultural pests, weeds, herbicides, pesticides, chemical treatment, ecological control, integrated pest management (IPM), first-generation pesticides, scale insects, second-generation pesticides, broad spectrum, persistent, resurgence, secondary-pest outbreak, pesticide treadmill, Endocrine Disruptor Screening Program, bioaccumulation, biomagnifications, cultural control, control by natural enemies, genetic control, natural chemical control, predators, parasitoids, pathogens, plant-eaters, hormones, pheromones, juvenile hormone, ecdysone, economic threshold, insurance spraying, cosmetic spraying, pest-loss insurance, organic, Organic Foods Protection Act, Federal Insecticide, Fungicide, and Rodenticide Act, Federal Food, Drug, and Cosmetic Act (FFDCA), Delaney clause, prior informed consent (PIC), Rotterdam Convention

Discussion, Activities, and Labs:

1. Discuss with the class what we mean by pest. Why do we label particular organisms pests? What are the characteristics of a pest? Most pests are organisms that directly compete with humans. This is an important point for students to understand.

2. Discuss with the students various culture controls of pests. Ask them why they take showers, comb hair, wash clothes, and change bedding. Why do we have laws requiring window screens (if windows open), housing codes that require doors that seal and no cracks or holes in walls, and rules requiring treatment of sewage and drinking water? What are food preservation techniques but a form of cultural control? There are a large number of cultural controls for human pests that are so normal and effective that we don't recognize they exist.

3. Have students go to a grocery store, hardware store, garden center, and so forth to make a list of all the pesticides on the shelf. Notes should be taken concerning active ingredients, inert ingredients, use restrictions, cautionary label (caution, warning, danger), and so on. Each student should research, using the library and the Internet, an alternative method to control one of the pests listed on a pesticide container or the active ingredients of one of the pesticides.

Suggested Lecture Format:

I. The Need for Pest Control
    Because of the implementation of new farming practices, food production has increased dramatically, and with it, the need for pest control has increased dramatically in the past 50-60 years. Pest control has taken on two basic forms: chemical treatment or integrated pest management. **See Discussion Topic #1.**

    A. The Importance of Pest Control—"Many of the changes in agricultural technology, such as monoculture and the widespread use of genetically identical crops, have boosted yields and also brought an increase in the proportion of crops lost to pests." See Figure 13-2 and Figure 13-3.

    B. Different Philosophies of Pest Control—Two basic means are used to control pests: chemical treatment and integrated pest management (IPM).

II. Chemical Treatment: Promises and Problems
    Use of chemical pesticides, including DDT have simultaneously allowed for higher food production and for increased pest resistance, human health conditions, and effects on the broader environment. Recently, we have focused on the use of synthetic organic chemical pesticides with little resolution to our long standing issues with pesticides.

    A. Development of Chemical Pesticides and Their Successes—"Finding effective materials to combat pests is an ongoing endeavor." We have moved from first-generation pesticides, largely based on

142

damaging heavy metals, to second-generation pesticides which were developed using synthetic organic chemistry. See Table 13-1.

1. The DDT Story—DDT was discovered and shown to be a broad spectrum and persistent chemical that appeared to damage pest populations but not humans.
   i. In War…During World War II DDT helped to combat pests from body lice to the causative agents of Dengue Fever and Malaria.
   ii. And in Peace…At home DDT was sprayed to prevent defoliating insects, to kill mosquitoes, to limit the spread of tree diseases, and to prevent agricultural pests.

B. Problems Stemming from Chemical Pesticide Use—"The problems associated with the use of synthetic organic pesticides can be categorized as follows: development of resistance by pests, resurgences and secondary-pest outbreaks; and adverse environmental and human health effects."

1. Development of Resistance by Pests—"The most fundamental problem for growers is that chemical pesticides gradually lose their effectiveness."
   i. Evolution at Work—"Resistance builds up because pesticides destroy the sensitive individuals of a pest population, leaving behind only those few that already have some resistance to the pesticide. Resistant insect populations develop rapidly because insects have a phenomenal reproductive capacity."
   ii. The Last Roundup®—"Over the years of pesticide use, the number of resistant species has climbed steadily. Many major pest species are resistant to all of the principal pesticides."

2. Resurgences and Secondary-Pest Outbreaks—"After a pest has been virtually eliminated with a pesticide, the pest population not only recovers, but also explodes to higher and more severe levels. This phenomenon is known as resurgence. To make matters worse, small populations of insects that were previously of no concern because of their low numbers suddenly start to explode, creating new problems. This phenomenon is called a secondary-pest outbreak."
   i. Treadmill—Synthetic organic chemicals "do not eradicate the pests. Instead, they increase resistance and secondary-pest outbreaks, which lead to the use of new and larger quantities of chemicals, which in turn lead to more resistance and more secondary-pest outbreaks and so on." See Figure 13-7.

3. Adverse Human Health Effects—"As with all toxic substances, pesticides can be responsible for both acute and chronic health effects."
   i. Acute Effects—"More than 96,300 persons suffered acute poisonings from pesticides in the United States during 2007."
   ii. Chronic Effects—"Among the chronic effects of pesticides is the potential for causing cancer, as indicated by animal testing…other chronic effects include dermatitis, neurological disorders, birth defects, and infertility."
   iii. Endocrine Disruptors—Many pesticides can interfere with reproductive hormones.

4. Adverse Environmental Effects—The story of aerial spraying of DDT demonstrates the hazards of widespread pesticide use.
   i. DDT, Continued—"Because of accumulation, small, seemingly harmless amounts received over a long period of time may reach toxic levels."
   ii. Up the Chain—"Bioaccumulation, which occurs in the individual organism, may be compounded through a food chain." See Figure 13-9.
   iii. Silent Spring—"The book, Silent Spring, became an instant best-seller. Its basic message was that, if insecticide use continues as usual, there might someday come a spring with no birds-and with ominous consequences for humans as well."

143

5. Nonpersistent Pesticides: Are They the Answer?—"Because the persistent pesticides have been banned, the agrochemical industry has substituted nonpersistent pesticides for the banned compounds."
    i.   Toxicity—"The total environmental impact of a pesticide is a function not only of its persistence, but also of its toxicity, its dosage, and the location where it is applied."
    ii. Bird Kill—Birds have been especially vulnerable to pesticides. Also, other insects (like bees) that are not pests, have been harmed.

III. Alternative Pest Control Methods
Ecological control of pests is a way of using natural factors to control pests in such a way that is not harmful to humans and allows for sustainable agriculture.

A. Cultural Control—"A cultural control is a nonchemical alteration of one or more environmental factors in such a way that the pest finds the environment unsuitable or is unable to gain access to its target." See Figure 13-11.
    1. Control of Pests Affecting Crops, Gardens, and Lawns—To avoid the overuse of herbicides for lawns, simple techniques can be employed.
        i.   Crops—Managing crop residues over winter, using clean mulch, and crop rotation can all help to maintain pests on crops.
        ii. Border Patrol—"Most of the pests that are hardest to control were unwittingly imported from other parts of the world, and many other species in other regions would be serious pests is introduced into the United States."

B. Cultural Control of Pests Affecting Humans—Humans have built pest control into their normal routines. Similar practices need to become routine with agricultural pest control as well. See Figure 13-13. **See also Discussion Topic #2.**

C. Control by Natural Enemies—"There are four well-defined types of natural enemies: predators, parasitoids, pathogens, and plant eaters."
    1. Protect the Natives—"The problem with using natural enemies lies in finding organisms that provide control of the target species without attacking other, desirable species."
    2. Import Aliens as a Last Resort—"Quite often, effective natural enemies have been found by systematically combing the home region of an introduced pest and finding its various predators or parasites."

D. Genetic Control—Most plant-eating insects and plant pathogens attach only one species or a few closely related species. This specificity implies a genetic incompatibility between the pest and any species that are not attacked."
    1. Control with Chemical Barriers—Some plants produce natural chemicals to repulse their pests.
    2. Control with Physical Barriers—"Physical barriers are structural traits that impede the attack of a pest."
    3. Control with Sterile Males—Flooding a population with sterile males can be an effective control strategy.
    4. Strategies Using Biotechnology—"Genetic engineering makes it possible to introduce genes into crop plants from other plant species, bacteria, and viruses."
        i.   Roundup® Again—"One biotech strategy has been to give a crop species resistance to a broad-spectrum herbicide."

144

ii. Not So Fast…The downsides to biotech innovations are that they "are not well suited to subsistence agriculture in developing countries…also, there is the definite possibility of developing 'superweeds' that are resistant to the herbicides or plant viruses."

E. Natural Chemical Control—The aim of natural chemical control is to isolate, identify, synthesize, and then use an insect's own hormones or pheromones to disrupt its life cycle. Two advantages of natural chemicals are that they are nontoxic and that they are highly specific to the pest in question."

IV. Socioeconomic Issues in Pesticide Use
More and more, agriculture is moving away from pesticides and towards integrated pest management and organically grown food as consumer concern over pesticides increases.

A. Pressures to Use Pesticides—"The question to be asked when facing any pest species is: Is the species causing significant damage? Even if there is no evidence of immediate damage from a pest, a grower who believes that his or her plantings are at risk is likely to resort to insurance spraying." See Figure 13-19.

B. Integrated Pest Management—"IPM aims to minimize the use of synthetic organic pesticides without jeopardizing crops. This is made possible by addressing all the interacting sociological, economic, and ecological factors involved in protecting crops."
    i. Indonesia—"Indonesia has provided a viable IPM model for other rice-growing countries." See Figure 13-21. **See also Discussion Topic #3.**

C. Organically Grown Food—"Many farmers are turning away from the use of pesticides, chemical fertilizers, antibiotics, and hormones as they raise grain, vegetables, and livestock for the organic food trade."
    i. USDA Organic—The Organic Foods Protection Act and the National Organic Standards Board established standards for foods and products to be considered certified organic.

V. Pesticides and Policy
Policies have been put in place in the last 50-60 years that address the effect of pesticides on human health, the need for proper training for those who work with pesticides, and the need to keep food free of pesticide residues.

A. FIFRA—"The Federal Insecticide, Fungicide, and Rodenticide Act…established by Congress…requires manufacturers to register pesticides with the EPA before marketing them."

B. FFDCA—The Federal Foods, Drug, and Cosmetic Act and the Delancy clause "prohibited many pesticides from being used on foodstuffs when those pesticides had been found to cause cancer in laboratory tests with animals."

C. FQPA—"The National Research Council examined this dilemma and recommended in 1987 that the anticancer clause be replaced with a 'negligible risk' standard."
    1. Care for Kids—"The focus is on children both because they typically consume more fruits and vegetables per unit of body weight than do adults and because studies have shown that children are frequently more susceptible to carcinogens and neurotoxins."

145

D. Pesticides in Developing Countries—"The United States currently exports thousands of tons of pesticides (active ingredients) each year. Some of these are products banned in the United States itself."

    1. PIC—Prior informed consent requires "exporting countries and all potential importing countries of actions they have taken to ban or restrict the use of pesticides or other toxic chemicals."

    2. Code of Conduct—"In spite of early opposition from the pesticide industry and exporting countries, an international Code of Conduct on the Distribution and Use of Pesticides, which addressed in detail conditions of safe pesticide use, was approved by the FAO in November 2002."

E. Final Thoughts—There is an increasing press towards ecological pest management and keeping food pesticide free.

Review Questions: Possible Answers

1. *Define pests. Why do we control them?*

    Pests are "any organism that is noxious, destructive, or troublesome" to humans. Many pests are organisms that directly compete with humans. These pests consume food humans grow, gather, hunt, etc. We compete for the same food source. Some organisms are considered pests because they carry human diseases, (e.g., mosquitoes, ticks, flies). Other pests bother us because they create messes, (e.g. squirrels, raccoons, birds).

2. *Discuss two basic philosophies of pest control. How effective are they?*

    One method looks for "a magic bullet that will eradicate or greatly lessen the numbers of the pest organism." This philosophy relies on chemical control of pest populations. The other major method used to control agricultural pests is ecological pest management. This method focuses on the pest's life cycle and its ecological relationships. Building soil and maintaining a diverse ecosystem are integral to this technique. Ecological pest management uses agents that "are highly specific for the pest species being fought or they manipulate one or more aspects of the ecosystem."

    Integrated pest management begins with sustainable ecosystem management but as a last resort will use chemical pest management techniques. A farmer who has not used ecosystem-sustaining farming methods has not practiced ecological pest management or integrated pest management even if he/she has not used pesticides during a growing season.

3. *What were the apparent virtues of the synthetic organic pesticide DDT?*

    "DDT appeared to be nothing less than the long-sought 'magic bullet,' a chemical that was extremely toxic to insects yet seemed nontoxic to humans and other mammals. It was inexpensive to produce. It was broad spectrum, meaning that it was effective against a multitude of insect pests. It was also persistent, meaning that it did not break down readily in the environment and hence provided lasting protection."

4. *What adverse environmental and human health effects can occur as a result of pesticide use?*

    The adverse environmental problems that can occur as a result of pesticide use include the development of resistance by pests, resurgence, and secondary pest outbreaks. The adverse human health effects include chronic effects such as cancer dermatitis, neurological disorder, birth defects, and infertility. Additionally, immune suppression is possible along with disruption of the endocrine system.

5. *Define bioaccumulation and biomagnification.*

Biomagnification is the movement of a chemical through the food chain; as an organism eats on the trophic level below it, it takes in the chemicals that are in those organisms, magnifying the concentration of the chemical. Bioaccumulation is biomagnification plus bioconcentration (the movement of a chemical against a concentration gradient).

6. *Why are non-persistent pesticides not as environmentally sound as first thought?*

    "For several reasons, however, non-persistent pesticides are not as environmentally sound as they might appear. First of all, they are persistent enough to 'ride the food supply from farmer to consumer.'" Second, "many of the non-persistent pesticides are far more toxic than DDT. This higher toxicity, combined with frequent applications needed to maintain control, presents a significant hazard to agricultural workers and other exposed to these pesticides. Non-persistent pesticides may still have far-reaching environmental impacts. For example, to control outbreaks of grasshoppers that eat sunflowers, farmers in Argentina began spraying monocrotophos, an acutely toxic organophosphate pesticide in 1995. Shortly afterwards, thousands of dead Swainson's hawks were seen in the sunflower fields. It was estimated that 20,000 hawks died in one year, about 5% of the world's population of the species. Another problem is that "desirable insects may be just as sensitive as pest insects to non-persistent pesticides. Finally, non-persistent chemicals are just as likely to cause resurgences and secondary-pest outbreaks as are persistent pesticides, and pests become resistant to non-persistent pesticides just as readily, too."

7. *Describe the four categories of natural, or biological, pest control Cite examples of each and discuss their effectiveness.*

    "The four general categories of natural of biological pest control are (1) cultural control, (2) control by natural enemies, (3) genetic control, and (4) natural chemical control."

    Cultural control: "combing and brushing hair, bathing, wearing clean clothes eliminate head and body lice, fleas, and other parasites. Changing of bed linens regularly protects against bedbugs. Properly and systematically disposing of garbage and keeping a clean house with all the cracks sealed and with good window screens are effective methods for keeping down populations of roaches, mice, flies, mosquitoes, and other pests. Sanitation requirements in handling and preparing food are cultural controls designed to prevent the spread of disease. The refrigeration, freezing, canning, and drying of foods are cultural controls that inhibit the growth of organisms that cause rotting, spoilage, and food poisoning." Cultural control has been very effective.

    "The following examples illustrate the range of possibilities for controlling pests with natural enemies: Tiny predator beetles have been imported in an attempt to control the hemlock wooly adelgid," various caterpillars have been controlled by parasitic wasps, the prickly pear cactus and numerous other weeds have been controlled by plant-eating insects, rabbits in Australia are controlled by an infectious virus, water hyacinth, which has blanketed many African lakes, is coming under control following the introduction of Brazilian weevils, and mealy bugs in Africa are controlled by a parasitic wasp. Natural enemies have been effective but the importation of a natural enemy might create new problems; finding a natural enemy can be difficult.

    Genetic control includes disease-resistant varieties, or physical or chemical barriers produced by the host plant or animal. Leafhoppers are significant worldwide pests of cotton, soybeans, alfalfa, clover, beans, and potatoes; but they can damage only plants that have relatively smooth leaves. If hooked hairs or "glandular hairs that exude a sticky substance" are selected for in breeding then the leafhopper could not do as much damage. This has been used for disease resistance in potatoes, corn, honey bees, and many other species.

    Natural chemical controls include hormones and pheromones. Hormones, (e.g., juvenile hormone and ecdysone) can disrupt the development of insects. Pheromones can be used as attractants or repellants or induce confusion. Pheromones have more potential than hormones.

8. *Define the term economic threshold as it relates to pest control. What is cosmetic spraying and insurance spraying?*

    "Damage should be deemed significant only when the economic losses due to the damage considerably outweigh the cost of applying a pesticide. This point is called the **economic threshold**. If significant damage is not occurring, natural controls are already operating, and the situation is probably best left as is."

    "Even if there is no evidence of immediate damage from a pest, a grower who believes that his or her plantings are at risk is likely to resort to **insurance spraying**—the use of pesticides to prevent losses to pests."

147

"Growers know that blemished produce means less profit, so they indulge in **cosmetic spraying**—the use of pesticides to control pests that harm only the item's outward appearance."

9. *What are the four steps in IPM? Explain how IPM worked in Indonesia.*
    "The EPA refers to a four-tiered approach in describing IPM: 1. Set action thresholds, 2. Monitor and identify pests, 3. Prevention, 4. Control."

    "Faced with declining success in controlling the brown plant bopper, Indonesian rice growers have switched from heavy pesticide spraying to a light spraying regime that preserves the natural enemies of the insect."

10. *What is organic food, and how is it now certified?*
    Organic food is food that has been grown without the use of synthetic pesticides, chemical fertilizers, antibiotics, and hormones. Organic food is certified by certifiers that have been approved by the National Organic Program under the Organic Food Production Act of 1990. Farmers and processors have to follow the rule and cannot use any synthetic material that is not on the list. "To market certified organic foods, farmers now must have their operations scrutinized by USDA-approved inspectors. Only then may they use the USDA seal on their products."

11. *How does FIFRA attempt to control pesticides? What new perspective does FQPA bring to the policy scene?*
    FIFRA required that pesticides be "evaluated both for their intended uses and for their impacts on human health and the environment" and that "those who use the pesticides—especially agricultural workers—must be appropriately trained and protected from the risk of close contact."
    FQPA focuses on protecting consumers from exposure to pesticides on/in food. "The following are the major requirements of the act:
    a. The new safety standard is 'a reasonable certainty of no harm' for substances applied to food.
    b. Special consideration must be given to the exposure of young children to pesticide residues.
    c. Pesticides or other chemicals are prohibited if they can be shown to carry a risk of more than one case of cancer per million people when consumed at average levels over the course of a lifetime.
    d. All possible sources of exposure to a given pesticide must be evaluated, not just from food.
    e. A special attempt must be made to assess the potential harmful effects of the so-called 'hormone disrupters.'"
    One problem corrected by FQPA was the different standards applied to raw and processed food. Processed food could have no detectable levels of suspected cancer-causing substances (the Delaney clause). The detection limits for chemical were getting smaller and smaller, triggering the Delaney clause, yet there was little scientific evidence that such small quantities of suspected carcinogens were a health hazard. Another problem corrected by FQPA was to change the focus for standard setting from the typical 70-kg man to the most susceptible population—children. Additionally, all exposures have to be considered when setting exposure limits. If a pesticide is found in your drinking water, the exposure limit for the amount allowed in food has to take this into consideration.

12. *Discuss recent policy regarding the export of pesticides to development countries.*
    "The international community has erected a more effective system, through the cooperative work of two U.N. agencies: the FAP and the UNEP. There is now a process of prior informed consent (PIC), whereby exporting countries inform all potential importing countries of actions they have taken to ban or restrict the use of pesticides or other toxic chemicals. Governments in the importing country respond to the notification via the U.S. agencies, which then disseminate all the information they receive to the exporting countries and follow up by monitoring the export practices of those countries."
    An additional problem has been addressed by FAO's "International Code of Conduct." "(C)onditions of safe pesticide use were addressed in detail. The code makes clear the responsibilities of both private companies and countries receiving pesticides in promoting their safe use. Unlike the PIC Convention, this code calls for voluntary action and so is not legally binding, but it has already proven useful in holding private industry and importing countries to standards of safe use."

Thinking Environmentally: Possible Answers

1. *Consider the ethics of the United States' exportation of pesticides. A large portion of this exported material is banned in the United States itself. If the choice was up to you to continue this or put it to an end, what would you do? Remember that such pesticides have at least a positive immediate benefit to these countries. Are they a necessary evil?*

    Answers will vary as this is an opinion question. Students should establish the benefits and disadvantages of using pesticides in any country, including the developing countries.

2. *Almost one-third of the chemical pesticides bought in the United States are for use in houses and on gardens and lawns. What should manufacturers and users do to ensure the limited and prudent use of pesticides?*

    One possible way to ensure the limited and prudent use of pesticides by consumers is to not sell concentrates. This avoids the problem of incorrect dilutions. The EPA already limits the types of pesticides that are approved for consumer purchase. This could be limited further and the quantities that may be purchased could be limited.

3. *Should the government give farmers economic incentives to switch from pesticide use to IPM? How might that work?*

    This is an opinion question. Types of incentives could be financial assistance in installing physical barriers and cultural control. Farmers could receive subsidies for the use of biological controls. The use of genetic controls could be subsidized by lower or no costs seeds, etc.

4. *Investigate how bugs and weeds are controlled on your campus. Are IPM techniques being used? Organic fertilizers? If not, consider lobbying for their use.*

    The office of physical plant or grounds would have this type of information. Most larger campuses are not using IPM techniques. It could be interesting to discuss how one might implement an IPM program at a large institution.

5. *Imagine you're the mayor of a mid-sized suburban town where mosquitoes invade from neighboring marshes. What kind of restrictions would you place on local pesticide use? Defend your answer.*

    Again, this is an opinion answer. The benefits and disadvantages of using pesticides to control a potentially disease causing mosquito population should be discussed.

CHAPTER 14
Harnessing Energy for Human Societies

Chapter Outline:

I. Energy Sources and Uses
    A. The Three Kings: Coal, Oil, and Gas
        1. Coal
        2. Oil Rules
        3. Gas, Naturally
    B. Electrical Power Production
        1. Generators
            i. Turbogenerators
        2. Fluctuations in Demand
            i. Demand Cycle
            ii. Blackout
        3. Clean Energy?
            i. Efficiency
    C. Matching Sources to Uses
        1. Energy Flow
II. Exploiting Crude Oil
    A. How Fossil Fuels Are Formed
        1. Renewal
    B. Crude-Oil Reserves Versus Production
        1. Recovery
    C. Declining U.S. Reserves and Increasing Importation
        1. The Oil Crisis of the 1970s
        2. Adjusting to Higher Prices
            i. Recovery
        3. Back to Old Ways
        4. Back to the Future
        i. Recession
    D. The Consequences of U.S. Dependency
        1. Costs of Purchase
        2. Persian Gulf Oil
            i. Two More Wars
        3. Other Sources
    E. Oil Resource Limitations and Peak Oil
        1. Hubbert's Peak
        2. U.S. Geological Survey
        3. Downward Trajectory
III. Other Fossil Fuels
    A. Natural Gas
        1. Natural-Gas-Run Cars
        2. Synthetic Oil
            i. The Costs
    B. Coal
        1. Strip Mining

Key Topics:

1. Energy Sources and Uses
2. Exploiting Crude Oil
3. Other Fossil Fuels
4. Energy Policy and Security

Instructional Goals:

1. All energy use has environmental and social costs.

2. Energy type and energy use should be matched to improve the efficiency of energy consumption.

3. Fossil fuels are nonrenewable resources.

4. Conservation is the energy source with the greatest potential for creating new energy supplies, and it has the least number of environmental costs.

Concepts and Connections:

     Matching energy sources and the end use of energy is an interesting concept to many students. The logic of greater efficiency in boiling water directly rather than boiling water to produce electricity to boil water is intuitive. Helping students understand the high energy cost in using electricity for uses not requiring electricity can assist their critical thinking development.

     Energy is connected to everything we do. Humans are seemingly unique in that we tap energy sources beyond our internal food-derived energy. This ability to use energy sources outside of the food we consume results in a variety of environmental costs. Air pollution is an obvious cost incurred as we extract, refine, or consume fuel. Our fossil fuel consumption is the major source of the observed increases in tropospheric greenhouse gasses. When we mine for coal, oil shale, or oil sands, major disruptions of ecosystems are possible. Water pollution can result from oil spills, acid mine drainage, and fuel transport accidents. Hazardous materials and wastes are generated during the production, transport, and use of fossil fuels.

     Another way to look at environmental issues surrounding energy consumption is to list and evaluate the potential environmental consequences from the production, transport, and use. Each fuel has different impacts and it can be quickly determined that no single energy source is a panacea. Even conservation, the largest single energy source available, has costs. For example, to insulate a home requires the manufacturing of the insulation material. The manufacturing process requires energy and material—both having environmental costs.

Concepts in Context:

The existence of fossil fuels is dependent on ecosystem structure and function (Chapters 3 and 4). Dramatic environmental change produced the correct conditions for fossil fuel formation, and this can be linked to the dramatic changes observed in species diversity (Chapter 6). Disruption of terrestrial ecosystems (Chapters 5 and 7), including soil (Chapter 11), and aquatic (Chapter 7) ecosystems, can occur during the production, transport, and use of fossil fuels.

The rate of fossil fuel consumption can be linked to human population growth (Chapter 8) and consumption rates per person. Demographic transition (Chapter 8), as observed in developed countries, included increases in individual rates of fuel consumption. Alternative views of how to reach a stable population size (Chapter 9) do not include increases in individual rates of fuel consumption. Humans are very dependent on fossil fuels, especially in developed nations, for the production of food (Chapter 12), fertilizers, and pesticides (Chapter 13).

Water pollution (Chapter 20) can result during the production, transport, and use of fossil fuels. Personal watercraft vehicles are not only a source of noise pollution in recreational areas; they are also a substantial source of the oil and gasoline contamination of lakes and rivers. Hazardous materials and waste (Chapter 22) are components of fossil fuel. Even the nonhazardous portion of these fuels creates solid waste (Chapter 21) problems. Air pollution (Chapter 19) resulting from the burning of fossil fuels results in a variety of adverse health effects. Another aspect of air pollution from fossil fuel consumption is the increased concentration of greenhouse gasses observed in the troposphere (Chapter 18).

Key Terms and Vocabulary:

electrical power, energy carrier, primary energy source, electrical generator, turbine, turbogenerator, smart grid, condenser, thermal pollution, conservation reserve, primary recovery, enhanced recovery, balance-of-payment deficit, integrated gasification combined cycle (IGCC) plant, The National Energy Policy Report, Energy Independence and Security Act of 2007, Corporate Average Fuel Economy (CAFE)

Discussion, Activities, and Labs:

1. Ask the students to list inefficient energy conversions. Some suggestions include boiling water on an electric stove, using electricity to heat hot water for a shower, using electricity for space heating, and using fossil fuels to generate hydrogen for storage in a hydrogen fuel cell and then using the fuel cell to power an automobile. Ask students to suggest more efficient matches between energy sources and use. Ask students to list uses of electricity for which we cannot substitute a primary energy source. Some suggestions include computers, stereos, and light bulbs. Ask the students to list some consumer items that require electricity but do not plug into an electrical socket. Some suggestions include solar-powered calculators and solar-powered phones or lights (seen along highways).

2. Divide the class into groups of three to four students. Provide each group with an energy budget. The energy budgets could reflect the quantity of energy used per person in different countries. Using a variety of developed and developing countries' energy budgets would be interesting because not all developed or developing countries consume the same quantity of energy per person. Provide each group of students with a list of activities that consume energy. From this list the students are to select the energy-consuming activities that are the most important to them. The goal is to determine, based upon limited energy availability, what activities are

152

most desirable and how many people can be supported on the energy budget. Ask each group to appoint a spokesperson so the decisions, and justifications, made by each group can be discussed with the whole class.

3. Have each student list the ways they use energy. This list should include at least 20 items. Each student should choose five energy uses from their list that they could least live without. For each of the five uses the student is to research, using the Internet and library, ways he/she could reduce the quantity of energy used to perform the task. The goal is to determine how to maintain the most essential components of a person's lifestyle while reducing the individual's energy demand.

Suggested Lecture Format:

I. Energy Sources and Uses
   All energy use has environmental and social costs. **See Discussion Topic #1.**

   A. The Three Kings: Coal, Oil, and Gas—All of the fossil fuels have reigned for their energy uses. See Figure 14-4 and Figure 14-5.
      1. Coal—"By the end of the 1800s, coal had become the dominant fuel, and it remained so into the 1940s."
      2. Oil Rules—"In the 1800s, the simultaneous development of three technologies—the internal combustion engine, oil-well drilling, and the refinement of crude oil into gasoline and other liquid fuels—combined to provide an alternative to steam power."
      3. Gas, Naturally—"Natural gas is largely methane, which produces only carbon dioxide and water as it combusts; thus, it burns more cleanly than coal or oil."

   B. Electrical Power Production—"The electricity itself is an energy carrier—it transfers energy from a primary energy source (coal or waterpower for instance) to its point of use.
      1. Generators—"Electric generators were invented in the 19th century."
         i. Turbogenerators—"In the most widely used technique for generating electrical power, a primary energy source is employed to boil water, creating high-pressure steam that drives a turbine…coupled to the generator." See Figure 14-6 and Table 14-1.
      2. Fluctuations in Demand—"The utility is responsible for balancing the electrical supply and demand, regardless of daily or seasonal fluctuations."
         i. Demand Cycle—"The typical pattern of daily and weekly electrical demand in the United States is shown in Figure 14-7."
         ii. Blackout—"Power brownouts and blackouts are a serious threat to an economy that is now highly dependent on computers and other electronic devices."
      3. Clean Energy?—Electricity is clean at the point of use, but its environmental impact really depends on the type of primary energy used.
         i. Efficiency—"The problem of transferring pollution from one place to another becomes even more pronounced when you consider efficiency because the production of electricity from burning fossil fuels has an efficiency of only 30-35%."

   C. Matching Sources to Uses—"It is necessary to consider more than just the source of energy because some forms of energy lend themselves well to one use, but not to others."
      1. Energy Flow—The major pathways from the primary energy sources to the various end uses are shown in Figure 14-9. **See Discussion Topic #2.**

II. Exploiting Crude Oil
Energy type and energy use should be matched to improve the efficiency of energy consumption.

   A. How Fossil Fuels Are Formed—"The reason crude oil, coal, and natural gas are called fossil fuels is that all three are derived from the remains of living organisms." See Figure 14-10.
      1. Renewal—Although fossil fuels are being made continuously, "it takes 1,000 years to accumulate the amount of organic matter that the world now consumes each day."

   B. Crude-Oil Reserves Versus Production—Geologists estimate the amount of crude oil expected to be found in the future based on their survey of the land. "The estimates may be far off the mark because there is no way to determine whether estimated reserves actually exist except by exploratory drilling."
      1. Recovery—"Conventional pumping (primary recovery) can remove only 25% of the oil in a field. Further removal, of up to 50% of the oil in the field, is often possible, but it is more costly because it involves manipulating pressure in the oil reservoir by injecting brine or steam which forces oil into the wells. See Table 14-2.

   C. Declining U.S. Reserves and Increasing Importation—"Up to 1970 the United States was largely oil independent…In 1970, however, new discoveries fell short, so production decreased, while consumption continued to grow rapidly." See Figure 14-11.
      1. The Oil Crisis of the 1970s—"Imported oil began to cost more in the early 1970s, and then, in conjunction with an Arab-Israeli war in 1973, OPEC initiated an embargo of oil sales to countries such as the United States, that gave military and economic support to Israel."
      2. Adjusting to Higher Prices—In response to the oil crisis, we increased domestic production, created a national stockpile of oil, and tried to reduce consumption of oil. See Figure 14-2.
         i. Recovery—An oil glut in the 1980s occurred as a result of lower demand and increased supply of oil.
      3. Back to Old Ways—During the 1980s we reduced conservation and exploitation efforts resulting in increasing prices of oil.
      4. Back to the Future—"The collapse in oil prices of the 1990s set the stage for another developing crisis: a rise in oil prices that began in late 1998."
         i. Recession—"The countries of the world slid into a recession that was called the worst in 75 years. The impact on oil prices was profound."

   D. The Consequences of U.S. Dependency—"As the U.S. dependency on foreign oil rises, we are faced with problems at three levels: 1) The costs of purchasing oil, 2) the risk of supply disruptions due to political instability in the Middle East and, 3) ultimate resource limitations in any case."
      1. Costs of Purchase—"The cost for crude oil represents about 36% of our current balance-of-payment deficit. When we buy oil from a foreign country, we are draining our own economy."
      2. Persian Gulf Oil—"Maintaining access to Middle Eastern oil is also a major reason for our efforts toward negotiating peace agreements between various parties in that region."
         i. Two More Wars—"Within a month, U.S. and British forces invaded Afghanistan, which had been harboring Osama bin Laden and elements of Al Qaeda. Then, in 2003, a U.S.-British coalition invaded Iraq in order to overthrow Saddam Hussein's rule and eliminate suspected weapons of mass destruction."

154

3. Other Sources—"The United States has turned more and more to non-Middle Eastern oil suppliers. Recently, Canada replaced Saudi Arabia as the number-one exporter of oil to the United States."

E. Oil Resource Limitations and Peak Oil—"Most of the 'new' oil in the United States is coming from innovative computer mapping of geological structures and horizontal drilling technology that enable oil to be identified and withdrawn from small isolated pockets that were previously missed within oil fields."
   1. Hubbert's Peak—"On the basis of their estimates and the known amount already used…a Hubbert curve indicated that peak oil production will occur sometime in the current decade." See Figure 14-15.
   2. U.S. Geological Survey—"In 2000, on the basis of extensive geological studies, the U.S. Geological Survey released an assessment of world oil and gas that included 'undiscovered reserves'-that is, reserves from fields that have not yet been found."
   3. Downward Trajectory—"At the current rate of use, the proved reserves can supply only 40 years of oil demand."

III. Other Fossil Fuels
Fossil fuels are nonrenewable resources.

A. Natural Gas—"Natural gas is continually emitted from oil- and gas-bearing geological deposits and new drilling is opening up to more deposits."
   1. Natural-Gas-Run Cars—"With the installation of a tank for compressed gas in the trunk and some modifications of the engine fuel-intake system-a car will run perfectly well on natural gas."
   2. Synthetic Oil—"With the aid of the Fisher-Tropsch process, natural gas can be converted to a hydrocarbon that is liquid at room temperature and pressure-basically synthetic oil."
      i. The Costs—"Applying natural gas to the transportation sector…may extend the oil phase of our economy but it will not be a sustainable solution."

B. Coal—"Current U.S. reserves are calculated to be 264 billion tons, and at the 2007 rate of production, the supply could last 230 years. Unlike oil and natural gas, we produce more coal each year than we use, and we export about 5% of coal production annually."
   1. Strip Mining—"This method totally destroys the ecology of the region, as forests are removed and streams are buried by the coal wastes."
   2. Coal Power—"Once it is mined, coal is transported to large power plants. A typical 1,000 MW plant burns 8,000 tons of coal a day—a mile long train's worth of coal every day."

C. Oil Shale and Oil Sand—The United States has extensive deposits of oil shale…a fine sedimentary rock containing a mixture of solid, wax-like hydrocarbons called kerogen. "Oil sand is a sedimentary material containing bitumen, an extremely viscous, tarlike hydrocarbon" that can be heated and refined like crude oil.

IV. Energy Policy and Security
Conservation is the energy source with the greatest potential for creating new energy supplies, and it has the least number of environmental costs.

155

A. Security Threats—"There are several security threats that the United States incurs through its dependence on fossil fuel energy."

    1. Oil Dependence—"The years 2006-2008 brought oil prices to a new high, threatening a repeat of this economic roller coaster."

        i. Terrorism—"Nuclear power plants, hydropower, dams, oil, and gas pipelines, refineries, tankers, and the electrical grid—all of these present attractive targets for terrorists intent on doing damage to the people and the economy of the United States."

    2. Global Climate Change—"The long-term prospect of using fossil fuels to meet our energy needs poses a huge risk to our economic, environmental, and national security because of global climate change." See Figure 14-3 and Figure 14-19.

B. Energy Policies—"Because energy supply and demand is such a nation-wide matter, only public policy has the sweeping power to effect changes that will make a difference."

    1. Supply-Side Policies—Policies ranging from the Cheney Report to the Energy Policy Act, and the Energy Independence and Security Act have dominated supply-side policies.

        i. Business as Usual?—"Supply-side policies, especially those dealing with fossil fuel energy are 'business-as-usual' solutions to our energy security issues."

    2. Demand-Side Policies—"What we really want is not energy, but comfortable homes, transportation to and from where we need to go, manufactured goods, computers that work, and so forth. As a result, many energy analysts argue that we should stop thinking in terms of where we can get additional supplies of the old fuels…and think about how we can satisfy these needs with a minimum expenditure of energy and the least environmental impact." **See Discussion Topic #3.**

C. Final Thoughts—"Conserving energy is extremely important, but keep in mind that reducing our use of fossil fuels is not eliminating that use."

Review Questions: Possible Answers

1. *How have the fuels to power homes, industry, and transportation changed from the beginning of the Industrial Revolution to the present?*

    Homes: Homes were heated originally with wood. In the industrialized world this changed with the beginning of the Industrial Revolution. Coal became a dominant method of home heating. In the 1950s this changed to electricity, oil, and natural gas.

    Industrial: At the start of the Industrial Revolution wood was used to fuel the steam engine. When wood resources were depleted, coal was substituted. (This transition was not without social and economic disruption.) The transition to coal was complete by the end of the 1800s, and the dominance of coal as a fuel did not end until the 1940s.

    Transportation: Wind (ships) and horses were the primary method of transportation until the Industrial Revolution. Trains became an important mode of transportation; wood and then coal were used initially. Ships are powered by fossil fuels. Petroleum, primarily in the form of gasoline, has dominated transportation since the 1940s.

2. *What are the three primary fossil fuels, and what percentage does each contribute to the U.S. energy supply?*

    Coal—22%   Natural gas—23%   Petroleum—40%

3. *Electricity is a secondary energy source. How is it generated and how efficient is its generation?*

Coal, oil, or nuclear power is used to boil water to produce steam that turns the turbines of a turbogenerator. Hydroelectric power plants use water to turn turbines that generate electricity. "(I)t takes three units of primary energy to create one unit of electrical energy that is actually put to use."

4. *Name the four major categories of primary energy use in an industrial society, and match the energy sources that correspond to each.*

"Primary energy use is commonly divided into four categories: (1) transportation, (2) industrial processes, (3) commercial and residential use (heating, cooling, lighting, and appliances), and (4) the generation of electrical power, which goes into categories (2) and (3) as secondary energy use. Transportation . . . depends entirely on petroleum, whereas nuclear power, coal, and waterpower are limited to the production of electricity." Some coal may be used for home heating, as are electricity, wood, oil, and natural gas. Most commercial and residential use is electricity. Industrial processes use oil, natural gas, and electricity. Some oil, natural gas, and biomass are used for the generation of electricity.

5. *What is the distinction between estimated reserves and proven reserves of crude oil, and what factors cause the amounts of each to change?*

"The science of geology provides information about the probable locations and extent of ancient shallow seas. On the basis of their knowledge and their field experience, geologists make educated guesses as to where oil or natural gas may be located and how much may be found. These educated guesses are the world's estimated reserves. The estimates may be far off the mark, because there is no way to determine whether estimated reserves actually exist, except by exploratory drilling. (I)f exploratory drilling strikes oil, further drilling is conducted to determine the extent and depth of the oil field. From that information, a fairly accurate estimate can be made of how much oil can be economically obtained from the field. That amount then becomes proven reserves." If the economics of oil extraction change, then the amount of proven reserves can change.

6. *How does the price of oil influence the amount produced?*

"The price of a barrel of oil determines the extent to which reserves are exploited. No oil company will spend more money to extract oil than it expects to make selling the oil."

7. *What are the trends in oil consumption, in the discovery of new reserves, and in U.S. production before 1970? After 1970? What is a Hubbert curve?*

"Up to 1970, the United States was largely oil independent. That is, exploration was leading to increasing proven reserves, such that production could basically keep pace with growing consumption. In 1970, however, new discoveries fell short, so production decreased, while consumption continued to grow rapidly. This downturn vindicated predictions of late geologist M. King Hubbert, who proposed that oil exploitation in a region would follow a bell-shaped curve. Hubbert observed the pattern of U.S. exploitation and predicted that U.S. production would peak between 1965 and 1970. At that point, about half of the available oil would have been withdrawn, and production would decline gradually as reserves were exploited."

Production is still increasing worldwide but it is expected to peak during this decade. Consumption is growing and is expected to continue to grow.

8. *What did the United States do in the early 1970s to resolve the disparity between oil production and consumption? What events caused the sudden oil shortages of the mid 1970s and then the return to abundant, but more expensive, supplies?*

"To fill the energy gap between rising consumption and falling production, the United States depended increasingly on imported oil, primarily from Arab countries of the Middle East. Because imported oil costs only $2.30 per barrel ($9.18 in 2002 dollars) in the early 1970s and Middle Eastern reserves were more than adequate to meet the demand, this course seemed to present few problems."

"A group of predominantly Arab countries known as the Organization of Petroleum Exporting Countries (OPEC) formed a cartel and agreed to restrain production in order to get higher prices. Imported oil began to cost more in the early 1970s, and then, in conjunction with an Arab-Israeli war in 1973, OPEC initiated an embargo of oil sales to countries, like the United States, that gave military and economic support to Israel. The effect was almost instantaneous, because we depend on a fairly continuous flow from wells to points of consumption. Spot shortages occurred, which quickly escalated into widespread panic because of our widespread dependence on cars and trucks. We were willing to pay almost anything to have oil shipments resumed." By continuing to limit oil production all through the 1970s, OPEC was able to keep supplies tight enough to force prices higher and higher.

9. *Why did an oil glut occur in the mid-1980s, and what were its consequences in terms of oil prices and the continuing pursuit of the responses to the crisis of the 1970's?*

An oil glut occurred because consumption declined due to the efforts of the mid to late-1970s. Oil prices dropped and the pursuit of the responses listed in Question 8 was dropped. We curtailed exploration; production from older, more expensive oil fields was stopped; conservations efforts and incentives were abandoned; tax incentives and other subsidies for the development or installation of alternative energy sources were terminated, destroying many new businesses; and the need for conservation and for the development of alternative ways to provide transportation seems to have largely passed from the mind of the public."

10. *What have been the directions of U.S. production, consumption, and importation of crude oil since the mid-1980s?*

Alaska oil production peaked in 1988 and continues to decline, production of crude oil in the U.S. continues to drop, consumption has increased as people buy more consumer goods and cars that are less fuel efficient, and importation of crude oil has increased. "At the time of the first oil crisis, in 1973, the United States depended on foreign sources for about 35% of its crude oil. In 1993, it passed the 50% mark, and it is now at 60%. According to the Department of Energy, the period from 1973 to 1995 saw a reduction in energy growth by 18%, saving the economy $150 billion a year in total energy expenditures."

11. *Describe the situation with respect to natural gas and coal for United States in terms of domestic supplies, the consequences of developing and using the fuels, and the ability of those sources to supplement oil.*

"Considerable resources of natural gas and comparatively vast resources of coal and shale sands are still available in the United States." We have approximately 50 years of natural gas reserves and 250 years of coal reserves in the United States. "Natural gas has been rising as a fossil fuel of choice—so much so, that 16% of our annual use now comes from imports, almost all by pipeline from Canada. Natural gas can be used to meet some fuel needs for transportation." Natural gas can also be used to heat homes and hot water and power electrical power plants. Natural gas is the least polluting of all the fossil fuels.

"Unlike oil and natural gas, we produce more coal each year than we use, and we export about 4% of coal production annually." Both underground and surface mining have severe environmental consequences. Underground mining also has significant impacts on worker health and safety. Coal is primarily used for electrical generation and is unlikely to be useful for transportation—the largest user of petroleum. The ability to supplement oil supplies by using coal is very limited.

12. *What are the security risks and consequences of our growing dependence on foreign oil? How do they relate to the Persian Gulf War of 1991? To terrorism? To the 2003 U.S.-Iraqi war?*

The security risks include terrorism within the United States and terrorism directed at U.S. citizens while outside of the country. Additional security risks include the impact on our economy when prices increase or boycotts are instituted. Our growing dependence on foreign oil increases our economic vulnerability. Foreign oil also means that it needs to be transported long distances, with the potential for accidents and deliberate sabotage.

There are also costs in terms of tax dollars. "The Middle East is a politically unstable region of the world. As noted earlier, it was the unexpected Arab boycott that plunged us into the first oil crisis in 1973. Maintaining access to Middle Eastern oil is also a major reason for our efforts toward negotiating peace agreements between various parties in that region. Recognizing this political instability, the United States maintains a military capability to ensure our access to Persian Gulf oil. This capability was tested in the fall of 1990 when Saddam Hussein of Iraq invaded Kuwait, then producing 6 million barrels per day. The U.S.-led Persian Gulf War of early 1991 threw Hussein's armies out of Kuwait and gave the United States an ongoing presence in the Persian Gulf region. It was this presence, however, that eventually angered the radical Islamic terrorist Al Qaeda organization and led to the September 11, 2001, attack on the World Trade Center and the Pentagon."

"In 2003, a U.S.-British coalition invaded Iraq in order to overthrow Saddam Hussein's rule and eliminate suspected weapons of mass destruction (which were never found). As the momentum was building for the

158

invasion, protesters around the world rallied to the cry 'No blood for oil,' implying that the real motivation behind the pending war was to gain access to Iraq's rich oil reserves. With the war now over, some hindsight suggests that oil was part of the picture."

13. *What phenomenon may restrict the consumption of fossil fuels before resources are depleted?*
   Public policy changes may restrict consumption of fossil fuels before resources are depleted. We are very dependent on imported oil, which increases our economic vulnerability and increases the risk of terrorism. All of our energy infrastructure, nuclear power plants, hydropower dams, oil and gas pipelines, refineries, tankers, and the electrical grid "present attractive targets for terrorists intent on doing damage to people and the economy of the United States."
   "The long term prospect of using fossil fuels to meet our energy needs poses a huge risk to our economic, environmental, and national security because of global climate change."

14. *Compare the Bush administration's energy policy with the Energy Policy Act of 2005 and the Energy Independence and Security Act of 2007 relative to supply-and demand-side strategies.*
   "The Cheney report (CR) estimated that, over the next 20 years, oil consumption will increase 30%, natural gas consumption by 50%, and electricity demand will rise 45%. The Cheney report recommends ways to meet these rising demands, and the new Energy Policy Act (PA) acted on most of these recommendations but not always favorably."
   "Exploring and developing domestic sources of oil and gas
       CR: Open the ANWR and offshore locations to oil and gas exploration and production.
       PA: Promotes taking an inventory of offshore oil and gas resources but no drilling in ANWAR (yet).
   Increasing use of the vast coal reserves for energy
       CR: Add between 1,300 and 1,900 new coal-fired electric power plants in the next 20 years.
       PA: Promotes energy from coal via clean technologies, loan guarantees, and research incentives.
   Continuing subsidies to oil and nuclear industries
       CR: Provide tax incentives to encourage energy production from fossil fuels and nuclear fuels.
       PA: Guarantees $6.9 billion in tax incentives and billions more in loans for these industries.
   Removing environmental and legal obstacles to energy development
       CR: Streamline the permitting process for drilling and hydropower licensing and employ eminent domain to establish new electrical transmission lines.
       PA: Provide tax credits for hydropower plants, streamlines permitting for drilling.
   Providing access to remote sources of natural gas
       CR: Expedite the planning and construction of a natural-gas pipeline to bring Alaskan natural gas to the lower 48 states.
       PA: Requires periodic reporting of progress in the pipeline construction, which now depends on state and private monies. Establishes federal control of siting and permitting new LNG terminals."
   "Supply-side policies, especially those dealing with fossil-fuel energy are 'business-as-usual' solutions to our energy security issues. They do little or nothing to reduce our vulnerability to oil price disruptions, terrorist actions, and global climate change. Demand-side policies, by contrast, have the advantage of reducing our energy needs and making it more possible to move to a future in which renewable energy can become the ruling technology. At the same time, these policies will decrease our vulnerability to terrorists and to disruption of the oil market. They will also save money and reduce pollution from burning fossil fuels."
   The Cheney report and the Energy Policy Act address ways to lower energy demand:
   Increasing the mileage standards for motor vehicles
       CR: Study and provide recommendations to increase the Corporate Average Fuel Economy (CAFE) standards for motor vehicles, but in ways that will avoid any negative impact on the U.S. automotive industry.
       PA: The House and Senate overwhelmingly opposed raising the CAFE standards, but authorized continued "study" of the issue. The act did, however, grant consumer tax credits for fuel-efficient hybrid and other advanced technology vehicles. For example, a buyer of a 2007 Toyota Camry hybrid would receive a tax credit of $2,600.
   Increasing the energy efficiency of appliances and buildings
       CR: Promote higher efficiency standards for appliances when possible, and cover additional appliances.

159

PA: Provides tax breaks for manufacturers of energy-efficient appliances, encourages EPA to continue its Energy Star program, which also addresses energy-efficient buildings. Also provides tax breaks for those making energy efficiency improvements to their homes.

Encouraging industry to use combined heat and power (CHP) technologies

CR: Provide tax credits and more flexibility in permitting CHP projects.

PA: No significant positive action on CHP, but amends a previous act (PURPA) that required utilities to buy power from CHP plants. Also encourages combined cycle technology that used coal gasification for producing the natural gas.

Promoting greater use of non-fossil-fuel sources of energy (nuclear and renewable energy)

CR: Build more nuclear power plants, and increase and subsidize alternative energy sources.

PA: "A tax credit for the first 6,000 megawatts of new nuclear capacity for the first eight years of operation, insurance to protect companies building new reactors from the risk of regulatory delays, and federal loan guarantees for up to 80% of the construction costs of new power plants. (A)uthorizes $1.25 billion towards the construction of a special nuclear plant that would produce hydrogen from water (from Chapter 13), establishes a Renewable Fuel Standard for ethanol and biodiesel, continues funding for research and development on renewable energy, extends the production tax credit for electricity generated with wind and biomass for another two year, extends the Energy Star building energy efficiency program to include schools, retail establishments, private homes, and health care facilities, provides tax credits for many types of home improvements that improve energy efficiency, provides tax credits for geothermal heat pumps, solar water heating, and PV systems, develops efficiency standards for many more appliances, provides tax credits for manufacturers of some energy-saving appliances (but not air conditioners!), continues funding for the Freedom Car and Freedom Fuel projects, provides for a temporary income tax credit applicable to the purchase of new hybrid of fuel-cell-powered vehicles, and contains provisions aimed at enabling geothermal energy to compete with fossil fuels in generating electricity."

15. *To what degree has energy conservation served to mitigate energy dependency? What are some prime examples of energy conservation? To what degree may conservation alleviate future energy shortages and the cost of developing alternative sources of energy?*

"According to the Department of Energy, the period from 1973 to 1995 saw a reduction in energy growth by 18%, saving the economy $150 billion a year in total energy expenditures."

Energy conservation is the single greatest source of energy available. It has the ability to reduce the environmental consequences of all types of energy sources. If we double the fuel efficiency of the automobile from 27.5 mpg to 55 mpg (the mileage of some hybrids), we have halved the environmental impact of driving the same number of miles. We have also doubled the life span of our petroleum reserves used for transportation. Even something as simple as carpooling with one other person doubles the fuel efficiency of the trip. Walking, which also improves cardiovascular health and could help reduce obesity, would decrease energy consumption.

Combined heat and power (CHP or cogeneration) is another way to conserve. "According to CHP methodology, a factory or large building installs a small power plant that produces electricity and heats the building with 'waste' heat. Such systems can achieve an efficiency of 80%! Use of this technology boosts the efficiency of conversion of fuel energy to electrical energy from around 30% to as high as 50%."

Other energy conservation measures include insulation, double-pane windows, substitution of fluorescent lights for incandescent lights, more efficient appliances, recycling, and water conservation.

Thinking Environmentally: Possible Answers

1. *Statistics show that less developed countries use far less energy per capita than developed countries. Explain why this is so.*

Less developed countries use far less energy per capita than developed countries because they have smaller houses (less heating, cooling, and lighting energy required) and people typically have fewer appliances, fewer cars, and fewer electronic devices. People in developing countries typically do not have several televisions per family (or person) or several cars per family. The likelihood that a child has a television, computer, stereo, hair dryer, and toys that require electricity is greater in the developed world than the developing world.

The amount of driving and traveling per person is less in developing countries. Distances traveled for work and vacations are less; families live nearby and the number of trips per year is less.

2. *Between 1980 and 1999, gasoline prices in the United States declined considerably relative to inflation, and then rose dramatically in the 2000s. Predict what they will do in the next 10 years, and rationalize your prediction.*

It is unlikely that gasoline prices will decline in the next 10 years because we are likely to reach our maximum oil production and demand will continue to increase. Demand will soon exceed available supply, resulting in increased cost per gallon. Price per gallon of gasoline will soon equal what people in other countries pay. Prices will continue to increase as we reach and move beyond the Hubbert Peak.

One way for oil prices to drop would be if demand for oil dropped. This would require a major shift in how we travel and how far we travel. If Americans could walk to work and/or to stores, the demand for gasoline would drop. If our cars were more fuel efficient—in the range of 100 miles per gallon—it might be possible for demand not to exceed the supply. This could result in lower gasoline costs or costs remaining level.

3. *Suppose your region is facing power shortages (brownouts). How would you propose solving the problem? Defend your proposed solution on both economic and environmental grounds.*

One method to regulate energy use and to reduce the impact of power shortages would be to install thermostats that could be controlled by the utility companies. If a power shortage is imminent, the thermostat settings could be lowered or raised by a few degrees. This would reduce the energy demand tremendously but would not be as noticeable to the individual as rolling brownouts or blackouts. This method could also be used to reduce peak loads, thus reducing the number of power plants needed.

It would also be possible to alter pricing. To use power during peak demand times would cost the consumer more. Dishwashers could be run at night when demand was less, and the cost to run the dishwasher would be less. Some businesses could alter when they use the greatest amount of electricity, (e.g., automated production runs could occur at night rather than at peak demand times).

Consumers and businesses could be encouraged to switch to energy efficient appliances and lighting. A program to pay a portion of the cost of the new appliance or lighting would encourage the switch. A recycling program for large appliances (refrigerators, washers, and dryers) could be instituted with the recycling of copper and other metals paying for the recycling operation, and possibly offsetting the costs of the program.

A program to increase the efficiency of electronics and computers could be instituted. A recycling program for these consumer goods would reduce the impact from switching and could offset the cost of the program.

Reducing the number of power plants needed or the amount of energy that is produced would reduce the quantity of air pollution (all but hydroelectric). The amount of environmental damage from siting the power plant and from extracting the fuel (all but hydroelectric) would be reduced. Recycling appliances and other consumer goods would reduce the impact of disposal of the discarded appliances and the manufacture of the new appliances.

4. *List all the environmental impacts that occur during the "life span" of gasoline—that is, from exploratory drilling to the consumption of gasoline in your car.*

Exploratory work has a small impact on the environment through the drilling operation and the need to have access to the area. Roads, if created for the exploratory work, fragment habitats and increase human access to areas.

Extraction impacts the immediate environment by the building of roads (fragmentation of habitat), the disruption of habitat for the drilling and extraction, and possible spills. Once oil is extracted there is a need to transport the oil, usually via a pipeline to a collection point. Building and maintaining pipelines disrupt habitats during their construction. If the pipeline needs to be heated (as in Alaska), then there will be additional impacts during the daily operation of the pipeline.

Once the oil has been collected at a central point it needs to be transported to a refinery. This could involve ocean transport or further transport via pipelines. Ocean transport includes the possibility of accidents,

161

sabotage, and environmental contamination from normal operation (seawater used as a ballast in the tanker). The refinery is a major source of air pollution and is likely to result in local habitat destruction along with water pollution.

Transportation of refined oil to the point of consumer purchase is typically done with tanker trucks. There is always the possibility of an accident resulting is a spill of refined fuel. The soil and water will be contaminated during this process.

Air pollution results from the dispensing and use of gasoline.

5. *Explore the positions of the following regarding an increase in CAFE requirements: the fossil fuel industry, the automobile-manufacturing companies, the steel industry, Congress, the Union of Concerned Scientists, and the National Academy of Sciences. How do they differ, and why?*

The fossil fuel industry, the automobile-manufacturing companies, the steel industry, and Congress oppose an increase in CAFE requirements, while the Union of Concerned Scientists and the National Academy of Sciences support an increase in the CAFE requirements.

The fossil fuel industry wants to sell as much gasoline as possible. CAFE would not help the industry in meeting this goal because fuel consumption would decline. The automobile industry would need to change its manufacturing process, thus incurring costs. The industry would also have to change how it advertises vehicles, as the engine power (thus fuel consumption) is a major selling point for a substantial number of Americans. We have been taught that an engine with more power is better. The steel industry does not support increasing the CAFE standards because one major method of reducing energy consumption is to reduce the weight of a vehicle. Plastic replaces steel. Congress (or at least most members) does not support increasing the CAFE standards because this would adversely impact business in their district—or many members believe it will. Congress people without a connection to the auto industry may have made a deal with other members of Congress for their support on other issues.

The National Academy of Sciences and the Union of Concerned Scientists are looking only at energy security, impact on air quality, global climate change, and so on. They are not evaluating the impact on a particular industry or Congressional district but the impact on the United States as a whole.

CHAPTER 15
Nuclear Power

Chapter Outline:

I. Nuclear Energy in Perspective
   A. The History of Nuclear Power
      1. The Nuclear Age
      2. Curtailed
      3. Currently…
      4. Global Picture

II. How Nuclear Power Works
   A. From Mass to Energy
      1. The Fuel for Nuclear Power Plants
         i. Nuclear Fuel
         ii. Nuclear Bomb
      2. The Nuclear Reactor
         i. Moderator
         ii. Fuel Rods
         iii. Control Rods
      3. The Nuclear Power Plant
         i. LOCA
   B. Comparing Nuclear Power with Coal Power

III. The Hazards and Costs of Nuclear Power Facilities
   A. Radioactive Emissions
      1. Biological Effects
         i. High Dose
         ii. Low Dose
         iii. Exposure
      2. Sources of Radiation
         i. Getting Nuked?
   B. Radioactive Wastes
      1. Half-Life
   C. Disposal of Radioactive Wastes
      1. Tanks and Casks
      2. Radioactivity and the Military
         i. From Russia, with Curies
         ii. Megatons to Megawatts
      3. High-Level Nuclear Waste Disposal
         i. Yucca Mountain
         ii. Yucca Rejected
   D. Nuclear Power Accidents
      1. Chernobyl
         i. Consequences

   ii. Could It Happen Here?

  E. Safety and Nuclear Power

   1. Passive Safety

   2. New Generations of Reactors

   3. Terrorism and Nuclear Power

    i. Response

    ii. Making a Bomb

  F. Economics of Nuclear Power

   1. Longevity?

   2. Decommissioning

   3. New Life

IV. More Advanced Reactors

  A. Breeder (Fast-Neutron) Reactors

  B. Reprocessing

  C. Fusion Reactors

   1. The d-t Reaction

   2. Tokamak

    i. Pot of Gold?

V. The Future of Nuclear Power

  A. Opposition

   1. Mismatch?

  B. Rebirth of Nuclear Power

   1. Nuclear Energy Policies

Key Topics:

1. Nuclear Energy in Perspective
2. How Nuclear Power Works
3. The Hazards and Costs of Nuclear Power Facilities
4. More-Advanced Reactors
5. The Future of Nuclear Power

Instructional Goals:

1. Nuclear power plants produce energy by creating steam from water and using the steam to turn a turbogenerator. This process is similar to other (except hydro) fuel sources.

2. Nuclear power uses fission—the splitting of a uranium-235 atom into two smaller atoms—to produce electricity. Fusion is the fusing of hydrogen into helium and occurs on the sun. The power plants cannot explode.

3. Radioactive emissions, alpha and beta particles and gamma rays, can adversely impact biological systems.

4. Nuclear power plants do not emit greenhouse gasses. Fewer tons of ore need to be mined to fuel a nuclear power plant than a coal-fired power plant. Under normal operating conditions, a coal-fired power plant emits more radiation than does a nuclear power plant.

5. Concerns about the generation of electricity from nuclear power come from the possibility of accidents and the lack of secure disposal options. If the new reactor designs are used to build a new generation of nuclear power plants, there is less concern about the possibility of an accident.

Concepts and Connections:

Energy issues can be connected to all other issues. The health of the economy is tied to the availability of energy. First determining the most appropriate source of energy for our needs—matching sources to end use—is important before we decide that more electrical generation is necessary.

The historical aspects of nuclear power are as important as the technical, social, and economic aspects. Nuclear power is a result of the development of nuclear weapons. The U.S. government, after World War II, attempted through the Peace Atom campaign to convince the public that nuclear technology could be used for peaceful purposes. The original use of nuclear power (as a weapon of mass destruction) continues to influence the public's attitude about nuclear power.

The environmental movement, at various times, has supported the use of nuclear power for electricity production. During the 1960s the Sierra Club supported the use of nuclear power. By the mid-1970s few, if any, environmental groups supported nuclear power. Now there are again environmental groups who are supporting the use of nuclear power as a non-greenhouse-gas-emitting alternative to coal.

Concepts in Context:

The matching of energy source to end use (Chapter 14) is important to the discussion of nuclear power. When electricity is used in inefficient ways, we increase the level of environmental concern surrounding nuclear power because more electricity needs to be generated. The environmental consequences of generating electricity from fission can be compared to the environmental consequences of generation electricity from coal, oil, or natural gas (Chapter 14). The environmental consequences from alternative energy sources (Chapter 16) should also be compared to nuclear power.

All forms of energy use have environmental consequences. Some of the consequences are due to mining and the resultant destruction of ecosystems (Chapters 3, 4, and 5). Uranium mining has affected the environmental health of miners and those living near the tailings (Chapter 17). The number of people and the quantity of energy used per person (Chapter 8) influence the quantity and types of energy used by humans.

Key Terms and Vocabulary:

Isotopes, mass number, milling, yellow cake, enrichment, moderator, fuel elements, fuel rods, pressurized-water reactors, loss-of-coolant accident (LOCA), radioactive wastes, high-level wastes, low-level wastes, radioactive decay, half-life, Megatons to Megawatts, The Nuclear Waste Policy Act of 1982, active safety, passive safety, Embrittlement, Energy Independence and Security Act

165

Discussion, Activities, and Labs:

1. Divide the class into groups of three to four students. Each group is to list the benefits (nuclear medicine, food irradiation, research, electricity generation) obtained from using nuclear technology and the potential dangers (damage to DNA if exposed). After each list has been completed, the students need to consider if the benefits outweigh the dangers. Even if a group decides the benefits do not outweigh the dangers, have each group discuss the pros and cons of placing a nuclear waste facility in their region. (Even if no additional radioactive wastes are created, there are substantial quantities already in need of a disposal site.) Have each group list the characteristics of a good disposal site and the possibility of these characteristics being found locally.

2. Divide the class into groups of three to four students. Have the students list the pros and cons for using nuclear power and coal to generate electricity. All the environmental and human health problems of both should be listed. All the ways each energy source avoids an environmental or human health problem should be listed. Each group is to choose either nuclear or coal as the source of energy used to generate electricity. The group must articulate the reason for their choice and the most important (critical) reason for the choice. (For some students this will seem like an impossible choice. They will wish to generate electricity using alternative fuels. A choice between nuclear and coal should be made because we sometimes need to pick between "unacceptable" choices.) Each group appoints a spokesperson to explain to the class why the particular choice was made.

3. Divide the class into groups of three to four students. Have 2 to 3 groups of student the list of pros and cons of nuclear power, 2–3 groups list the pros and cons of coal, 2 to 3 groups list the pros and cons of natural gas, and 2–3 groups list the pros and cons of petroleum. Bring the class back together and compare the lists and select the preferred source(s) of energy.

4. Have each student write a dialogue about nuclear power. One individual in the dialogue supports the use of nuclear technology to produce energy while the other individual does not. Each person in the dialogue articulates the logical reasons for their position. For example, a student might write the following exchange. Sue: "I've been thinking about how silly it is to operate nuclear power plants when we don't have a secure disposal site. I don't understand why we think it is reasonable to generate a waste that we don't know how to handle safely." Carol: "I don't understand your concern. The government has a facility it is developing and we will have a place for the wastes soon. Tell me why you think we won't be able to securely dispose of the wastes." From here each person in the dialogue would articulate the reasoning behind his or her viewpoint.

Suggested Lecture Format:

I. Nuclear Energy in Perspective
    Nuclear power plants produce energy by creating steam from water and using the steam to turn a turbogenerator. This process is similar to other (except hydro) fuel sources. **See Discussion Topic #1.**

    A. The History of Nuclear Power—"It was anticipated that nuclear power could produce electricity in such large amounts and so cheaply that we would phase into an economy in which electricity would take over virtually all functions, including the generation of other fuels, at normal costs." See Figure 15-2.
        1. The Nuclear Age—"In the 1960s and early 1970s, utility companies moved ahead with plans for numerous nuclear power plants. Officials estimated that by 1990 several

166

hundred plants would be online and by the turn of the century as many as a thousand would be operating."

2. Curtailed—"In the United States, 28 units (separate reactors) have been shut down permanently for a variety of reasons."

3. Currently… —"At the end of 2008, 104 nuclear power plants were operating in the United States."

4. Global Picture—Despite concerns about a major nuclear accident in Chernobyl and a major scare at Three-Mile Island in the U.S., demands for electricity are increasing and nuclear power may be an answer. See Figure 15-4.

II. How Nuclear Power Works

Nuclear power uses fission—the splitting of a uranium-235 atom into two smaller atoms—to produce electricity. Fusion is the fusing of hydrogen into helium and occurs on the sun. The power plants cannot explode. See Figure 15-5.

A. From Mass to Energy—"Nuclear energy involves changes at the atomic level through one of two basic processes: fission and fusion."

1. The Fuel for Nuclear Power Plants—"All current nuclear power plants employ the fission (splitting) of uranium-235."

   i. Nuclear Fuel—"To make nuclear 'fuel' uranium ore is mined, purified into uranium dioxide, and enriched."

   ii. Nuclear Bomb—"When U-235 is highly enriched, the spontaneous fission of an atom can trigger a chain reaction."

2. The Nuclear Reactor—"A nuclear reactor for a power plant is designed to sustain a continuous chain reaction but not allow it to amplify into a nuclear explosion."

   i. Moderator—"The moderator slows down the neutrons that produce fission so that they are traveling at the right speed to trigger another fission." See Figure 15-6.

   ii. Fuel Rods—"To achieve the geometric pattern necessary for fission, the enriched uranium dioxide is made into pellets that are loaded into long metal tubes. The loaded tubes are called fuel elements or fuel rods." See Figure 15-7.

   iii. Control Rods—"The chain reaction in the reactor core is controlled by rods of neutron-absorbing material, referred to as control rods, inserted between the fuel elements."

3. The Nuclear Power Plant—"In a nuclear power plant, heat from the reactor is used to boil water to provide steam for driving conventional turbogenerators." See Figure 15-8.

   i. LOCA—A loss-of-coolant accident can happen if a crack occurs and there is a loss of water in the reactor.

B. Comparing Nuclear Power with Coal Power—In terms of the fuel needed, the carbon dioxide emissions, the sulfur dioxide and other emissions, the amount of radioactivity released, and the solid wastes produced coal power is much more environmentally devastating than nuclear power. However, the risk of nuclear fallout still looms large with nuclear power. **See Discussion Topic #2 and #3.** See also Figure 15-9.

III. The Hazards and Costs of Nuclear Power Facilities

Radioactive emissions, alpha and beta particles and gamma rays, can adversely impact biological systems.

A. Radioactive Emissions—"Direct products of the fission are generally unstable isotopes of their respective elements." See Figure 15-10. See also Figure 15-1 and Figure 15-2.
    1. Biological Effects—"A major concern of the public regarding nuclear power is that large numbers of people may be exposed to low levels of radiation, thus elevating their risk of cancer and other disorders."
        i.   High Dose—"If the whole body is exposed to high levels of radiation, a generalized blockage of cell division occurs that prevents the normal replacement of repair of blood, skin, and other tissues."
        ii. Low Dose—"In lower doses, radiation may damage DNA, the genetic material inside cells." Cells with damaged (mutated) DNA may then begin dividing and growing out of control, forming malignant tumors or leukemia."
        iii. Exposure—"Health effects are directly related to the level of exposure."
    2. Sources of Radiation—"The average person in the United States receives a dose of about 3.6 mSv per year."
        i.   Getting Nuked?—"Careful measurements have shown that public exposure to radiation from normal operation of a power plant is less than 1% of natural background radiation"

B. Radioactive Wastes—As long as wastes are kept isolated from living organisms until they have the chance to decay they are safe.
    1. Half-Life—"The rate of radioactive decay is such that half of the starting amount of a given isotope will decay within a certain period."

C. Disposal of Radioactive Wastes—"The development of nuclear power went ahead without ever fully addressing the issue of what would be done with the radioactive wastes. The current problem of nuclear waste disposal is twofold:" short-term containment and long-term containment.
    1. Tanks and Casks—"For short-term containment, spent fuel is first stored in deep swimming-pool like tanks on the sites of nuclear power plants."
    2. Radioactivity and the Military—"Some of the worst failures in handling radioactivity have occurred at military facilities in the United States and in the former Soviet Union."
        i.   From Russia, with Curies—"Russian military weapons facilities have been even more responsible" than the U.S.
        ii. Megatons to Megawatts—"The end of the Cold War has brought the welcome dismantling of nuclear weapons by the United States and the nations of the former Soviet Union."
    3. High-Level Nuclear Waste Disposal—Although burying waste has been established as the best solution, a high quality storage facility has not yet been agreed upon.
        i.   Yucca Mountain—A mountain in Nevada is the only place being seriously considered for nuclear waste disposal but there has been much debate about its opening from the people of Nevada.
        ii. Yucca Rejected—"The Obama administration decided to terminate the Yucca Mountain program, citing health and safety concerns as the reason."

168

D. Nuclear Power Accidents—"On March 28, 1979, the Three Mile Island Nuclear Power Plant near Harrisburg, Pennsylvania, suffered a partial meltdown as a result of a series of human and equipment failures and a flawed design."
  1. Chernobyl—Prior to 1986 many speculated about the worst possible nuclear accident. "On April 26, 1986, events at a nuclear power plant in Ukraine (then a part of the Soviet Union) made such speculation irrelevant. Since that day, Chernobyl has served as a horrible example of nuclear energy gone awry." See Figure 15-13.
    i. Consequences—"As the radioactive fallout settled, 135,000 people were evacuated and relocated…the soil remains contaminated with radioactive compounds. Only 2 engineers were directly killed by the explosion but 28 of the personnel brought in to contain the reactor in the aftermath of the explosion died of the radiation within a few months."
    ii. Could It Happen Here?—"Nuclear scientists argue that the answer is no because U.S. power plants have a number of design features that should make a repeat of Chernobyl impossible."

E. Safety and Nuclear Power—"As a result of Three Mile Island and other, lesser incidents in the United States, the NRC has upgraded safety standards not only in the technical design of nuclear power plants, but also in maintenance procedures and in the training of operators." **See Discussion Topic #4.**
  1. Passive Safety—"Involves engineering devices and structures that make it virtually impossible for the reactor to go beyond acceptable levels of power, temperature, and radioactive emissions."
  2. New Generations of Reactors—"Generation IV plants are now being designed and will likely be built within the next 20 years."
  3. Terrorism and Nuclear Power—Because of the great potential for exposure, nuclear power plants and waste disposal facilities could be serious targets of terrorism.
    i. Response—"Following September 11, the NRC immediately beefed up the requirements for security around every power plant—adding more guards, more physical barriers, and vehicle checks at greater distances from the plant."
    ii. Making a Bomb—"About 15 pounds of plutonium would be sufficient to make a crude bomb."

F. Economics of Nuclear Power—"Nuclear power involves a financial risk that utility executives have been hesitant to take."
  1. Longevity?—Nuclear power plants have not lasted the 40 years that they were expected to. Most have shut down after a 20 year lifespan.
  2. Decommissioning—To shut down nuclear power plants is costly; many owners are opting to make repairs rather than shut them down.
  3. New Life—A more favorable political climate and concerns over pollution and energy supplies have made nuclear power a better prospect than it was in the recent past.

IV. More Advanced Reactors

169

Nuclear power plants do not emit greenhouse gasses. Fewer tons of ore need to be mined to fuel a nuclear power plant than a coal-fired power plant. Under normal operating conditions, a coal-fired power plant emits more radiation than does a nuclear power plant.

    A. Breeder (Fast-Neutron) Reactors—"The breeder reactor is designed so that (nonfissionable) ^{238}U absorbs the extra neutrons, which are allowed to maintain their high speed.

    B. Reprocessing—"A number of countries are reprocessing spent fuel through chemical processes, recovering plutonium and mixing it with ^{238}U to produce mixed-oxide fuel that is about 55 plutonium and suitable for further use in many nuclear power plants."

    C. Fusion Reactors—"The aim of fusion technology is to carry out fusion in a controlled manner in order to provide a practical source of heat for boiling water to power steam turbogenerators."
        1. The d-t Reaction—Hydrogen is abundant and hydrogen fusion could solve many energy problems, but ^{2}H and ^{3}H are required for what is called a d-t reaction.
        2. Tokamak—This design allows a containment of hydrogen while it is being superheated in order to fuse with helium. Such methods have not yet proven to be energy efficient.
            i. Pot of Gold?—"Fusion is, at best, a very long-term and uncertain option."

V. The Future of Nuclear Power
Concerns about the generation of electricity from nuclear power come from the possibility of accidents and the lack of secure disposal options. If the new reactor designs are used to build a new generation of nuclear power plants, there is less concern about the possibility of an accident.

    A. Opposition—Opposition to nuclear power exists on many fronts.
        1. Mismatch?—"Opponents of nuclear power also cite the basic mismatch between nuclear power and the energy problem. The main energy problem for the United States is an eventual shortage of crude oil for transportation purposes, yet nuclear power produces electricity, which is not yet used for transportation."

    B. Rebirth of Nuclear Power—If we come to a point in the future where we decide that current sources of energy supply are too polluting, nuclear power may become a viable option for the future. Several key changes must be made before nuclear power can be successful and widely used, however.
        1. Nuclear Energy Policies—"Although no new plants will be built by 2010, it begins to look like nuclear power in the United States may rise like a phoenix from the ashes of its recent decline."

Review Questions: Possible Answers

1. *Compare the outlook regarding the use of nuclear power in the United States and globally in each of the following decades: 1960s, 1980s, and early 21st century.*

United States: 1960s—the U.S. government was interested, after World War II, in converting the technology developed for military purposes into civilian uses. The belief was that the cost of generating electricity from nuclear power would be so cheap that it could be used instead of other forms of fuel. The building of nuclear power plants did not begin until the U.S. government limited the legal liability of those corporations and utilities owning the power plants (Price Anderson Act—1957). Additionally, the U.S. government assumed responsibility for all high-level nuclear waste generated by commercial nuclear power plants. "In the 1960s and early 1970s, utility companies moved ahead with plans for numerous nuclear power plants. By 1975, 53 plants were operating in the United States, producing about 9% of the nation's electricity and another 170 plants were in various stages of planning of construction." **1970s**—by the mid-1970s the future of nuclear power was no longer rosy. Three bills were passed in California in 1976 halting future construction of nuclear power plants unless the waste product problem was solved. Many existing orders for power plants were cancelled. Construction was terminated in some instances. **1980s**—the building and operation of nuclear power plants continued to be curtailed. Shoreham was closed after only 32 hours of operation. The citizens in Sacramento, California voted to close Rancho Seco, which had been operated by the local public utility company. **1990s**—in the 1990s the last nuclear power plant under construction was brought on line. **The present**—the outlook is a bit rosier today because of the problems with coal generation and high electrical demand. With the passage of the Energy Policy Act of 2005, there is a possibility of additional nuclear power plants being constructed in the United States.

Globally: Thirty-one nations have nuclear power plants in operation or under construction. "Including those in the United States, the world has a total of 440 operating nuclear plants, with an additional 32 under construction. After the catastrophic accident at Chernobyl in April 1986, nuclear power is being rethought in many countries. Yet the demand for electricity is more robust than ever, and the other means of generating electricity have their own problems."

2. *Describe how energy is produced in a nuclear reaction. Distinguish between fission and fusion.*
   Fission—"a large atom of one element is split to produce two small atoms of different elements"
   Fusion—"two small atoms combine to farm a larger atom of a different element"
   Energy is produced in a nuclear reaction by changes at the atomic level. "In both fission and fusion, the mass of the product(s) is less than the mass of the starting material, and the lost mass is converted to energy in accordance with the law of mass-energy equivalence."

3. *How do nuclear reactors and nuclear power plants generate electrical power?*
   A nuclear power plant boils water to make steam to turn a turbogenerator. The technology differs from other (non-hydro) electrical generating plants in the source of the energy used to boil water.

   Fission is used to produce the energy in a nuclear power plant. "In fission, a large atom of one element is split to produce two smaller atoms of different elements." Uranium-235 is the heavy atom used in the fission process. A neutron hits the nucleus of uranium-235, causing the release of neutrons and creating new daughter elements. In a nuclear power plant the quantity and speed of neutrons is controlled so the reaction rate is controlled. Control rods, inserted into the reactor core, absorb neutrons, thereby controlling the rate of the fission chain reaction. The moderator slows the speed of neutrons. The heat generated from fission is absorbed by water, usually in a double-loop system, and steam is generated.

4. *What are radioactive emissions, and how are most humans exposed to them?*
   Radioactive emissions are the direct products of fission; they "are generally unstable isotopes of their respective elements." The "unstable isotopes become stable by ejecting subatomic particles (alpha particles, beta particles, and neutrons), or high-energy radiation (gamma rays), or both."
   Background radiation from cosmic rays and naturally occurring uranium and radon gas provides the largest exposure to radioactive emissions. Medical sources are the second largest source. "Nuclear power is by no means the only source of radiation: There is also normal background radiation from radioactive materials, such

171

as the uranium and radon gas that occur naturally in the earth's crust, and cosmic rays from outer space. For most people, background radiation is the major source of radiation exposure. In addition, we deliberately expose ourselves to radiation from medical and dental X rays, by far the largest source of human-induced exposure and, for the average person, equal to one-fifth the exposure from background sources. The average person in the United States receives a dose of about 3.6 mSv per year."

5. *How are radioactive wastes produced? And what are the associated hazards?*
   Radioactive emissions are the direct products of fission; they "are generally unstable isotopes of their respective elements." The "unstable isotopes become stable by ejecting subatomic particles (alpha particles, beta particles, and neutrons), or high-energy radiation (gamma rays), or both."

   Exposure to radiation increases the risk of cancer. Low doses of radiation may damage DNA. Some people argue that there are doses of radiation below which there would be no adverse effect because of the DNA repair mechanisms that exist. Others argue that no safe level of exposure exists. High doses of radiation can block cell division, resulting in death.

6. *Describe the two stages of nuclear waste disposal.*
   Short-term Containment: "Allows the radioactive decay of short-lived isotopes. In 10 years, fission wastes lose more than 97% of their radioactivity. Wasters can be handled much more easily and safely after this loss occurs. For short-term containment, spent fuel is first stored in deep swimming pool-like tanks on the sites of nuclear power plants. The water in these tanks dissipates waste heat (which is still generated to some degree) and acts as a shield against the escape of radiation. After a few years of decay, the spent fuel may be placed in air-cooled dry casks for interim storage until long-term storage becomes available."
   Long-term Containment: "Provide(s) protection from the long-lived isotopes. Government standards require isolation for 20 half-lives. (Plutonium has a half-life of 24,000 years.)" We have not begun any long-term containment in the United States.

7. *What problems are associated with the long-term containment of nuclear wastes? What is the current status of the disposal situation?*
   Currently all commercial nuclear power plant spent fuel is contained in on-site storage ponds. High-level radioactive waste from spent fuel and low-level wastes, such as tools and clothing, need to be isolated from the environment. One of the by-products of fission is plutonium, which has a half-life of 24,000 years. Because it is necessary to isolate radioactive substances for 20 half-lives, plutonium needs to be safely stored for 480,000 years. No long-term disposal site exits. The site being developed by the U.S. government, Yucca Mountain, is surrounded by a great deal of controversy. Some of the concerns expressed about the Yucca Mountain facility include nearby earthquake faults, a geologically active volcano; rock formation above the storage rooms that would allow rainwater to permeate the wastes, resulting in groundwater contamination; and the need to ship spent nuclear fuel across the country. (The vast majority of nuclear power plants are in the eastern portion of the country, while Yucca Mountain is in Nevada.)

   "In July 2002, President George W. Bush signed a resolution (passed by Congress) voiding a veto by Nevada's Governor that had attempted to block further development at the site (Yucca Mountain). The Yucca Mountain facility has officially been designated to be the nation's nuclear waste repository. The site could begin receiving wastes from commercial facilities all over the country in the year 2018, according to the latest DOE estimate. Nevada's governor and congressional delegation vow to continue their fight in the courts. In the meantime, the NRC has approved a plan by a private consortium to establish an interim site for storage of dry casks on the Skull Valley Goshute Reservation in Utah. Private Fuel Storage, the company that will build the facility, argues that the deal will remove a major obstacle to further growth of the nuclear industry (and greatly benefit the Goshutes tribe). Predictably, Utah's governor and congressional delegation are doing everything they can to prevent this from happening. Interestingly, an underground storage facility in New

172

Mexico, the Waste Isolation Pilot Plant, has been receiving shipments of highly radioactive wastes from nuclear weapons facilities since 1999, with no apparent problems."

8. *Describe what went wrong at Three Mile Island and Chernobyl.*

"While conducting a test of standby diesel generators, engineers disabled the power plant's safety system, withdrew the control rods, shut off the flow of steam to the generators, and decreased the flow of coolant water in the reactor. However, they did not allow for the radioactive heat energy generated by the fuel core, and the reactor began to heat up. The extra steam that was produced could not escape and had the effect of rapidly boosting the energy production of the reaction. In an attempt to quell the reactor, the engineers quickly inserted the carbon-tipped control rods. The carbon tips acted as moderators, slowing down the neutrons that were produced in the reaction. The neutrons, however, were still speedy enough to trigger more fission reactions, and the result was a split-second power surge to 100 times the maximum allowed level. Steam explosions then blew the 2,000-ton top off the reactor, the reactor melted down, and a fire was ignited in the graphite, burning for days."

"Three Mile Island nuclear power plant suffered a partial meltdown as a result of human and equipment failures and a flawed design. The steam generator shut down automatically because of a lack of power in its feed-water pumps, and eventually a valve on top of the generator opened in response to the gradual buildup of pressure. Unfortunately, the valve remained stuck in the open position and drained coolant water from the reactor vessel. There were no sensors to indicate that this pressure-operated relief valve was open. Operators responded poorly to the emergency, shutting down the emergency cooling system at one point and shutting down the pumps in the reactor vessel. One instrument error compounded the problem: Gauges told operators that the reactor was full of water when, actually, it needed water badly. The core was uncovered for a time and suffered a partial meltdown." The Rancho Seco nuclear power plant in Sacramento, California, had the same flawed design, which had not been corrected completely before the voters closed the facility in 1989, 10 years after the Three Mile Island accident.

9. *What features might make nuclear power plants safer? What about terrorism?*

A passive safety system might make a power plant safer. This "involves engineering devices and structures that make it virtually impossible for the reactor to go beyond acceptable levels of power, temperature, and radioactive emission; there operation depends only on standard physical phenomena, such as gravity and resistance to high temperatures."

Terrorism is a potential threat. "General consensus is that a jetliner could not penetrate the very thick walls of the containment vessel protecting the reactor. It could, however, destroy the control building and bring on a" loss of coolant accident. "Even worse, every power plant has a spent-fuel storage pool containing at least as much highly radioactive material as the nuclear core. These pools are not at all as heavily protected as the reactor vessel. If a pool lost its water, the fuel could heat up and cause a fire that could release greater amounts of cesium-137 than the Chernobyl accident, according to an NRC report."

10. *What are the four generations of reactors? Describe the advantages of Generations III and IV.*

Generation I was the earliest reactors "developed in the 1950s and 1960s; few are still operation. The majority of today's reactors are Generation II vintage, the large baseline power plants, of several designs. Generation III refers to new designs with passive safety features and much simpler, smaller power plants—among them the so-called advanced light-water reactors (ALWRs)." The Generation III designs are also smaller so that heat is conducted "outward into the soil; in this manner, the reactors could not incur a core meltdown. Generation IV plants, initiated by the U.S. Department of Energy, are now being designed and will likely be built within the next 20 years. One example of a Generation IV reactor is the pebble-bed modular reactor (PBMR), which will feed spherical carbon-coated uranium fuel pebbles gradually through the reactor vessel, like a gum-ball machine. The PBMR will be cooled with fluidized helium, an inert gas, which will also spin the turbines. These reactors will be small, will produce about 160 MW of power, and are expected to be cheap to build, passively safe, and inexpensive to operate. The modules can be built in a factory and shipped to the location of the power plant."

11. *Discuss the economic reasons that have caused many utilities to opt for coal-burning, rather than nuclear-powered, plants.*

Utility companies might opt for coal burning, rather than nuclear-power, plants because "increasing safety standards for the construction and operation of nuclear power plants caused the cost of plants to increase at least fivefold, even after inflation is considered. Adding to the rise in costs is the withdrawal of government subsidies to the nuclear industry. Third, public protests frequently delayed the construction or start-up of new power plants. Such delays increased costs still more, because the utility was paying interest on its investment of several billion dollars even when the plant was not producing power. Finally, safety systems may protect the public, but they do not prevent an accident from financially ruining the utility." Nuclear power plants were originally estimated to have a half-life of 40 years but "more than 100 nuclear power plants have been shut down after an average operating lifetime of 17 years." Decommissioning is an unknown cost.

12. *How do fast-neutron and fusion reactors work? Does either one offer promise for alleviating our energy shortage?*

"The breeder reactor is designed so the (nonfissionable) U-238 absorbs the extra neutrons, which are allowed to maintain their high speed. (Such reactors are now called 'fast-neutron reactors'). When this occurs, the U-238 is converted to plutonium, which can then be purified and used as a nuclear fuel, just like U-235. Thus, the fast-neutron reactor (breeder) converts nonfissionable U-238 into fissionable PU-239, and because the fission of U-235 generally produces two neutrons in addition to the one needed to sustain the chain reaction, the breeder may produce more fuel than it consumes." It is not likely that breeder reactors will alleviate our energy shortage because they have greater safety and security problems than nuclear power plants and they "are more expensive to build and operate."

Fusion reactors would use tritium and deuterium to produce helium and energy. For one design the difficulty is "to contain the hydrogen while it is being heated to tremendously high temperatures." No materials are known that can withstand this high heat without vaporizing. Currently, it still takes more energy to run the magnets or lasers (the other two designs) than is obtained by the fusion process. We are still many years from the development of this energy source. "Developing, building, and testing a fusion power plant would require at least another 10 to 20 years and many billions of dollars. Additional plants would require more years. Thus, fusion is, at best, a very long-term option. Many scientists believe that fusion power will always be the elusive pot of gold at the end of the rainbow. The standard joke about fusion power is that it is the energy source of the future, and always will be!"

13. *Explain why nuclear power does little to address our largest energy shortfall.*

"The main energy problem for the United States is an eventual shortage of crude oil for transportation purposes, yet nuclear power produces electricity, which is not used for transportation. If we were moving toward a totally electric economy that included even electric cars, nuclear-generated electricity could be substituted for oil-based fuels. Unfortunately, electric cars have not yet proved practical, and the outlook for them in the near future remains uncertain. Consequently nuclear power simply competes with coal-fired power in meeting the demands for base-load electrical power. Given the high costs and additional financial risks of nuclear power plants, coal is cheaper, and the United States does have abundant coal reserves."

14. *Discuss changes in nuclear power that might brighten its future.*

"If nuclear energy is to have brighter future, it will be because we have found the continued use of fossil fuels to be so damaging to the atmosphere that we have placed limits on their use but have not been able to develop adequate alternative energy sources Nuclear supporters point out that U.S. nuclear power plants prevent the annual release of 164 million tons of carbon, 5.1 million tons of sulfur dioxide, and 2.4 million tons of nitrogen oxides. President George W. Bush has made expanding nuclear energy a major component of his energy policy, by taking the following steps: (1) proposing the Nuclear Power 2010 program, with plans to identify new sites for nuclear power plants, to streamline regulations associated with site licensing, and to

174

encourage industry to build new plants that could become operational by 2010; (2) moving toward a resolution of the nuclear waste problem by approving the Yucca Mountain site for a repository; and (3) signing into law the Energy Policy Act of 2005, which includes a wide range of incentives to enable the Nuclear Power 2010 program: a tax credit for the first 6,000 megawatts of new nuclear capacity for the first eight years of operation, insurance to protect companies building new reactors from the risk of regulatory delays, and federal loan guarantees for up to 80% of construction costs of new power plants. The new act also authorizes $1.25 billion towards the construction of a special nuclear plant that would produce hydrogen from water, a key part of the coming fuel cell technology for automobiles. These incentives amount to $13 billion."

Thinking Environmentally: Possible Answers

1. *Evaluate the risks of nuclear power. Are we overly concerned or not concerned enough about nuclear accidents? Could an accident like Chernobyl happen in the United States?*

    The risks of nuclear power are primarily some type of loss of coolant accident and the release of radioactive materials into the environment and the need to isolate of radioactive wastes from humans and the environment.

    As to whether or not we are overly concerned or not concerned enough, this is an opinion question that will depend upon the individual's risk assessment. Some individuals will feel that we are too concerned while others will feel that we are not concerned enough. A justification for one's opinion is important. Are the consequences of exposure to radiation too high? Are the human and environmental costs higher from coal?

    An exact replica of the Chernobyl accident could not occur in the United States because we do not have graphite reactors, nor do we have nuclear power plants without a containment building. It is possible (and it has happened) that reactor operators have responded poorly to events taking place within the reactor. It is possible for the material in the rod storage pools to be released to the environment in a way that would be similar to what occurred at Chernobyl because the pools are not within a containment building.

2. *Would you rather live next door to a coal-burning plant or a nuclear power plant? Defend your choice.*

    Answers to this question will vary. There are pros and cons to living next door to a nuclear power plant versus a coal fired plant. Each person's risk assessment will differ.

3. *Global climate change has been cited by nuclear power proponents as one of the most important justifications for further development of the nuclear power option. Give reasons for their belief, and then site some reasons that would counter their argument.*

    Nuclear power plants, unlike coal, gas, and petroleum fired electrical power plants, do not produce greenhouse gases. While this is true, the consequences to humans and the environment due to an uncontrolled release of radiation could be viewed as at least as severe as the consequences from global climate change. The need to isolate the waste products from a nuclear power plant for a half million years may be viewed as equally or more problematic than global climate change.

4. *Go to the website http://www.pbmr.com and investigate the reactor described there. Where is it being designed, and where will it likely be used first? What are its features?*

    Pebble Bed Modular Reactor (Pty) Ltd of South Africa was established in 1999 with the intention to develop and market small-scale, high-temperature reactors both locally and internationally. The 700-member PBMR project team is based in Centurion near Pretoria, South Africa.

    The PBMR is a High Temperature Reactor (HTR), with a closed-cycle, gas turbine power conversion system. Although it is not the only HTR currently being developed in the world, the South African project is internationally regarded as the leader in the power generation field. Very high efficiency and attractive economics are possible without compromising the high levels of passive safety expected of advanced nuclear designs.

175

This nuclear power plant design can use three different fuel sources— uranium, thorium, or plutonium. The fuel is "contained within spherical pebbles made of pyrolitic graphite. An inert gas, helium, nitrogen, or carbon dioxide, circulates through the spaces between the fuel pebbles. This carries heat away from the reactor. Ideally, the heated gas is run directly through a turbine. However, if the gas from the primary coolant can be made radioactive by the neutrons in the reactor, usually it is brought to a heat exchanger, where it heats another gas, or steam. The exhaust of the turbine is quite warm and may be used to warm buildings or chemical plants, or even run another heat engine." Helium is used as the coolant, not water. (All quotes are from the web site.)

The first pebble-bed reactor is likely to be used in South Africa. China has a test reactor operating, as do Netherlands, Germany, Japan, and Russia. Other countries working on this technology include the United States, the United Kingdom, France, Japan, Canada, Argentina, South Korea, Republic, Switzerland, and Brazil. The facility in the United States is likely to be at the Idaho National Engineering Lab.

CHAPTER 16
Renewable Energy

Chapter Outline:

I.   Putting Solar Energy to Work
   A.   Solar Heating of Water
   B.   Solar Space Heating
      1.   Building = Collector
      2.   Earth-Sheltered Housing
      3.   Energy Stars
   C.   Solar Production of Electricity
      1   Photovoltaic Cells
         i.   Uses
         ii.   Cost
         iii.   Inverters
         iv.   Utilities
         v.   New PV Technologies
      2.   Concentrated Solar Power (CSP)
         i.   Solar Trough
         ii.   Power Tower
         iii.   Dish-Engine System
      3.   The Future of Solar Energy
         i.   Matching Demand
II.   Indirect Solar Energy
   A.   Hydropower
      1.   Trade-offs
         i.   More Dams?
         ii.   Dam Report
   B.   Wind Power
      1.   Design
      2.   Drawbacks
   C.   Biomass Energy
      1.   Burning Firewood
         i.   Fuelwood Crisis
      2.   Burning Wastes
      3.   Producing Methane
III.   Renewable Energy for Transportation
   A.   Biofuels
      1.   Ethanol
         i.   Farm Products
         ii.   Second-Generation Biofuel
         iii.   Air Quality
      2.   Biodiesel

B. Hydrogen: Highway to the Future
    i. A Good Idea, But…
    ii. Plants Do It
    iii. Electrolysis
    iv. Solar Energy to Hydrogen
    v. Model U
      1. Fuel Cells
        i. Freedom CAR
IV. Additional Renewable-Energy Options
    A. Geothermal Energy
      1. Heat Pumps
    B. Tidal and Wave Power
      1. Ocean Waves
    C. Ocean-Thermal-Energy Conversion
V. Policies for a Sustainable Energy Future
    A. Final Thoughts

Key Topics:

1. Putting Solar Energy to Work
2. Indirect Solar Energy
3. Renewable Energy for Transportation
4. Additional Renewable-Energy Options
5. Policies for a Sustainable-Energy Future

Instructional Goals:

1. Solar energy is, for all practical purposes, an inexhaustible energy source. The difficulties with using solar relate to the desired end uses of energy and the technical issues involved in the conversion of radiant energy to electricity.

2. Several sources of energy are available that depend upon the Sun. Hydropower is dependent on the hydrological cycle, which is dependent upon the Sun's energy for the movement of water molecules. Wind power is dependent upon the Sun because winds are partially generated by the Sun's differential heating of the earth's atmosphere. Biomass energy uses the energy captured from the Sun in photosynthesis.

3. Other renewable energy resources present energy solutions for the future, but there are drawbacks and hurdles to overcome for all of them.

4. Policies aimed at stabilizing greenhouse gases, developing sustainable and renewable energy, will be critical for the future.

Concepts and Connections:

Renewable energy captures the imagination of many students. Obtaining energy without depleting the supply is attractive. A discussion of the links between renewable energy supplies and sustainable ecosystems is important. The potential conflict between using farmland for the production of biofuels and growing food can be an interesting discussion because all the issues concerning the sustainable production of food, (e.g. erosion, soil fertility, energy use, and land use), are important for the production of biofuels.

Any discussion of renewable and alternative energy needs to include the environmental consequences resulting from the production and use of the energy. No energy production or use is without environmental consequences.

It is interesting to discuss with students their perceived energy needs. The kinds and quantity of consumer goods, transportation, food, and housing purchased by each of us place demands on the types and quantities of energy produced. Linking our daily decisions to how much energy is used can be an eye-opening experience.

Concepts in Context:

The concepts and issues in this chapter on renewable energy can be linked to nuclear power (Chapter 15) and fossil fuels (Chapter 19). There are common issues between all energy forms. Some of the common issues include environmental impact (Chapters 3, 4, 5, and 7), air pollution (Chapter 19), greenhouse gases (Chapter 18), water pollution (Chapter 20), recycling and solid waste (Chapter 21), and hazardous waste (Chapter 22).

The size of the human population (Chapter 8) and energy use per person are also important to consider when deciding how to obtain the energy. Food production in the developed world, and increasingly so in the developing world, is tied to the use of energy (Chapter 12). Pesticides (Chapter 13) and fertilizers have a direct link to energy use; both of these farm inputs need energy for their production, distribution, and soil/plant application. Energy production and use can be tied to environmental health (Chapter 17). Economic decisions (Chapter 2) are closely tied to the cost and availability of energy.

Key Terms and Vocabulary:

solar constant, flat-plate collectors, earth-sheltered housing, Energy Star, energy conservation, photovoltaic, PV cell, solar-trough, power grid, pumped-storage power plants, wind turbines, wind farms, reformulated gasoline, fuel cells, hydrogen economy, geothermal energy, tidal barrage, ocean thermal-energy conversion, energy conservation and efficiency, 2005 Energy Policy Act, 2007 Energy Independence and Security Act, The American Recovery and Reinvestment Act of 2009, carbon tax

Discussion, Activities, and Labs:

1. Discuss with the students the possibility that we will run out of energy. Try to elicit from the students what people mean when they say we are running out of energy. People typically mean that we are running out of

fossil fuel. There are sufficient energy options that actually running out of energy is unlikely. The more likely scenario would be that we don't make a smooth transition from a fossil fuel economy to a renewable energy economy. Ask the students to suggest ways to make the transition smooth. Ask the students to suggest possible policy changes, consumer behavioral changes, building code changes, and attitude changes that may be necessary to make the transition.

2. Discuss the pros and cons of all energy sources. All energy sources produce pollutants in the production of the component parts. Some energy sources do not produce pollutants during use, for example, passive solar. Discuss the need to match the end use with the energy source. What is a sustainable energy policy? Would it have a few or many sources of energy? Would it attempt to reduce energy demand?

3. Divide the class into groups of three to four students. Provide each student with plans and materials to build a solar cooker. It should be possible to complete the building of a solar cooker during a class period. A thermometer should be included within the solar cooker building materials. Tell the students that during the next class period they will be cooking something in the solar cooker. Each group will be expected to devise an experiment concerning the solar cooker. They can test variables such as the effect of cooker panel angle in relation to the sun, of shading, of a sheltered area, of additional insulation, of the opening the solar cooker lid, and so on. During the next class period have each group choose to cook different items. Pick items that can be cooked within a short period of time. The students should record the effect of their variables on the temperature inside the solar cooker and on the length of time necessary to cook the food item.

4. Divide the class into groups of three to four students. Ask each group to devise a sustainable energy plan for the United States. Encourage them to be inventive. Look for ways to reduce energy demand by encouraging people to live closer to work, live in cities rather than suburbs, or improve the energy efficiency of cities. What forms of energy would be emphasized? What forms of energy would form a smaller part of their energy plan?

Suggested Lecture Format:

I. Putting Solar Energy to Work
Solar energy is, for all practical purposes, an inexhaustible energy source. The difficulties with using solar relate to the desired end uses of energy and the technical issues involved in the conversion of radiant energy to electricity. **See Discussion Topic #3.**

    A. Solar Heating of Water—"A solar collector for heating water consists of a thin, broad box with a glass or clear plastic top and a black bottom in which water tubes are embedded." See Figure 16-5 and Figure 16-6.

    B. Solar Space Heating—"The same concept for heating water with the sun can be applied to heat spaces. Flat- plate collectors such as those used in water heating can be used for space heating." See Figure 16-7.
       1. Building = Collector—A well designed building with proper positioning and insulation can be the most efficient collector. See Figure 16-8.
       2. Earth-Sheltered Housing—"Uses earth as a form of insulation and orients the building for passive solar energy." See Figure 16-9.

3. Energy Stars—"In 2001, the EPA extended its Energy Star program to buildings and began awarding the Energy Star label to public and corporate edifices."

C. Solar Production of Electricity—"Currently a few methods are feasible…and are proving to be economically viable."

   1. Photovoltaic Cells—Look "like a simple wafer of material with one wire attached to the top and one to the bottom. As sunlight shines of the wafer, it puts out an amount of electrical current roughly equivalent to that emitted by a flashlight battery." See Figures16-10 and 16-11.

      i. Uses—"Panels of PV cells provide power for rural homes, irrigation pumps, traffic signals, radio transmitters, lighthouses, offshore oil-drilling platforms" and more.

      ii. Cost—The cost of "25 cents per kilowatt-hour…must be compared with that of other power alternatives (6-12 cents per kilowatt-hour for residential electricity)."

      iii. Inverters—"The inverter acts as an interface between the solar PV modules and the electric grid or batters. It must change incoming direct current…to alternating current compatible with the electricity coming from the grid and/or the devices that will be powered by the PV system." See Figure 16-12.

      iv. Utilities—Although more and more utilities are moving toward using PV technology on a large scale, installation on rooftops has the most promise. See Figure 16-13.

      v. New PV Technologies—Three new technologies are helping to bring the cost of PV electricity down: thin-film PV cells, SLIVERs, and glass coated with light-absorbing dyes.

   2. Concentrated Solar Power (CSP)—Reflection can be used to focus sunlight and to transfer heat to turbogenerators.

      i. Solar Trough—"The curvature of the trough is such that all of the sunlight hitting the collector is reflected onto a pipe running down the center of the system."

      ii. Power Tower—"A power tower is an array of sun-tracking mirrors that focuses the sunlight falling on several acres of land onto a receiver." See Figure 16-14.

      iii. Dish-Engine System—Consists "of a set of parabolic concentrator dishes that focus sunlight onto a receiver." See Figure 16-15.

   3. The Future of Solar Energy—Although the demand for solar energy is growing dramatically, drawbacks are present.

      i. Matching Demand—Solar power can provide for more and more of our daytime energy needs while wind and other renewable resources can reduce the need for fossil-fueled energy during the night.

II. Indirect Solar Energy

Several sources of energy are available that depend upon the Sun. Hydropower is dependent on the hydrological cycle, which is dependent upon the Sun's energy for the movement of water molecules. Wind power is dependent upon the Sun because winds are partially generated by the Sun's differential heating of the earth's atmosphere. Biomass energy uses the energy captured from the Sun in photosynthesis.

A. Hydropower—"About 6% of the electrical power generated in the United States currently comes from hydroelectric dams, most of it from about 300 large dams concentrated in the Northwest and Southeast." See Figure 16-16.
   1. Trade-offs—Using dams to generate electricity have both advantages and disadvantages environmentally.
      i. More Dams?—Building more dams is being restricted by a lack of good sites as well as by controversy worldwide.
      ii. Dam Report—"The report found dams to be a mixed blessing, concluding that large dams should be built only if no other options exist."

B. Wind Power—"The United States is the world leader in wind energy, with Germany close behind. In the past seven years, global wind power capacity has increased at a rate of 28% per year." See Figure 16-17 and Figure 16-18.
   1. Design—"Many different designs of wind machines have been proposed and tested, but the one that has proved most practical is the age-old concept of wind-driven propeller blades."
   2. Drawbacks—Drawbacks of wind include a lack of wind at times, the displeasing look of large wind farms, and the potential hazard to birds.

C. Biomass Energy—Burning firewood, paper, organic waste, and the generation of methane are all forms of biomass energy. See Figure 16-19.
   1. Burning Firewood—"Wherever forests are ample relative to the human population, firewood—or fuel-wood, as it is called—can be a sustainable energy resource, and indeed, wood has been a main energy resource over much of human history."
      i. Fuelwood Crisis—"There was serious concern in the later decades of the 20th century about deforestation due to wood gathering, but although there are local shortages, it appears that global use of fuel-wood peaked in the late 1990s and is now declining."
   2. Burning Wastes—"Facilities that generate electrical power from the burning of municipal wastes (waste-to-energy conversion) are discussed in Chapter 21."
   3. Producing Methane—"When the disposal of manure, the production of energy, and the creation of fertilizer can be combined in an efficient cycle, great economic benefit can be achieved."

III. Renewable Energy for Transportation
Renewable energy in the form of biofuels and hydrogen present possibilities for the future, but there are drawbacks and hurdles to overcome for each.

A. Biofuels—"Complex organic matter (primarily plants, but also animal wastes) can be processed to make fuels for vehicles."
   1. Ethanol—"Gasahol, 10% ethanol and 90% gasoline, has been promoted and marketed in the Midwest since the late 1970s."
      i. Farm Products—Corn-based ethanol could be a "net loser in its impact on climate change."
      ii. Second-Generation Biofuel—"A more likely long-run technology for producing ethanol is the use of cellulosic feed-stocks such as agricultural crop residues, grasses (such as

182

switchgrass), logging residues, fast-growing trees, and fuel-woods from forests." See Figure 16-21.

       iii. Air Quality—Ethanol can also replace MTBE as a fuel additive to make gasoline cleaner.

    2. Biodiesel—Soybean oil, recycled vegetable oil, and even poultry waste have been converted into fuel.

B. Hydrogen: Highway to the Future—"Neither carbon dioxide nor hydrocarbon pollutants are produced during the burning of hydrogen."

       i. A Good Idea, But…There is no natural source of hydrogen gas on the earth and producing hydrogen gas in itself requires a lot of energy.

       ii. Plants Do It—It might be possible to generate hydrogen gas by mimicking the process of photosynthesis.

       iii. Electrolysis—Another method for producing hydrogen gas is "to pass an electrical current through water and cause the water molecules to dissociate. Hydrogen bubbles come off at the negative electrode (the cathode), while oxygen bubbles come off at the negative electrode."

       iv. Solar Energy to Hydrogen—Setting up solar troughs hooked up to produce hydrogen gas by electrolysis is possible.

       v. Model U—This Ford model "sports a 2.3 liter internal combustion engine that runs on hydrogen and is equipped with a hybrid electrical drive."

    1. Fuel Cells—"An alternative to burning hydrogen in conventional internal combustion engines uses hydrogen in fuel cells to produce electricity and power the vehicle with an electric motor." See Figure 16-22.

       i. Freedom CAR—"Originally, it was a partnering effort between the government and the auto companies to promote research toward fuel-cell-powered vehicles, with a goal of 2010 for commercial introduction."

IV. Additional Renewable-Energy Options

Geothermal energy, tidal and wave power and ocean-thermal-energy-conversion all provide possible energy solutions for the future.

A. Geothermal Energy—There are naturally occurring areas where almost boiling water is close to the surface of the earth and can be used to drive turbogenerators. See Figure 16-23.

    1. Heat Pumps—Pipes can be drilled into the earth and used to heat water as a heat exchange system. See Figure 16-24.

B. Tidal and Wave Power—"A phenomenal amount of energy is inherent in the twice-daily rise and fall of the ocean tides, brought about by the gravitational pull of the Moon and the Sun."

    2. Ocean Waves—"It might be possible to harness some of (wave energy), but the technological challenge is daunting."

C. Ocean-Thermal-Energy Conversion—"Is the name of an experimental technology that uses this temperature difference (between the surface of the water heated by the sun and the colder deep water) to produce power."

V. Policies for a Sustainable Energy Future
Policies aimed at stabilizing greenhouse gases, developing sustainable and renewable energy, will be critical for the future. **See Discussion Topics #1, #2, and #4.**

    A. National Energy Policy—The 2005 Energy Policy Act and the 2007 Energy Independence and Security Acts "have become the major expression of federal energy policy, although many other laws promoting renewable energy and conservation have been enacted."

    B. Final Thoughts—"Are the preceding developments, even the suggested carbon tax, enough to enable us to achieve a sustainable-energy system and to mitigate global climate change? Very likely, no. Yet many of them are moving us in the stewardly direction that is vital to the future of the global environment."

Review Questions: Possible Answers

1. How does solar energy compare with fossil-fuel energy in satisfying basic energy needs? What are the three fundamental problems in harnessing solar energy?

    Solar energy compares quite well with fossil fuel energy in satisfying basic energy needs. "Just 40 minutes of sunlight striking the land surface of the United States yields the equivalent energy of a year's expenditure of fossil fuels." The three fundamental problems in harnessing solar energy are its collection, conversion, and storage.

2. How do active and passive solar hot-water heaters work?

    "A solar collector for heating water consists of a thin, broad box with a glass or clear plastic top and a black bottom with water tubes embedded within. Such collectors are called flat-plate collectors. Faced toward the Sun, the black bottom gets hot as it absorbs sunlight . . . and the clear cover prevents the heat from escaping." Water is thus heated and is conveyed to a tank where it is stored. An active system, the heated water is moved by means of a pump. In a passive system, natural convection currents are used."

3. How can a building best be designed to become a passive solar collector for heat?

    "The basic principle is to have windows facing the Sun. In the winter, because of the Sun's angle of incidence, sunlight can come in and heat the interior of the building. At night, insulated drapes or shades can be pulled down to trap the heat inside. The well-insulated building, with appropriately made doors and windows, would act as its own best heat-storage unit. Excessive heat load in the summer can be avoided by using an awning or overhang to shield the windows from the high summer Sun."

    "A common criticism of solar heating is that a back up heating system is still required for periods of inclement weather. Good insulation is a major part of the answer to this criticism." The added construction cost is 5–10% above normal.

4. How does a PV cell work, and what are some present applications of such cells?

    A PV cell works by sunlight shining on the wafer. "Each cell consists of two very thin layers of semiconductor material separated by a junction layer. The lower layer has atoms with single electrons in the outer orbital that are easily lost. The upper layer has atoms lacking electrons in their outer orbital; these atoms readily gain electrons. The kinetic energy of light photons striking the two-layer 'sandwich' dislodges electrons

184

from the lower layer, creating an electrical potential between the layers. The potential provides the energy for an electrical current to flow through the rest of the circuit."

Photovoltaic cells are common in pocket calculators, watches, and toys. Photovoltaic cells are used to provide power for homes, irrigation pumps, traffic signals, radio transmitters, lighthouses, offshore oil-drilling platforms, and other locations that are distant from power lines. Future applications include home-sized systems on rooftops.

"To accelerate the market share of solar power, the cost of solar cells needs to drop dramatically." This is expected to happen within the next decade or so.

5. *What is happening in recent years in the PV market? How are utilities encouraging PV power?*
    "Utilities in California, New York, New Jersey, and Connecticut have established programs that provide incentives to customers to install 2- to 4-kW PV systems on their roofs. A 2-kW system provides about half of the annual energy needs of a residence, and in case the homeowner is generating more than needed, the utility buys the excess electricity at the retail rate. A federal program, the Million Solar Roofs Initiative, aims at encouraging the installation of solar energy units on a million residential and commercial rooftops by 2010, but the initiative provides few financial incentives, focusing instead on 'partnering' with other organizations, such as the utilities in California and New York, and providing technical and advisory assistance. With 350,000 systems already installed by 2003, the program already appears to have seriously underestimated the potential for PV solar system installation. The Solar America Initiative, another federal program, works at the industrial and institutional level to promote the adoption of PV electrical systems, using U.S. technology. The goal of the initiative is to 'prove 5-1- GW of new electric capacity (equivalent to the amount of electricity needed to power 1-2 million homes) to the U.S. grid,' by 2015."

6. *Describe the solar-trough system, how it works, and its potential for providing more power.*
    The solar-trough collector system has "collectors that are long, trough-shaped reflectors tilted toward the Sun. The curvature of the trough is such that all the sunlight hitting the collector is reflected onto a pipe running down the center of the system. Oil or some other heat-absorbing fluid circulating through the pipe is thus heated to very high temperatures. The heated fluid is passed through a heat exchanger to boil water and produce steam for driving a turbogenerator. The potential for the solar-trough system is quite good because the cost of producing a kilowatt-hour is barely more than the cost from coal-fired facilities. These facilities need to be located where there is plenty of sunlight.

7. *What is the potential for developing more hydroelectric power in North America versus developing countries, and what would be the environmental impacts of such development?*
    Few sites remain that are suitable for hydroelectric facilities in North American or elsewhere. "Only 2% of the nation's rivers remain free flowing, and many of these are now protected by the Wild and Scenic Rivers Act of 1968, a law that effectively gives certain scenic rivers the status of national parks. Proposals for new dams outside of the United States are embroiled in controversy over whether the projected benefits justify the ecological and social trade-offs."

8. *Where is wind power being harvested, and what is the future potential for wind farms?*
    Germany has the greatest amount of wind being harvest followed by Spain and then the United States. The Midwest is a prime location within the United States for wind power. "The American Wind Energy Association calculates that wind farms located throughout the Midwest could meet the electrical needs for the entire country, while the land beneath the turbines could still be used for farming." The potential for wind power is quite good. Its price is currently competitive; "There are no technical, economic, or resource limitations that would prevent wind power from supplying at least 12% of the world's electricity by 2020."

9. *What are some ways of converting biomass to useful energy, and what is the potential environmental impact of each?*

The four ways of converting biomass to useful energy are burning of firewood, municipal wastepaper, and other organic waste; generating methane from anaerobic digestion of manure and sewage sludge; and producing alcohol from fermenting grains and other starchy materials.

The environmental impact from burning firewood is deforestation. The environmental consequences from burning municipal wastepaper is that the paper could be recycled (saving resources and more energy than can be obtained from burning) and the potential for dioxin production if the temperatures are not high enough. Generating methane from manure and sewage sludge would be problematic if methane is released prior to its use (potent greenhouse gas) and metals in sewage sludge might be problematic. Producing alcohol from fermenting grains has all the problems associated with farming plus it diverts farmland from food production.

10. *What biofuels are used for transportation, and what is the potential for increasing biofuels in the United States?*

The biofuels used for transportation are ethanol from corn and biodiesel from used vegetable oil. The production costs to make ethanol are almost twice as great as gasoline.

"In 2005–2006, 4.3 billion gallons of ethanol for fuel, the equivalent of 100 million barrels of oil, were used in the United States. Some 14% of the nation's corn crop is dedicated to this use; an ethanol factory also produces corn oil and livestock feed. Ethanol plants under construction will increase the production capacity to 6.3 billion gallons. A production tax credit of 51 cents a gallon helps ethanol compete with gasoline."

"Currently, ethanol represents about 1.6% of U.S. gasoline consumption. This could rise to 13% if the country's entire corn crop were devoted to ethanol production—an impossible assumption, given the importance of corn for animal fed and export. With some 75 million acres devoted to corn harvest in the U.S., there is little suitable farmland for significant expansion."

11. *How can hydrogen gas be produced via the use of solar energy? How might hydrogen be collected and stored to meet the need for fuel for transportation in the future?*

"We would start by building arrays of solar-trough or photovoltaic generating facilities in the deserts of the southwestern United States, where land is cheap and sunlight plentiful. The electrical power produced by these methods would then be used to produce hydrogen gas by electrolysis. The most efficient way to move the hydrogen is through underground pipelines; hundreds of miles of such pipelines already exist where hydrogen is transported for use in chemical industries."

"An alternative to burning hydrogen in conventional internal combustion engines uses hydrogen in fuel cells to produce electricity and power the vehicle with an electric motor. Fuel cells are devices in which hydrogen or some other fuel is chemically recombined with oxygen in a manner that produces an electrical potential rather than initiating burning."

12. *How do fuel cells work, and what is being done to adapt them to power vehicles?*

"An alternative to burning hydrogen in conventional internal combustion engines uses hydrogen in fuel cells to produce electricity and power the vehicle with an electric motor. Fuel cells are devices in which hydrogen or some other fuel is chemically recombined with oxygen in a manner that produces an electrical potential rather than initiating burning. Emissions consist solely of water and heat! Because fuel cells create much less waste heat than conventional engines do, energy is transferred more efficiently from the hydrogen to the vehicle—at a rate of 45 to 60%, versus the 20% for current combustion engines vehicles. To power a vehicle, hundreds of fuel cells are combined into a fuel cell stack. The vehicle must also include a hydrogen storage device, a cooling system (fuel cells also generate heat), and a device to force oxygen into the fuel cells."

13. *What is geothermal energy, and what are two ways is it being harnessed?*

Geothermal energy "occurs where the hot molten rock of Earth's interior is close enough to the surface to heat groundwater." Two ways in which geothermal is being used are electrical production and space heating.

14. *What is the potential for developing tidal power in the United States?*

There are no suitable locations for tidal barrage. One location in Alaska is being investigated for the building of a concrete impoundment enclosure that sites on the ocean bottom. San Francisco is exploring the possibility of a turbine beneath the Golden Gate Bridge.

15. *How does renewable energy answer the key global and national energy issues?*

"Renewable energy means sustainable energy, and a sustainable energy future does not include significant fossil-fuel energy." Renewable energy reduces our dependence on fossil fuel imports and increases our energy security.

16. *Describe current policy for renewable energy and energy efficiency, as an outcome of the passage of the Energy Policy Act of 2005. What crucial issues were omitted from the act?*

"For renewable energy and efficiency, current energy policy (policies enacted in law) does the following:
- Establishes a Renewable Fuel Standard (RFS) for ethanol and biodiesel of 4 billion gallons in 2006, rising to 8 billion gallons by 2012.
- Continues funding for research and development on renewable energy, including major funding increases for solar energy and biomass programs.
- Extends the production tax credit for electricity generated with wind and biomass for another two years.
- Extends the Energy Star building energy efficiency program to include schools, retail establishments, private homes, and health care facilities.
- Provides tax credits for many types of home improvements that improve energy efficiency.
- Provides tax credits for geothermal heat pumps, solar water heating, and PV systems.
- Develops efficiency standards for many more appliances and provides tax credits for manufacturers of some energy-saving appliances (but not air conditioners!).
- Continues funding for the Freedom Car and Freedom Fuel projects.
- Provides for a temporary income tax credit applicable to the purchase of new hybrid or fuel-cell-powered vehicles.
- Contains provisions aimed at enabling geothermal energy to compete with fossil fuels in generating electricity."

What the Energy Policy Act of 2005 does not do:
- It did not establish a federal Renewable Portfolio Standard (RPS). This would require utilities to provide an increasing percentage of power from non-hydroelectric renewable sources (wind, solar biomass). However, the states are setting the bar for the RPS: 20 states and the District of Columbia have implemented RPS requirements.
- It did not increase CAFE standards, but simply authorized continued 'study' of the issue.
- It did not take any direct action on global warming, although it can be argued that every provision that promotes greater energy efficiency and the use of renewable energy sources is going to reduce greenhouse gas emissions in the U.S.

Thinking Environmentally: Possible Answers

1. *What do you believe needs to happen before solar power becomes a thoroughly mainstream form of energy production? Defend your answer.*

Student responses will vary. Look for a discussion of the cost of solar energy versus traditional electricity and for a discussion about research dollars that need to be invested in renewable energy resources.

2. *What do you think could be a viable solution for backup power systems for solar heaters in the event of bad weather?*

Student responses will vary. Students should discuss possible renewable resource options listed in this chapter that do not depend on weather.

3. *How much promise does hydrogen power hold? Is its eventual sustainability just a myth or something to be pursued?*

Although hydrogen could possibly be an inexhaustible resource for energy, determining a cost-effective, safe, and efficient way to use hydrogen as a fuel presents a major challenge. New solutions on the horizon, as discussed in this chapter do present promise.

4. *Imagine you are charged with building a facility run entirely by renewable resources (with the possible exception of backup power). How would you evaluate which sources have the most potential?*

Student responses will vary. Students should discuss possible renewable resource options listed in this chapter including conservation by earth sheltering, solar power, wind power, and other types of power that can be used in commercial facilities.

5. *Audit all the energy needs in your daily life. How much energy do you consume? Describe how each need might be satisfied by one or another renewable-energy option. (Check the internet for tools for this exercise.)*
The answer to this question will vary from individual to individual.

CHAPTER 17
Pollution and Prevention

Chapter Outline:

I.   Links Between the Environment and Human Health
    A.   Environmental Health
        1.   The Picture of Health
        2.   Public Health
            i.   Other Countries
            ii. Life Expectancy
            iii. Two Worlds
    B.   Environmental Hazards
        1.   Cultural Hazards
        2.   Biological Hazards
            i.   Tuberculosis
            ii. Malaria
        3.   Physical Hazards
            i.   Out of Nowhere
            ii. In Harm's Way
        4.   Chemical Hazards
            i.   Carcinogens
        5.   Cancer
            i.   Carcinogenesis
II. Pathways of Risk
    A.   The Risks of Being Poor
        1.   Wealth
        2.   Priorities
    B.   The Cultural Risk of Tobacco Use
        1.   Marlboro Country?
        2.   Secondhand Smoke
        3.   Goodbye, Joe
        4.   Legally Speaking
        5.   FCTC and MPOWER
    C.   Risk and Infectious Diseases
        1.   Even Here?
        2.   Tropical Diseases
        3.   Net Results
        4.   Good News
    D.   Toxic Risk Pathways
        1.   Indoor Air Pollution
            i.   Developing Countries
            ii. Asthma
            iii. Worms, Anyone?

          iv. Toxicology

     E. Disaster Risk

III. Risk Assessment

     A. Risk Assessment by the EPA

        1. Hazard Assessment: Is This Really a Hazard?

           i. Ask the Mice

           ii. Just Test People?

        2. Dose-Response and Exposure Assessment: How Much for How Long?

        3. Risk Characterization: What Does the Science Say?

     B. Public-Health Risk Assessment

        1. The DALY

     C. Risk Management

     D. Risk Perception

        1. Hazard Versus Outrage

           i. Media's Role

           ii. Public Concern and Public Policy

     E. The Precautionary Principle

        1. Stewards of Health

Key Topics:

1. Links Between the Environment and Human Health
2. Pathways of Risk
3. Risk Assessment

Instructional Goals:

1. Environmental hazards are broadly defined and include cultural, biological, physical, and chemical hazards.

2. Poverty, personal choices, societal affluence, and economic structure influence an individual's risk of injury, disease, or death from an environmental hazard.

3. Risk analysis is based upon a four-step process: hazard assessment, dose-response assessment, exposure assessment, and risk characterization. The process, while based upon scientific data, includes many value judgments concerning the validity of the available data, the biological significance of the data, the need for safety factors, and the variables to be included in the analysis.

4. Risk management merges public policy with risk assessment. While all members of society have not learned the skills to generate the data used in risk analysis or know how to complete a risk analysis, all people can participate in the public policy aspects of risk management. The risk analysis provides only one piece of the necessary information in forming public policy.

5. Risk perception is critical for determining the risks that will be tolerated. Understanding how people perceive risk and addressing the concerns of people are essential in solving risk management dilemmas.

6. The precautionary principle, long accepted in Europe as a guide for public policy, is gaining ground in the United States. This principle states that when an activity has a reasonable risk of causing harm to people or the environment, lack of scientific certainty cannot be used to justify lack of action to prevent harm. One advantage of decision making influenced by the precautionary principle over risk-based decision making is that the precautionary principle includes the outrage component of public response. The perception of risk is included in the decision making process.

Concepts and Connections:

Human environmental health impacts can be related to all environmental issues. Air and water pollution have direct human impacts, and we will typically see adverse consequences to nonhuman species when air or water quality are sufficiently poor that adverse human impacts are visible. Even when the environmental changes are insufficient to directly impact humans we may see adverse consequences in other species. If limiting factors, habitats, food webs, biogeochemical cycles, predator-prey relationships, or succession are altered we may see human health impacts as a secondary outcome due to the ecosystem not being able to provide the goods and services needed for human survival.

Environmental health can be more broadly defined to include ecosystem health. This allows us to use some of the same tools and thought processes to study the impact of human activities on ecosystems.

Concepts in Context:

All issues covered in an environmental science course can be linked to the material in this chapter. Anything that adversely impacts ecosystems by changing limiting factors, habitats, or the relationships between organisms (Chapter 3) can result in reductions in food production (Chapter 12), thus impacting human health. Activities that impact the biogeochemical cycle (Chapter 4) or change ecological succession (Chapter 5), causing reductions in the available goods and services (Chapter 7), may result in compromised human health. Human population growth (Chapter 8) influences the impact of human activities on ecosystems and human health. The health of the soil (Chapter 11) will influence our ability to grow food (Chapter 12), therefore impacting human health. How we use water (Chapter 10) has direct impacts on human and ecosystem health. Biodiversity, or the lack thereof, (Chapter 6) may influence our ability to find new disease treatments and maintain the sustainability of the ecosystems that support humans (Chapter 5).

How and which types of energy used (Chapters 14, 15, and 16) influence quality of the environment; air, water, and land pollution are obvious environmental impacts from energy production and use. We observe increases in human disease rates from air (Chapter 19) and water pollution (Chapter 20). Improperly handled solid (Chapter 21) and hazardous (Chapter 22) waste may adversely impact human health. Pesticide use (Chapter 13) can directly and indirectly impact human health. Ozone depletion and global climate change (Chapter 18) are predicted to adversely impact human health and ecosystem health.

Economic and public policy (Chapter 2) decisions will influence human and environmental health. The building of sustainable communities and environmentally friendly lifestyles (Chapter 23) will improve human health.

Key Terms and Vocabulary:

pollution, pollutant, nonbiodegradable, environment, hazard, risk, vulnerability, morbidity, mortality, epidemiology, rotavirus, underweight, vector control, treatment strategies, toxicology, risk assessment, epidemiological study, animal testing, dose-response assessment, exposure assessment, risk characterization, risk management, risk perceptions, precautionary principle

Discussion, Activities, and Labs:

1. Discuss with the class the various factors influencing risk perception. If you ask the students to raise their hands if they feel safer when they are driving rather than someone else, most (if not all) will raise their hands. Ask them if this could possibly be true. What is the probability that everyone in the room is a safer driver than everyone else in the room—simultaneously? This short exercise should provide the students with some insight as to risk perception. Go through a selected number of the items under risk perception in the lecture below. You could ask who would rather not travel by airplane. Ask what factors have influenced their risk assessment. Some reasons might include passengers don't control the airplane (controllability), size of the disaster if it happens (severity), human error (origin), if an accident happens it is because the airline isn't doing maintenance to save money (benefit), not a frequent flyer (exposure), and don't need to fly (necessity). Ask the students to list the reasons why a smoker might find the risk from smoking acceptable (voluntary, small number of people at risk per incident, control, smoker benefits, familiar, frequent exposure). Ask the students to list the reasons why a nonsmoker might find the risk from passive cigarette smoke unacceptable (involuntary, no control, no benefit, tobacco companies make money from people accepting the risk, infrequent exposure, delayed effect, large number of people affected, not a necessity). A person getting ready to stop smoking will have a more mixed perception of the risk. This last example should provide the student with an understanding as to how people can perceive a risk so differently and why it is so difficult to create public policy when risks are perceived differently.

2. In the United States we currently make policy decisions using a risk-based decision making process. The precautionary principle is an alternative policy making process that is very controversial in the United States but very accepted in Europe. Describe to the students the precautionary principle and Type I and II errors. (Anytime a decision is made there is a possibility that an error will have been made. A Type I error is the theoretical possibility that a decision is made to accept that something is happening when nothing is happening. A Type II error is the theoretical possibility that a decision is made that nothing is happening when something is happening. The kind of error that is preferable depends on the perspective of the individual. For example, to an utility company it would be an error [Type I] to act if global warming is happening when it may not be. To an ecologist, evolutionary biologist, agronomist, or another individual who views the consequences of global climate change as severe, it would be an error [Type II] to act as if global warming is not happening (when it could be.) Describe to the students the risks involved with making a wrong decision about global climate change. Ask the students to describe the economic and social impact of acting as if global climate change is occurring (when it is not)—diversion of money from other tasks to reducing greenhouse gas emissions, cost of energy conservation, economic dislocations from reducing greenhouse gas emissions and energy conservation, and so on. Ask the students to describe the economic and social impact of acting as if global climate change is not occurring (when it is)—impacts on global and local ecosystems, impacts on the ability to grow food or obtain resources (timber), impacts from increased energy usage (air conditioning?).

3. Society has limited dollars available to mitigate risks. This exercise combines risk perception with economic realities. Divide the students into groups of three to four. Provide each group with a list of a variety of environmental risks and ranking of those risks by experts and the public. For each of the risks assign a dollar figure for the mitigation of the risk. The number of lives saved or improved by the mitigation of the risk should also be provided. (Because actual data may not exist for each risk, you could provide reasonable estimates as long as the students know that you have not provided known values.) Also provide each group with limited

192

supply money to mitigate the risks. The students are to decide how to spend the money and justify the decisions they make using the expert-derived and perceived (theirs and the information provided of public risk perception) risks.

4. Each student is to list his or her daily activities (e.g., consuming nonorganic food, driving a car, riding a bicycle, using a computer, swimming, smoking, drinking, washing produce before eating, washing hands after using the toilet, etc.). Using death as an outcome, provide the students with a rank order list of the level of risk from various activities. For example, smoking is more hazardous than consuming nonorganic food, and not washing your hands after using the toilet is riskier than consuming nonorganic food. (There are several tables in the text that could help rank risks.) For the most risky behaviors, have each student, using the list of factors influencing risk perception; determine why he/she might perceive his/her risky behavior as not very risky.

5. Have each student collect examples from the newspaper or other sources of decisions that have been made using risk-based decisions making and the precautionary principle (better safe than sorry).

Suggested Lecture Format:

I. Links Between the Environment and Human Health
    A. Environmental Health—"Within the human environment, there are hazards that can make us sick, cut our lives short, or contribute in other ways to human misfortune. In the context of environmental health, a hazard is anything that can cause 1) injury, disease, or death to humans; 2) damage to personal or public property; or 3) deterioration or destruction of environmental components."
        1. The Picture of Health—"Unfortunately, measuring all these dimensions of health for a society is virtually impossible. Thus, to study environmental health, we will focus on disease and consider health to be simply the absence of disease."
        2. Public Health—"Each state also has a health department, and most municipalities have health agents. In addition, there is a huge health care industry in the United States, with federal programs such as Medicare and Medicaid, hospitals, health maintenance organization, and local physician and other health professionals."
            i. Other Countries"Virtually every country has a similar ministry of health that acts on behalf of its people to manage and minimize health risks."
            ii. Life Expectancy—"In 1955, average life expectancy globally was 48 years. Today it is 68 years and rising gradually."
            iii. Two Worlds—"The countries of the world have undergone the epidemiologic transition to different degrees, with very different consequences."

    B. Environmental Hazards—"There are two fundamental ways to consider hazards to human health. One is to regard the lack of access to necessary resources as a hazard." Another way is to focus on the exposure to hazards in the environment.
        1. Cultural Hazards—"Many of the factors that contribute to mortality and disability are a matter of choice or at least can be influenced by choice. People engage in risky behavior and subject themselves to hazards." See Figure 17-3.
        2. Biological Hazards—"Approximately one-fourth of global deaths are due to infectious and parasitic diseases." See Table 17-1.

        i.   Tuberculosis—"Although AIDS has overtaken tuberculosis as the disease that causes the most adult deaths, tuberculosis continues to be a major killer." See Figure 17-5.

          ii.   Malaria—"Of the infectious diseases present in the tropics, malaria is by far the most serious, accounting for an estimated 247 million cases each year and 881,000 deaths." See Figure 17-6.

    3. Physical Hazards—"Natural disasters—including hurricanes, tornadoes, floods, forest fires, earthquakes, landslides, and volcanic eruptions—take a toll of human life and property every year. They are the outcome of hydrological, meteorological, or geological forces." See Figure 17-7. See also Table 17-2.

        i.   Out of Nowhere—"Each year in the United States, 780 tornadoes strike on average, spawned from the severe weather accompanying thunderstorms. Because of the tendency for cold, dry air masses from the north to mix with warm, humid air from the Gulf of Mexico, the central United States generates more tornadoes than anywhere else on Earth." See Figure 17-7.

          ii.   In Harm's Way—Both the increasing human population and the effect of human behavior on the environment are the causes for the increased human death toll from natural disaster. **See Discussion Topic #4.**

    4. Chemical Hazards—"Industrialization has brought with it a host of technologies that employ chemicals such as cleaning agents, pesticides, fuels, paints, medicines, and those used directly in industrial processes." See Figure 17-8.

        i.   Carcinogens—"Some chemical hazards are known carcinogens (cancer-causing agents)." "It is frequently hard to connect the cause with the effect. The Eleventh Report on Carcinogens…lists 51 chemicals (and 3 biological agents) now known to be human carcinogens and 188 more that are 'reasonably anticipated to be human carcinogens' because of animal tests."

    5. Cancer—"A cancer is a cell line that has lost its normal control over growth. Recent research has revealed the presence of as many as three dozen genes that can bring about a malignant (out-of-control) cancer; these genes are like ticking time bombs that may or may not go off."

        i.   Carcinogenesis—"Carcinogenesis (the development of a cancer) is now known to be a process with several steps, often with long periods of time in between. In most cases, a sequence of five or more mutations must occur in order to initiate a cancer."

II. Pathways of Risk

    A. The Risks of Being Poor—"One major pathway for hazards is poverty. The WHO has stated that poverty is the world's biggest killer. Environmental risks are borne more often by the poor, not only in the developing countries, but also in the developed countries of the world." See Figure 17-9.

        1. Wealth—"Overall, the wealthier a country becomes, the healthier is its population. However, in virtually all countries, those with wealth are able to protect themselves from many environmental hazards. People in developed countries tend to live longer, and when they die, the chief causes of death are diseases of old age."

        2. Priorities—"Education, nutrition, and the general level of wealth in a society do not tell the whole story, however. A nation may make a deliberate policy choice to put its resources into

improving g the health of its population, rather than, say, militarization or the development of modern power sources."

B. The Cultural Risk of Tobacco Use—"One cultural hazard, tobacco use, is the leading cause of death in the United States." See Figure 17-11.
1. Marlboro Country?—"Smoking has been shown to be responsible for 29% of cancer deaths in the United States Because of this, several measures have been taken to regulate this cultural hazard." Such measures include: raising cigarette taxes, reported warnings about the dangers of smoking, banning advertising of smoking on TV, promoting smoke-free areas, and banning smoking on airplanes.
2. Secondhand Smoke—"In January 1992, the EPA classified environmental tobacco smoke, meaning secondhand smoke, as a Class A (known human) carcinogen…'widespread exposure to secondhand smoke in the United States presents a serious and substantial public health risk'."
3. Goodbye, Joe—"The FDA launched efforts to curb tobacco sales to the under-aged. One early casualty was 'Joe Camel', a cartoon character that seemed to be targeted at the young."
4. Legally Speaking—"On the legal front, there has been some success—and some failure" regarding smoking.
5. FCTC and MPOWER—The WHO "Framework Convention on Tobacco Control (FCTC) was adopted in May 2003 by the World Health Assembly. "The treaty has been adopted by 168 countries and is aimed at reducing cigarette smoking and exposure to secondhand smoke. MPOWER stands for:
   - Monitor tobacco use and prevention policies
   - Protect people from tobacco smoke
   - Offer help to quit tobacco use
   - Warn about the dangers of tobacco
   - Enforce bans on tobacco advertising, promotion, and sponsorship
   - Raise taxes on tobacco

C. Risk and Infectious Diseases—"Epidemiology has been described as 'medical ecology' because the epidemiologist traces a disease as it occurs in geographic locations as well as tracing the mode of transmission and consequences of the disease in the field."
1. Even Here?—Despite money and technological advances, wide-scale biological hazards, even outbreaks of diarrhea, can still happen in developed countries.
2. Tropical Diseases—"The tropics, where most of the developing countries are found, have climates ideally suited for the year-round spread of disease by insects. Mosquitoes are vectors for several deadly and debilitating diseases, such as yellow fever, dengue fever, elephantiasis, West Nile virus, and malaria."
3. Net Results—"One highly promising effort funded by the WHO's Tropical Disease Research Program found that children provided with insecticide-treated nets over their beds (bed nets) experienced a substantial reduction in mortality from all causes. See Figure 17-4.
4. Good News—"In 2002, molecular biologists successfully sequenced the genomes of the *Anopheles* mosquito and the most lethal malaria parasite, *P. falciparum.*

D. Toxic Risk Pathways—"How is it that people are exposed to chemical substances that can bring them harm? Airborne pollutants represent a particularly difficult set of chemical hazards to control, as they are difficult to measure and difficult to avoid."

    1. Indoor Air Pollution—"The air inside the home and workplace often contains much higher levels of hazardous pollutants than outdoor air does!" See Figure 17-15.

        i. Developing Countries—"The most serious indoor air pollution threat is found in the developing world, where at least 3 billion people continue to rely on biofuels like wood and animal dung for cooking and heat."

        ii. Asthma—"One common consequence of indoor air pollution is asthma, which is currently at epidemic proportions in the United States, afflicting 20 million people each year."

        iii. Worms, Anyone?—"Recent research has suggested that frequent parasitic worm infections stimulate a well-regulated anti-inflammatory network in the immune systems of most people in the developing countries, protecting them against many allergic diseases like asthma."

        iv. Toxicology—"Even though substances found in indoor air are hazardous, the link between their presence in the air and the development of a health problem is harder to establish than with infectious diseases."

E. Disaster Risk—"Much of the human death and misery brought on by natural hazards could be prevented through rigorous disaster risk reduction strategies."

III. Risk Assessment—"Risk assessment is the process of evaluating the risks associated with a particular hazard before taking some action in a situation in which the hazard is present." **See Discussion Topic #1**. See also Figure 17-6.

A. Risk Assessment by the EPA—"Risk assessment began at the EPA in the mid-1970s as a way of addressing the cancer risks associated with pesticides and toxic chemicals."

    1. Hazard Assessment: Is This Really a Hazard?—"Hazard assessment is the process of examining evidence linking a potential hazard to its harmful effects."

        i. Ask the Mice—"A test involving several hundred animals (usually mice) takes about three years and costs more than $250,000. If a significant number of the animals develop tumors after having been fed the substance being tested, then the substance is either a possible or probably human carcinogen."

        ii. Just Test People?—Humans have been paid to test products for potential carcinogenicity, but the ethical issues associated with this are obvious.

    2. Dose-Response and Exposure Assessment: How Much for How Long?—"When animal tests or human studies show a link between exposure to a chemical and an ill effect, the next step is to analyze the relationship between the concentrations of the chemical in the test (the dose) and both the incidence and the severity of the response."

    3. Risk Characterization: What Does the Science Say?—It pulls "together all the information gathered in the first three steps in order to determine the risk and it accompanying uncertainties."

196

B. Public-Health Risk Assessment—The following criteria are used for risk assessment: potential global impact, high likelihood of causality, modifiability, and availability of data.
   1. The DALY—The disability-adjusted life year "represents the loss of one healthy year of a person's life." See Table 17-4.

C. Risk Management —"Risk management naturally follows (environmental risk assessment by the scientific community) and is the responsibility of lawmakers and administrators."

D. Risk Perception—People perceive more risk than ever, despite the fact that we are safer than ever. "The answer lies in people's risk perceptions—their intuitive judgments about risks."
   1. Hazard Versus Outrage—Peter Sandman asserts that perception of risk is "more of a matter of outrage than of a hazard."
      i. Media's Role—"The public perception of risk is strongly influenced by the media, which are far better at communicating the outrage elements of a risk than they are at communicating the hazard elements."
      ii. Public Concern and Public Policy—"Generally speaking, public concern, rather than cost-benefit analysis or risk–benefit analysis conducted by scientists, often drives public policy."

E. The Precautionary Principle—"There is a strong movement toward employing the precautionary principle in formulating public policy to protect the environment and human health." **See Discussion Topic #2 and Discussion Topic #5.**
   1. Stewards of Health—Governments and health care providers are "stewards whose responsibility is vitally important to environmental health." **See Discussion Topic #3**.

Review Questions: Possible Answers

1. Define pollution, pollutant, nonbiodegradable, and environment.
   Pollution is "the presence of a substance in the environment that, because of its chemical composition or quantity, prevents the functioning of natural processes and produced undesirable environmental and health effects." A **pollutant** is "any material that causes the pollution." If a substance is non-biodegradable it means that is "resists the attack and breakdown by detritus feeders and decomposers and consequently accumulates in the environment." Finally, the environment is "the whole context of human life—the physical, chemical, and biological setting of where and how people live."

2. Differentiate between a hazard and a risk. Where does vulnerability fit in?
   Hazard is anything that can cause "(1) injury, disease, or death to humans, (2) damage to personal or public property, or (3) deterioration or destruction of the environmental components. The existence of a hazard does not mean that undesirable consequences inevitably follow. Instead, we speak of the connection between a hazard and something happening because of that hazard as a **risk**, defined here as the probability of suffering injury, disease, death, or some other loss as a result of exposure to the hazard." Some people are more prone to being exposed to hazards because of the environment and cultural situation that they find themselves in. This is vulnerability. Risk=Hazard x Vulnerability.

3. Define morbidity, mortality, and epidemiology.

"**Morbidity** is the incidence of disease in a population and is commonly used to trace the presence of a particular type of illness, such as influenza or diarrheal disease. **Mortality** is the incidence of death in a population. **Epidemiology** is the study of the presence, distribution, and control of disease in populations."

4. *Describe the public health roles of the CDC and the WHO.*

The Centers for Disease Control (CDC) is "the lead federal agency (in the United states) for protecting the health and safety of the public. The primary responsibility for health risk management and prevention resides with the CDC and the state public health agencies. These agencies, for example, may require public-health measures such as immunizations and quarantines, and they are responsible for monitoring certain diseases and environmental hazards and for controlling epidemics. They also gather data and provide information on health issues to state and local health care providers."

WHO is the equivalent of the CDC at the international level. It will provide information and assistance to nations around the world in the area of immunization and monitoring diseases and epidemics. WHO is part of the United Nations and "is staffed by health professionals and other experts and is governed by the U.N. member states through the World Health Assembly."

5. *What are the four categories of human environmental hazards? Give examples of each.*

Cultural hazards—smoking obesity, alcohol and drug use, risky sexual practices, too little exercise, hazardous occupations, sunbathing, driving too fast. **Biological hazards**—diseases caused by bacteria, viruses, protozoans, fungi, worms, etc. **Physical hazards**—hurricanes, tornadoes, floods, forest fires, earthquakes, landslides, volcanic eruptions, climate change. **Chemical hazards**—chemicals that cause acute, subacute, chronic, or delayed responses in humans, carcinogens, teratogens, immunotoxins, hormonally active agents.

6. *List the top 10 risk factors that are responsible for global mortality and disease.*
   1) Underweight
   2) Unsafe sex
   3) Blood pressure
   4) Tobacco
   5) Alcohol
   6) Unsafe water, sanitation, and hygiene
   7) Cholesterol
   8) Indoor smoke from solid fuels
   9) Iron deficiency
   10) Overweight

7. *Document the efforts to control tobacco use both in the United States and globally.*

Tobacco is the leading cause of death in the United States and the fourth leading cause of death in the world. In the United States, "several measures have been taken to regulate (smoking). Tobacco products are highly taxed, for example, providing states with substantial revenues ($11.5 billion in 2003). Raising cigarette taxes has been shown to be one of the most effective ways to reduce smoking, especially in young people. Surgeons General of the United States have issued repeated warnings against smoking since 1964, and public policy has taken them seriously by requiring warning labels on smoking materials, banning cigarette advertising on television, promoting smoke-free workplaces, requiring nonsmokers' areas in restaurants, and banning smoking on all domestic airline flights. Since the warning began, the U.S. adult smoking population has gradually dropped from 42% to 21%. In January 1993, the EPA classified environmental tobacco smoke (ETS, meaning secondhand, or side-stream, smoke), as a Class A (known human) carcinogen."

"The battle against smoking is rapidly spreading worldwide. After years of efforts, the WHO Framework Convention on Tobacco Control (FCTC) was adopted in May 2003 by the World Health Assembly. This convention is a treaty that would reduce the spread of smoking by requiring signatory countries to raise taxes, restrict advertising, require larger health warnings on tobacco materials, and reduce ETS (steps already taken in

198

the United States). The treaty went into effect on February 27, 2005, and has been signed by 168 countries. Many countries have already taken action called for in the treaty: Ireland, Spain, Norway, and Italy have banned smoking in indoor public places, and other countries have begun banning advertising and printing warnings on cigarette packages."

8. *What is the significance of malaria worldwide, and what are some recent developments in the battle against this disease?*

In 2002, malaria is estimated to have caused 1,222,000 deaths (Table 15-1). "Of all the infectious diseases present in the tropics, malaria is by far the most serious, accounting for an estimated 300-500 million cases each year and more than a million deaths. Public health attempts to control malaria have been aimed at eradicating the anopheles mosquito with the use of insecticides. Malaria was once prevalent in the southern United States (including Philadelphia), but an aggressive campaign to eliminate anopheles mosquitoes and identify and treat all human cases of malaria in the 1950s led to the complete eradication of the disease there. Unfortunately, in the tropics, the mosquitoes have developed resistance to all of the pesticides employed and eradication has remained an elusive goal. DDT is still used in some developing countries to spray the walls of huts and houses, but its use in this manner is highly controversial because of the pesticide's well-known harmful environmental and health impacts. However, the spraying has proven to be highly effective. Resuming their use of DDT after several years with another pesticide, South Africa and Zambia were able to dramatically reduce their malaria caseloads. In 2002, molecular biologists successfully sequenced the genomes of the *Anopheles* mosquito and the most lethal malaria parasite, *P. falciparium*. Armed with this information, researchers are now able to target potential weak points in both organisms in the search for new vaccines and drugs. One highly promising effort funded by WHO's Tropical Disease Research program found that children provided with insecticide-treated nets over their beds experienced a substantial reduction in mortality from all causes. Elsewhere, WHO has documented increases in the incidence of malaria in association with land-use changes such as deforestation, irrigation, and the creation of dams. Research continues on the development of new, more effective antimalarial drugs and on the development of an effective vaccine. Recently, WHO initiated the 'Roll Back Malaria' campaign, designed not to eradicate the disease but to reduce the malaria-caused morality by half by 2010 and then to halve mortality again by 2015. The emphasis of this program is on getting research findings into policy and practice."

9. *Outline the four steps of risk assessment used by the EPA.*

The four steps are (1) hazard assessment, (2) dose-response, (3) exposure assessment, and (4) risk characterization. "Hazard assessment is the process of examining evidence linking a potential hazard to its harmful effects." Dose-response is "to analyze the relationship between the concentrations of chemicals in the test (the dose) and both the incidence and severity of the response." Exposure assessment "involves identifying human groups already exposed to the chemical, learning how their exposure came about, and calculating the doses and length of time of their exposure. The final step, risk characterization, is to pull together all the information gathered in the first three steps in order to determine the risk and its accompanying uncertainties.

10. *What methods are used to test chemicals for their potential to cause cancer?*

"We do not want to wait 20 years to find out that a new food additive causes cancer, so we turn to animal testing to find out now what might happen in the future. A test involving several hundred animals (usually mice) takes about 3 years and costs more than $250,000. If a significant number of the animals develop tumors after having been feed the substance being tested, then the substance is either a possible or probably human carcinogen, depending on the strength of the results. Although there are obvious differences between rodents and humans, all chemicals shown by epidemiological studies to be human carcinogens are also carcinogenic to

199

test animals, suggestion that animal tests have some predictive value for humans. In the past, chemical manufacturers that were interested in assessing the safety of pesticides (in order to have their products approved for use) paid human subjects to test the products. Such tests are far less expensive than the usual animal testing. (Volunteers may be paid only a few hundred dollars; mice apparently charge much higher fees!) A National Academy of Sciences panel addressed this topic in 1998, stating that the use of human volunteers 'to facilitate the interests of industry or of agriculture' is unjustifiable. The EPA agreed and banned any use of such tests. However, recently the Bush administration, responding to requests from manufacturers, has pressed the EPA to reevaluate its policy and allow human testing. A new rule from EPA forbids such testing on children and pregnant women (but allows it for others), satisfying the pesticide manufacturers. Another source of information is the chemical process itself: What are its physical and chemical properties, and what mode of action might the chemical process take in inducing cancer. Hazard assessment takes a 'weight-of-evidence' approach to determining the carcinogenic potential of a chemical of process. Standard descriptors are used in its conclusions, such as 'likely to be carcinogenic to humans.' In the end hazard assessment tells us that we may be a problem."

11. *Describe the process of risk assessment for public health as it was recently carried out by WHO. What is a DALY?*

WHO recently moved risk assessment from being a "function of environmental regulation" to "looking at all of the risk factors commonly known to be responsible for poor health and mortality and then asking the question, 'Of all the disease burden in this population, how much could be caused by this (particular) risk?' Certain risk factors were chosen for special attention, on the basis of the following criteria: potential global impact, high likelihood of causality, modifiability, and availability of data."

A DALY is "the disability adjusted life year. (O)ne DALY represents the loss of one healthy year of a person's life. This measure, now in common usage in the global health community, assess the burden of disease in terms of life lost due to premature mortality and time lived with a disability."

12. *Discuss the relationship between public risk perception and assessment, on the one hand, and public policy, on the other.*

"Generally speaking, public concern, rather than cost-benefit analysis or risk analysis conducted by scientists, drives public policy. The EPA's funding priorities are set largely by Congress, which reflects public concern. If public outrage is the primary impetus for public policy, some serious risks may get less attention than they deserve. In particular, risks to the environment are commonly perceived as much less important than they really are, because of the public's preoccupation with risks to human health."

13. *What is the precautionary principle, and how would employing the principle improve our approach to environmental public policy?*

The precautionary principle states, "Where an activity raises threats of harm to human health or the environment, precautionary measures should be taken even if some cause-and-effect relationships are not fully established scientifically. In this context, the proponent of an activity, rather than the public, should bear the burden of proof."

"The precautionary principle represents a potent tool for implementing stewardship in the environmental health arena. Although risk assessment is useful in many situations, it should not be used as a blanket policy. The precautionary principle enables us to act to prevent some potential environmental health problems, even at the risk of being wrong or at the risk of spending more than a problem technically deserves. The old saying, 'An ounce or prevention is worth a pound of cure' captures the sense of this approach. Where uncertainty is substantial and especially where the penalty for being wrong is great, it would seem wise to make the precautionary principle a guiding principle overseeing the entire risk assessment process."

Thinking Environmentally: Possible Answers

1. *Consider Table 17-4. Discuss each group's risk factors that are primarily a consequence of human choice. Pick one of these factors, and describe how you might proceed to bring it under control in an appropriate country.*

    The risk factors that are primarily someone's choice are unsafe sex; alcohol, drug, and tobacco use; blood pressure (parts); and cholesterol (parts); overweight; low fruit and vegetable intake (in most situations in developed countries); and physical inactivity.

    How a risk factor under the control of an individual can be reduced is very dependent upon cultural factors. For example, the reason a person might quit smoking will differ as a result of their cultural background. This was used by the Department of Health in California when they implemented the smoking cessation advertising campaign. In the Asian community of California it was very effective to emphasis the impact of the smoker's death on his family. (In the Asian community men are the primary smokers.)

    It is very important to know how a risk is perceived when designing a campaign to convince people to reduce their risks. Telling smokers about the health risks does not work. Smokers know the risks but the benefits obtained from smoking outweigh the health risks. The benefits from not being prepared for safe sex outweigh the risks; this is what needs to be addressed. The benefits from eating more calories today than are necessary to maintain our ideal weight outweigh the risks in the future that the excess calories will cause. Therefore, emphasizing the future benefits will not keep the person from overeating. The benefit must be one gained today.

2. *What global accountability is there for natural disaster relief? Consider the example of devastating weather in developing countries triggered by climate change (which could be instigated by the more prosperous).*

    Despite the fact that devastating weather seems to be linked to climate change and other environmental impacts of affluence, global accountability for natural disaster relief is limited and difficult to maintain.

3. *Suppose your town wanted to spray trees to rid them of a deadly pest. How would you use cost-benefit analysis to determine whether spraying is a good idea? Is there a better approach?*

    Cost-benefit analysis would compare all the costs to the program and all the benefits to the program. The benefits would include the number of people who are at risk of contracting the deadly disease, the number of years of life lost, the number of years of disability suffered, the loss of work productivity, the health care savings, and so on. The costs would include the financial costs to the program, the people who will become sick or die because of the spraying program, injuries (falling) from the spraying program, and so on. The problem with a cost-benefit analysis is that intangibles are not included. Ecological costs are left out, for example.

    A question to ask would be, what are other ways to reduce the number of deadly pests? What habitat and niche does the pest use? Can these be modified to eliminate the pest without causing other problems? Could some type of Integrated Pest Management Program be implemented?

4. *Consult the CDC web site (www.cdc.gov) and investigate one of the emerging infectious diseases. What risks do you take and what precautions should you take if traveling to an area where the disease has been found?*

    Not all the diseases listed by the CDC have information about precautions. Some of the diseases (*) have been added to the list because of bioterrorism potential. Below is a list of the CDC listed emerging or re-emerging diseases. Risk and precaution information has been included for some.

    - Drug-resistant infections (antimicrobial resistance)
    - Bovine spongiform encephalopathy (Mad Cow) and variant Creutzfeldt-Jakob disease (vCJD)—unclear what the risk is; avoid eating beef or beef products from a country with indigenous cases

201

- Campylobacteriosis
- Chagas disease—low risk; spray infested houses; insecticide-impregnated bed nets may reduce risk for travelers who cannot avoid camping or sleeping outdoors in poorly constructed houses in endemic areas
- Cholera*—low risk; mainly a risk if drinking contaminated water or eating poorly cooked or raw seafood in disease-endemic areas
- Cyrptococcosis
- Cryptosporidiosis (Crypto)
- Cylcosporiasis
- Cysticercosis—low risk; do not eat raw or undercooked port; wash hands, wash and peel all raw vegetables and fruit before eating; drink only bottled or boiled water
- Dengue fever
- Diptheria
- Ebola hemorrhagic fever—low risk; most often in rural areas of developing countries; found in Africa; reservoir host is unknown; avoid locations where an outbreak is occurring
- *Escherichia coli* infection
- Group B streptococcal infection
- Hantavirus pulmonary syndrome*—rare; rodent control is best prevention
- Hepatitis C
- Hendra virus infection
- Histoplasmosis—fungus is common in central and eastern U.S.; avoid areas with bird or bat droppings because this is where fungus grows
- HIV/AIDS
- Influenza
- Lassa fever*—low risk; Western Africa; exposure to infected rodents in most likely source of human infection
- Legionnaires' disease (legionellosis) and Pontiac fever
- Leptospirosis—"Travelers participating in recreational water activities, such as whitewater rafting, adventure racing, or kayaking, in areas where leptospirosis is endemic or epidemic could be at increased risk for the disease, particularly during periods of flooding." Avoid contact with contaminated water.
- Listeriosis—medium risk; thoroughly cook raw food from animals sources, wash raw vegetable thoroughly before eating, keep uncooked meats separate from vegetables and from cooked foods and ready-to-eat foods; avoid unpasteurized milk or foods made from unpasteurized milk, wash hands, knives, and cutting boards after handling uncooked food. Consume perishable and ready-to-eat food as soon as possible.
- Lyme disease
- Malaria
- Marburg hemorrhagic fever*—low risk; found in Africa but precise geographic range is unknown; reservoir host is unknown; avoid locations where an outbreak is occurring;
- Measles
- Meningitis
- Monkey pox
- MRSA (Methicillin Resistant *Staphylococcus aureus*)
- Nipah virus infection*
- Norovirus (formerly Norwalk virus) infection
- Pertussis

- Plague*—endemic in rodent populations in rural areas of Americas, Africa and Asia; risk is small; use DEET, avoid sick or dead animals or rodent nests and burrows, avoid visiting areas where recent plague epidemics or epizootics have occurred; bring antibiotic with you
- Polio (poliomyelitis)—should be fully immunized if going to country where polio still occurs
- Rabies—usually low risk but not if camping in rabies endemic countries, can be vaccinated
- Rift Valley fever—low risk; occurs primarily on the continent of Africa and into the Middle East; precautions include using insect repellent on exposed skin surfaces when outdoors, particularly during the day; Wear long-sleeved shirts and long pants when outdoors; when possible, stay in hotels or resorts that are well screened or air-conditioned and take measures to reduce and exclude mosquitoes; Use of bed nets is recommended if mosquito-proof accommodations are not available.
- Rotavirus infection—fairly common, usually not fatal in immune competent individuals; vaccination is possible
- Salmonellosis*
- SAR (Severe acute respiratory syndrome)
- Shigellosis*—fairly common infections; wash hands frequently; drink treated or boiled water only, eat only cooked vegetables and fruit or fruits that you peel yourself
- Smallpox*
- Sleeping sickness (Trypanosomiasis)
- Tuberculosis
- Tularemia*—occurs in the U.S., use insect repellent (ticks vector); cook food thoroughly; make sure water is from safe source
- Valley fever (coccidioimycosis)
- VISA/VRSA—Vancomycin-Intermediate/Resistant *Staphylococcus aureus*)
- West Nile virus infection
- Yellow fever—rarely causes illness in travelers; found primarily in South America and West and Central Africa during rainy season, vaccination is recommended; prevent exposure to mosquitoes, use DEET; wear long-sleeved shirts and long pants

CHAPTER 18
Global Climate Change

Chapter Outline:

I. Atmosphere, Weather, and Climate
    A. Weather
        1. Flowing Air
        2. Convection
        3. Jet Streams
        4. Put Together…
II. Climate Change Science
    A. Synopsis of Global Climate Change
        1. IPCC
            i. Third Assessment
            ii. A Nobel Effort
    B. Climates in the Past
        1. Further Back
            i. Rapid Changes
    C. Ocean and Atmosphere
        1. Thermohaline Circulation
            i. Abrupt Change
        2. What if…?
        3. Ocean-Atmosphere Oscillations
    D. The Earth as a Greenhouse
        1. Warming Processes
            i. Greenhouse Gases
        2. Cooling Processes
            i. Volcanoes
            ii. Aerosols
            iii. Solar Variability
        3. Thus…
    E. Evidence of Climate Change
        1. Satellites
        2. Ocean Warming
        3. Other Observed Changes
    F. Rising Greenhouse Gases
        1. Carbon Dioxide
            i. Carbon Dioxide Monitoring
            ii. Sources
            iii. Sinks
        2. Other Gases
            i. Water Vapor
            ii. Methane

Key Topics:

1. Atmosphere, Weather, and Climate
2. Climate Change Science
3. Response to Climate Change

Instructional Goals:

1. Few scientific questions have been answered sufficiently well enough so that no controversy exists. One must evaluate the evidence and make decisions using the preponderance of evidence.

2. Weather and climate are chaos-driven phenomenon. It is difficult to predict the impact of various changes in the factors affecting climate when small differences in initial conditions can result in large differences in

conditions later in time. Additionally, we don't know all the factors that influence climate and we don't know how each of the factors influences the other factors.

3. Gases in the troposphere act to keep heat from leaving the planet. Theory predicts that if the quantity of these gases in the atmosphere increases, the quantity of heat leaving the planet will decline. If global warming occurs, then both regional climatic changes and a rise in sea level are expected.

4. The scientific consensus is that the increase in temperatures observed over the last 50 years is part of a global warming trend.

Concepts and Connections:

Global climate is an interesting topic because it impacts the whole planet. What people in one country do (produce greenhouse gases for example) is predicted to impact the lives of people in a distant country. These two topics are also interesting because they are uncontrolled experiments. The risk and consequences of making an incorrect decision, or acting when we don't need to, or not acting when we should, are great.

Because we understand so little about climate and weather, our ability to understand climate-related data is limited. Theory tells us increasing the quantity of greenhouse gases (including water vapor in the form of clouds) would decrease the amount of heat leaving the troposphere. Theory also tells us that increasing the amount of cloud cover (planetary albedo) would increase the amount of solar radiation reflected to space. (The amount of solar radiation available on the surface of the planet would be reduced.) How all the factors interrelate to create climate and weather is unknown. All human activity is dependent upon climate. Our ability to grow food, the kinds of homes we build, the clothing we wear, and our daily comfort are dependent upon day-to-day weather and the overall climate of an area. Changing the overall climate of an area can have severe economic consequences.

Concepts in Context:

All issues concerning ecosystem function and sustainability (Chapters 3, 4, and 5) can be related to global climate change. Limiting factors, biogeochemical cycles, food webs, niches, habitats, and succession can be discussed in the context of global climate change. Evolution (Chapter 5) is influenced by changes in climate and rates of DNA mutation are influence by UV radiation levels. Rates of decomposition by decomposers (Chapter 3) will be influenced by climate and thus soil fertility (Chapter 11) will be affected. Because climate is influenced by and climate change influences the water cycle (Chapter 10), a discussion of these complexities is important.

Climate is an environmental resistance factor (Chapter 5) for human population size (Chapter 8). Climate change would influence food production (Chapter 12) and pest balance (Chapter 13). The kinds of food we choose to produce, (e.g., cattle), can influence the quantity of greenhouse gases produced. The goods and services we obtain from ecosystems (Chapter 7) would be adversely influenced by global climate change. The kinds of energy (Chapters 14, 15, and 16) we select influences levels of greenhouse gases. The way we dispose of our wastes, both sewage (Chapter 20) and trash (Chapter 21), influences the quantities of methane, a greenhouse gas, produced. Changes in climate can influence the quantity of disease-causing organisms in addition to influencing nutritional factors necessary for good health.

Our choices about how we live (Chapter 23) influence our ability to live sustainably. The economic choices (Chapter 2) made individually, as countries and as a world community, influence all aspects of the living world. Global climate change is an ideal example of this interconnectedness.

Key Terms and Vocabulary:

Troposphere, tropopause, stratosphere, weather, climate, meteorology, convection currents, jet streams, monsoons, climate, mitigation, adaptation, risk assessment, risk management, proxies, isotopes, Milankovitch cycles, conveyor, radiative forcing, greenhouse gases, planetary albedo, ocean acidification, positive feedback, equilibrium climate sensitivity, United Synthesis Product, adaptation, mitigation, precautionary principle, polluter pays principle, equity principle, Framework Convention on Climate Change (FCCC), Global Climate Change Initiative (GCCI), emissions intensity, Climate Change Science Program (CCSP), cap-and-trade program, adaptation, Least Developed Countries Fund, Special Climate Change Fund, Adaptation Fund, Climate Investment Funds

Discussion, Activities, and Labs:

1. Most students have a poor understanding of the atmosphere, which inhibits their understanding of global climate change. A discussion of what they know can help them eliminate misconceptions and build a correct understanding of the atmosphere. Ask the students what they think is in the atmosphere as you move farther from Earth. Ask them to explain their answers. (Discuss the chemical content of the troposphere and how greenhouse gases prevent reradiated heat from leaving the atmosphere. Discuss the chemical content of the stratosphere and the dynamic balance between molecular oxygen and ozone.)

2. Discuss the consequences of assuming that global warming is not happening, when it is, and the consequences of assuming that global warming is happening, when it is not. Which of these assumptions is closest to the Precautionary Principle? Which is closest to risk-based decision making? Help students to see that our assumptions about the consequences of making a wrong decision will influence which decision we favor. (A utility company is likely to favor assuming that global warming is not happening when it is because of the economic consequences of reducing greenhouse gas emissions).

3. Discuss the types of changes that could be implemented to reduce carbon emissions. Discuss which options would be the most effective. Which options would be the most disruptive to our current way of life? Rank the options from most to least desirable. Now consider the positive changes, beyond reducing carbon emissions, might occur as a result of the changes that will need to be made to reduce carbon emissions? Does this change the ranking?

4. Many students do not know that ice floating in the ocean will occupy approximately the same volume of water when it melts and that ice on land will increase the volume of water in the ocean when it melts and flows into the water. At the beginning of the class period, divide the class into groups of two to three students. Provide each group a beaker filled with ice, a beaker filled with water, and an empty beaker and tall marble column. (Anything with a flat surface that can be placed in a water-filled beaker without it floating will work. The top of the flat surface needs to be above the water line.) Place the marble column in the beaker and stack on the column as many pieces of ice that can fit without sliding off. Fill the ice filled beaker with water to its brim. The beaker containing the marble column should be filled no more than an inch from the top of the column. The level of water in the column-containing beaker should be marked. Each group of students writes a

207

© 2011 Pearson Education, Inc.

hypothesis concerning what they believe will occur to the water level as the ice in each beaker melts. At the end of the class, have the each group assess what has happened to the water from the melted ice cubes. Have each group discuss why the water behaved as it did. As a class discuss the results.

Suggested Lecture Format:

I.   Atmosphere, Weather, and Climate-**See Discussion Topic #1.**

A. Weather-"The day-to-day variations in temperature, air pressure, wind, humidity, and precipitation-all mediated by the atmosphere-constitute our weather. Climate is the result of long-term weather patterns in a region." See Figure 18-2. See also Table 18-1.

1. Flowing Air—"Some of the energy that is released from Earth's surface is transferred to the atmosphere."

2. Convection—"On a smaller scale, convection currents bring us the day-to-day changes in our weather as they move in a general pattern from west to east." See Figure 18-4.

3. Jet Streams—"Higher in the troposphere, Earth's rotation and air-pressure gradients generate veritable rivers of air, called jet streams, that flow eastward at speeds of more than 300 mph and that meander considerably."

4. Put Together… "Taking the general atmospheric circulation patterns and the resulting precipitation, then adding the wind and weather systems generating them, and finally mixing all this with the rotation of Earth and the tilt of the planet on its axis, which creates seasons-yields the general patterns of weather that characterize different regions of the world."

II. Climate Change Science

A. Synopsis of Global Climate Change—"In 2007, after sifting through thousands of studies about global warming, scientists from the IPCC published the Fourth Assessment Report (AR4) on climate change. They concluded that warming of the climate system is unequivocal." See Figures 18-5 and 18-6.

1. IPCC—The latest IPCC (Intergovernmental Panel on Climate Change) assessment working groups consist of more than 2,000 experts in the appropriate fields from 154 countries. These experts are unpaid and participate at the cost of their own research and other professional activities."

i.   Third Assessment—"In 2001, the IPCC released its Third Assessment Report." See page 455 for a summary of their results.

ii. A Nobel Effort—"In an unexpected move, the Nobel Committee awarded the 2007 Nobel Peace Prize to the IPCC and to former Vice President Al Gore for 'their efforts to build up and disseminate greater knowledge about man-made climate change, and to lay the foundation for the measures that are needed to counteract such change.'"

B. Climates in the Past—Since 1880, global average temperature has shown periods of cooling and warming, but since 1976, it has increased .6°C (1.1°F)." See Figure 18-5.

208

1. Further Back—Observation on climatic changes can be extended much further back in time with the use of proxies-measureable records that can provide data on factors such as temperature, ice cover, and precipitation. "The record based on these analyses indicated that Earth's climate has oscillated between ice ages and warm periods." See Figure 18-7a. "The most likely explanation for these major oscillations is the existence of known variation in Earth's orbit, where, in different modes of orbital configuration, the distribution of solar radiation over different continents and latitudes varies substantially."

   i. Rapid Changes—"Superimposed on the major oscillations is a record of rapid climatic fluctuations during periods of glaciations and warmer times. One such rapid change, called the *Younger Dryas* occurred toward the end of the last ice age." See Figure 18-7b.

C. Ocean and Atmosphere—"The oceans are the major source of water for the hydrologic cycle and the main source of heat entering the atmosphere."

   1. Thermohaline Circulation—"A thermohaline circulation pattern dominates oceanic currents, where thermohaline refers to the effects that temperature and salinity have on the density of seawater. This pattern, or conveyor system acts as a giant, complex conveyor belt, moving water masses from the surface to deep oceans and back again." See Figure 18-8.

      i. Abrupt Change—"North Atlantic marine sediments show evidence of the periodic invasion of ice bergs from the polar ice cap, which supplied huge amounts of fresh water as they melted."

   2. What if…?—"Among the likely consequences of extended global warming are increased precipitation over the North Atlantic and more melting of sea ice and ice caps. If such a pattern is sustained, it could lead to a weakening in the normal operation of the conveyor and a change in climate, especially in the northern latitudes."

   3. Ocean-Atmosphere Oscillations—"Regional climates are notoriously erratic on time scales from a few days to decades."

D. The Earth as a Greenhouse—"Factors that influence the climate include interactive internal components (oceans, the atmosphere, snow cover, sea ice, and external factors, solar radiation, the Earth's rotation, slow changes in our planet's orbit, and the gaseous makeup of the atmosphere)." See Figure 18-10. **See also Discussion Topic #3.**

   1. Warming Processes—The Earth's atmosphere works much like a car sitting in the sun with its windows down. When the sunlight comes in, it gets converted to heat energy and cannot escape back out through the windows of the car.

      i. Greenhouse Gases—"On a global scale, water vapor, CO_2, and other gases in the atmosphere play a role analogous to that of the glass in a greenhouse. Therefore, they are called greenhouse gases (GHGs)."

   2. Cooling Processes—"Sunlight reflected in this way (by clouds, snow, and ice) is called the planetary albedo, and it contributes to overall cooling by preventing a certain amount of warming in the first place."

      i. Volcanoes—"When Mount Pinatubo in the Philippines erupted in 1991, some 20 million tons of particles and aerosols entered the atmosphere and contributed to a significant drop in global temperature as radiation was reflected and scattered away."

209

ii. Aerosols—"Climatologists have found that industrial aerosols (from ground-level pollution) play a significant role in canceling out some of the warming from GHGs. Sulfates, nitrates, dust, and soot from industrial sources and forest fires enter the atmosphere and react with compounds there to form high-level aerosol haze." See Figure 18-10.

iii. Solar Variability—"Since the Sun is the source of radiant energy that heats the Earth, any variability in the Sun's radiation reaching the Earth will likely influence the climate."

3. Thus… "Global atmospheric temperatures are a balance between the positive and negative forcing from natural causes (volcanoes, clouds, natural GHGs, solar irradiance) and anthropogenic causes (sulfate aerosols, soot, ozone, increases in GHGs)."

E. Evidence of Climate Change—"The warming is happening everywhere, but is especially rapid at high latitudes in the Northern Hemisphere. Because of the continued increases in anthropogenic GHGs in the atmosphere, the observed warming is considered to be a consequence of an 'enhanced greenhouse effect'". **See Discussion Topic #2.**

1. Satellites—For a time, a discrepancy appeared to exist between satellite recorded temperatures of the troposphere and measured temperatures on the surface of the Earth. The CCSP study found that "no discrepancy exists because of errors in the satellite. Data have been identified and corrected."

2. Ocean Warming—"The long-term consequence is the impact of this stored heat as it eventually comes into equilibrium with the atmosphere, raising temperature over land and in the atmosphere even more. The immediate consequence is the rise in sea level that occurs because of thermal expansion."

3. Other Observed Changes—These changes include: Increases in warm temperature extremes, increased drought, shrinkage of Arctic Sea ice, melting of the Greenland Ice Sheet, rising temperatures in Antarctica, retreating glaciers, changing patterns of precipitation, more intense hurricanes, acidification of oceans as they absorb carbon dioxide, and the movement of fish towards the northern seas.

F. Rising Greenhouse Gases—"According to the IPCC AR4 Synthesis Report: 'Global GHG emissions due to human activities have grown since pre-industrial times, with an increase of 70% between 1970 and 2004." The most important of these gases is carbon dioxide."

1. Carbon Dioxide—"More than 100 years ago, Swedish scientist Svante Arhenius reasoned that differences in CO_2 levels in the atmosphere could greatly affect Earth's energy budget."

i. Carbon Dioxide Monitoring—"In 1958, Charles Keeling began measuring CO_2 levels on Mauna Loa, in Hawaii. Measurements there have been recorded continuously, and they reveal a striking increase in atmospheric levels of the gas. See Figure 18-6.

ii. Sources—"As Arhenius suggested, the obvious place to look for the source of increasing CO_2 levels is our use of fossil fuels." See Figure 18-5 and Figure 18-6.

iii. Sinks—Oceans and terrestrial ecosystems serve as 'carbon sinks'.

2. Other Gases—"Water vapor, methane, nitrous oxide, ozone, and chlorofluorocarbons CFCs) also absorb infrared radiation and add to the insulating effect of CO_2. Most of these gases have anthropogenic sources and are increasing in concentration." See Table 18-2.

    i.   Water Vapor—"Water vapor absorbs infrared energy and is the most abundant GHG. Although it plays an important role in the greenhouse effect, its concentration in the troposphere is quite variable."

    ii.   Methane—"Methane, the third-most important GHG, is 20 times more effective a GHG than is CO_2 molecule for molecule.

    iii.   Nitrous Oxide—"Nitrous oxide levels have increased some 18% during the last 200 years and are still rising at a rate of .8 ppb per year."

    iv.   Ozone-"Although ozone in the troposphere is short lived and varies at many locations, it is a potent GHG."

    3.   CFCs and Other Halocarbons—Anthropogenic halocarbons are long lived and destructive.

G.   Future Changes in Climate—"If global fossil fuel use continues on its present trajectory, emissions of GHGs will increase 35% by 2030. By 2050, this grows to over 100%." **See Discussion Topic #4.**

    1.   Modeling Global Climate—"Modeling climate is an essential strategy for exploring the potential future impacts of rising GHGs." See Figure 18-19.

       i.   Running the Models-"Every scenario employed in the models generates a rise in CO2 concentrations and a corresponding rise in mean global temperature." See Figure 18-20.

       ii.   Projections-"The amount of rise (in temperature) depending on energy choices and other factors, such a population growth." Rising global temperatures are linked to two major impacts: regional climatic changes and a rise in sea level."

       iii.   Sea Level-"There is great uncertainty about the magnitude of the rise in sea level. A half-meter rise in sea level will flood many coastal areas and make them much more prone to damage from storms, forcing people to abandon properties and migrate inland." "Once atmospheric GHG levels are stabilized, temperatures and sea levels will continue to rise for hundreds of years because of the slow response time of the oceans."

       iv.   What About the Antarctic?-"The Greenland and Antarctic Ice Sheets hold enough water to raise lea level by 230 feet (70 m)."

H.   Climate Change Impacts in the United States—"In 2002, the Bush administration launched the Climate Change Science Program (CCSP-now called the Global Change Research Program, or GCRP) to integrate the efforts of many federal agencies involved in the scientific effort to understand global climate change."

    1.   National Climate Change—"Most of the global impacts of climate change…have been observed in the United States." See Figure 18-22.

III. Response to Climate Change

    1.   Ethical Principles—Three basic principles indicate why we should respond to global warming: the precautionary principle, the polluter pays principle, and the equity principle.

A.   Mitigation—"It will be costly to take the actions needed to mitigate the causes of climate change and to adapt to changes that are unavoidable. But the costs of inaction will be far higher."

    1.   Achieving Stabilization—-"The states objective of the Framework Convention on Climate Change (FCCC) is to stabilize the GHG content of the atmosphere at levels and on a time

scale that would prevent dangerous anthropogenic interference with the climate system." See Figure 18-23 and Table 18-3.

    2. What Has Been Done?—The Framework Convention on Climate Change (FCCC) "agreed to the goal of stabilizing GHG levels in the atmosphere, starting by reducing GHG emissions to 1990 levels by the year 2000 in all industrialized nations.

        i. Kyoto Protocol—"The third Conference of Parties to the FCCC met in Kyoto, Japan, in December 1997 to craft a binding agreement on reducing GHG emissions. In Kyoto, 38 industrial and former eastern bloc nations agreed to reduce emissions of six GHGs to 5% below 1990 levels, to be achieved by 2012. See table 18-4.

        ii. Bali and Beyond—"In December 2007, a UN-sponsored climate conference held in Bali addressed the need for greater cuts in GHG emissions when the Kyoto Protocol expires in 2012."

    3. U.S. Policy—"The Bush administration announced in 2002 the Global Climate Change Initiative (GCCI). The flagship policy of this initiative is a reduction of 18% in emissions intensity over the next 10 years."

        i. A Sea Change—"The 111th Congress has taken up these issues, and the new White House administration has promised to bring a sea change in U.S. climate change policy. President Obama has made climate legislation a high priority and has signaled his commitment to the issue."

        ii. States and Corporations—Many individual states and corporations have made changes in regards to climate change and to encourage Congress to "fast track climate legislation."

    4. Mitigation Tools—"Table 18-5 presents a summary of most of the prominent mitigation tools."

        i. Wedges—"CMI broke the triangle into seven 'wedges', or mitigation strategies, each of which would reduce 1 billion tons of carbon emissions by 2055. See Figure 18-25.

B. Adaptation—"Adaptation means making adjustments in anticipation of changes brought on by the rising sea levels and temperatures of the next decades. It also means reducing vulnerability to the inevitable impacts of climate change."

    1. New Funds—"The FCCC established two new funds to address this concern: a Least Developed Countries Fund…and a Special Climate Change Fund…Subsequently the FCCC added the Adaptation Fund and the Climate Investment Funds."

    2. Poverty and Climate Change—"The World Band and a host of UN and other organizations released a report." See p. 479 for a list of their reported findings.

    3. Strategies—"The World Bank report suggests that 'the best way to address climate change impacts on the poor is by integrating adaptation measures into sustainable development and poverty reduction strategies.'"

C. Geoengineering—Engineering feats have been discussed which may alleviate some global warming problems, but "it is certain that we are conducting an enormous global experiment in geoengineering, and our children and their descendants will be living with the consequences."

Review Questions: Possible Answers

1. *Explain the possible connections between intense hurricanes and the effects of current warming.*

Several research groups have recently published studies that suggest a link between hurricanes and global warming, igniting a controversy that has not settled yet. They pointed out that the trend of increasing numbers of category 4 and 5 hurricanes coincides with the trend of rise in sea surface temperatures in tropical seas. The high sea surface temperatures result in more water vapor in the air, leading to conditions that create a rising column of warm, humid air that can be set by the Earth's rotation and lead to hurricane formation. Evidence is clear that the oceans have been absorbing an increasing amount of heat energy, resulting from the greenhouse effect of gases released by human enterprises.

2. *What are the important characteristics of the troposphere? Of the stratosphere?*

"The atmosphere is a collection of gases that gravity holds in a thin envelope around the Earth. The gases within the lowest layer, the troposphere, are responsible for moderating the flow of energy to Earth. The troposphere ranges in thickness from 10 miles in the tropics and 5 miles in high latitudes. . . . This layer contains practically all the water vapor and clouds in the atmosphere; it is the site and source of our weather. Above the tropopause is the stratosphere, a layer within which temperature increases with altitude, up to about 40 miles above the surface of Earth. The temperature increases primarily because the stratosphere contains ozone (O_3), a form of oxygen that absorbs high-energy radiation emitted by the Sun. Because there is little vertical mixing of air masses in the stratosphere and no precipitation from it, substances that enter it can remain there for a long time."

3. *Provide a brief synopsis of global climate change. What are the main issues and trends?*
"Earth is in the midst of an unsustainable rise in GHG levels, the result of our intense use of fossil fuels. In short, we completely depend on a host of technologies that are threatening our future. All projections of future fossil fuel use and GHGs point to global consequences that are serious, but not inevitable. The United States and other developed countries will not escape these consequences, but the gravest of them affect developing countries. A sustainable pathway is still open to use, and it involves a combination of steps we can take to mitigate the emissions and bring the atmospheric concentration of GHGs to a stable, even declining level."

4. *What has been discovered about global climate trends in the past? What is the contemporary trend showing?*

"Climate is far from constant. Some work done quite recently on ice cores has . . . provided . . . evidence that remarkable changes in the climate can occur within as little as a few decades. Superimposed on the major (climate) oscillations is a record of rapid climate fluctuations during periods of glaciations and warmer times. There is much natural variation in weather from year to year, and local temperatures do not necessarily follow globally averaged ones. It is a fact, however, that 17 of the hottest years on record have occurred since 1980; indeed, 1990–2000 was the hottest decade ever recorded—and that in spite of two cooler years following the eruption of Mount Pinatubo in the Philippines in 1991. Recently, oceanographers analyzed millions of oceanic temperature records from 1950 to 1995 and found that, between 1970 and 1995, the heat content of the global oceans increased dramatically."

5. *What is the conveyor system? How does it work? How does it connect with global warming?*

"A thermohaline circulation pattern dominates oceanic currents, where themohaline refers to the effects the temperature and salinity have on the density of seawater. This conveyor system acts as a giant, complex

213

conveyor belt, moving water masses from the surface to deep oceans and back again, according to the density of the mass. . . . salty (warm) water from the Gulf Stream moves northward on the surface and is cooled by Arctic air currents." As the water cools, it sinks because water increases in density as it cools (but its density decreases again when frozen). This cool water flows south "through the Atlantic, to the southern tip of Africa, where it is joined by cold Antarctic waters." It then ". . . spreads northward into the Indian and Pacific Oceans as deep currents." Gradually, the currents slow down and warm, becoming less dense and welling up to the surface, where they are further warmed and begin to move surface waters back again towards the North Atlantic. This movement transfers enormous quantities of heat toward Europe, providing a climate that is much warmer than the high latitudes there would suggest.

If a large quantity of freshwater in the North Atlantic appeared, the overall density of water in the North Atlantic would diminish, resulting in less water sinking. This would stop the conveyor because the water flowing north would be blocked. "North Atlantic marine sediments show evidence of the periodic invasion of icebergs from the polar ice cap that supplied huge amounts of freshwater as they melted. The evidence indicates that these invasions coincided with rapid cooling . . . and suggests that the conveyor system shifted southward, with deep water forming near Bermuda instead of Greenland. When this occurred, a major climate cooling happened with a few decades. One likely consequence of extended global warming is increased precipitation over the North Atlantic and more melting of sea ice and ice caps. If such a pattern is sustained, it could lead to a breakdown in the normal operation of the conveyor and a rapid change in climate, especially in the northern latitudes. . . . Indeed, oceanographers have seen a gradual decline in the salinity of the northern seas consistent with known glacial melt and a thinning of the ice in the Arctic Ocean."

6. *What is radiative forcing? Describe some warming and cooling forcing agents.*

"Radiative forcing is the influence a particular factor has on the energy balance of the atmosphere-ocean-land system. The factors can be positive, leading to warming, or negative, leading to cooling, as they affect the energy balance. If the factors change over time, they can lead to change in the climate."
Positive examples include increasing levels of water vapor, carbon dioxide, ozone, methane, nitrous oxide, chlorofluorocarbons, soot, and high-flying clouds.
Negative examples are increasing levels of particulates, sulfate aerosols, low-lying clouds, snow and ice (increases planetary albedo), and ozone depletion and volcanic eruption.

7. *What evidence do global land and ocean temperatures provide for a warming Earth?*

According to Figure 18-5, there has been a warming trend on both land and in the ocean since 1975 which has not been observed for the past 200 previous years.

8. *What additional changes contribute to the picture of human-caused warming?*

Based on proxies from times when temperatures were not recorded, we can see that oscillations between warm and cold periods have occurred. Indications of unusual land and oceanic temperatures in addition to evidence of unusually high and climbing levels of carbon dioxide and other anthropogenic greenhouse gases in the atmosphere, unusual weather patterns, melting sea ice, and the rise in global mean sea level are all major concerns pointing towards a warming phenomenon.

9. *Which of the GHGs are the most significant contributors to global warming? How do they work?*

214

"Water vapor is the most abundant greenhouse gas." Carbon dioxide is a significant contributor to global warming: CO_2 levels are "35% higher than they were before the Industrial Revolution and higher than they have been for over 400,000 years. Methane (CH_4), the third-most-important greenhouse gas, is a product of microbial fermentative reactions; its main natural source is wetlands."

"Light energy comes through the atmosphere and is absorbed by Earth and converted to heat energy at the planet's surface. The infrared heat energy radiates back upward through the atmosphere and into space. The GHSs that are naturally present in the troposphere absorb some of the infrared radiation and reradiate it back toward the surface; other gases (N_2 and O_2) in the troposphere do not."

10. *Describe the data for atmospheric CO_2. What are the significant sources and sinks for atmospheric CO_2?*

"In 1958, Charles Keeling began measuring CO_2 levels on Mauna Loa, in Hawaii. Measurements there have been recorded continuously, and they reveal a striking increase in atmospheric levels of the gas. The concentrations increased exponentially until the energy crisis in the mid-1970s, rose at a rate of 1.5 ppm/year for several decades, and recently began rising at a rate of 1.8 ppm/year and higher. The data also reveal an annual oscillation of 5-7 ppm, which reflects seasonal changes of photosynthesis and respiration of terrestrial ecosystems in the Northern Hemisphere. As of early 2007, atmospheric CO_2 levels were more than 380 ppm, 35% higher than they were before the Industrial Revolution and higher than they have been for over 400,000 years...."

Significant sources: Every kilogram of fossil fuel burned produces about 3 kg of CO_2 that enters the atmosphere. (The mass triples because each carbon atom in the fuel picks up two oxygen atoms in the course of burning and becomes CO_2.) Currently, 7.2 million metric tons (gigatons, or Gt) of fossil fuel carbon (GtC) are burned each year, all added to the atmosphere as CO_2 (about 3% of this total comes from cement production and is usually included in figures reported for fossil-fuel emissions). At least half of this amount comes from the industrialized countries. It is estimated that the burning of forest trees is another anthropogenic source that adds some 1.6 GtC annually to the carbon already coming from fossil fuel combustion.

Sinks: "Careful calculations show that if all the CO_2 emitted from burning fossil fuels accumulated in the atmosphere, the concentration would rise by at least 3 ppm per year, not the 2 ppm or less.... In the 1990s, this meant an addition of approximately 8 GtC per year added to the atmosphere by anthropogenic sources, yet only 3.3 GtC per year actually accumulated. Thus, there must be carbon 'sinks' that absorb CO_2 and keep it from accumulating at a more rapid rate in the atmosphere. Recent work with stable carbon and oxygen isotopes and careful measurements of atmospheric CO_2 around the globe have brought us much closer to quantifying annual fluxes in CO_2 and identifying the missing sinks. There is broad agreement that the oceans serve as a sink for much of the CO_2 emitted; some of this is due to the uptake of CO_2 by phytoplankton and its subsequent sinking, and some is a consequence of the under-saturation of CO_2 in seawater. There are limits to the ocean's ability to absorb CO_2, however, because only the top 300 m of the ocean is in contact with the atmosphere. Calculations indicate that, in the 1990s, the ocean sink accounted for an uptake of 2.2 $\pm$ 0.4 GtC annually. Measurements indicate that terrestrial ecosystems can also serve as a carbon sink. Indeed, these land ecosystems apparently stored a net 1.0 $\pm$ .5 GTC annually during the 1990s, a figure that includes the losses from deforestation and thus implies an average gross annual uptake of some 2.5 GtC during those years. For this reason, terrestrial ecosystems, and especially forests, are increasingly valued because of their ability to sequester carbon. Much of this carbon uptake is being attributed to increased rainfall associated with the warming trend in temperature."

11. *How are models employed in climate change research? Describe several scenarios for 21st century climate change.*

"Modeling climate is an essential strategy for exploring the potential future impacts of rising GHGs. Climatologists employ the same powerful computers used for weather forecasting and have combined global atmospheric circulation patterns with ocean circulation and radiation feedback from clouds to produce coupled general circulation models (CGCMs) that are capable of simulating long-term climatic conditions. . . . (T)he main purpose of the models is to project the future global climate."

"The A1 scenarios reflect a world in which population reaches its peak in mid-century and then declines; economic growth is rapid, and new technologies are employed. A1F1 shows a fossil-fuel intensive society, A1T reflects shifts to non-fossil-energy sources. The A2 series reflects a world of independent countries going their own way, with increasing population and varied economic growth and technological change. B1 reflects a world with population developments as in A1, but with rapid changes in economies and effective global cooperation to reach sustainability in all sectors. B2 has increasing populations and more regional adaptations, as in the A2 series, but with significant efforts to achieve sustainability. IS92a is a scenario carried over from the second IPCC assessment, for comparison purposes."

12. *What are the major IPCC projections for climate changes in the 21st century?*

"The major consequence of rising greenhouse gas levels during the 21st century is rising temperatures – the amount of rise depending on the energy choices and other factors, such as population growth. Rising global temperatures are linked to two major impacts: regional climatic changes and a rise in sea level."

"Equilibrium climate sensitivity—the change in mean global temperature that accompanies a doubling of atmospheric CO_2—is in the range of 2-4.5°C, most likely 3°C. The scenarios project a range of surface warming in 2100 compared with 1980–2000; for the B1, A1B, A2, and A1F1 scenarios the estimates are 1.5–2.8°C, 2.3–4.1°C, 3.0–5.0°C, and 3.5–5.8°C, respectively. The warming is expected to occur in geographical patterns similar to those of recent years: warming greatest at the higher latitudes and over land and least over the North Atlantic and southern oceans. Because of the warming climate, snow cover and sea ice will decrease and glaciers and ice caps will lose water, resulting in a rise in sea level. Permafrost in the Arctic is expected to thaw up to 90% of the upper layer. As the upper layers of the North Atlantic Ocean warm and become fresher, the thermohaline circulation is expected to slow down, but no models show it collapsing. Storm intensities are expected to increase, with higher wind speeds, more extreme wave heights, and more intense precipitation. The sea level rise, currently at a rate of 3 mm per decade, will certainly increase as a consequence of continue thermal expansion and snow and ice melt. Heat waves will become more frequent and longer lasting as the climate warms. Growing seasons will lengthen, and frost days will decrease in mid and high latitudes. Precipitation will decrease in already dry regions, and increase in wet regions; there will be an increase in extremes of daily precipitation."

13. *Summarize the key findings of the CCSP Synthesis (USP) report.*

"The United Synthesis Product (USP) provides a detailed look at the impacts of climate change on various sectors (e.g., transportation, agriculture, human health) and regions (e.g., Northwest, Southwest, Northeast, Alaska) of the United States." The report indicates that compared to 50 years ago: The average U.S. temperature and precipitation has risen, heavy precipitation has increased by 20%, extreme weather events have

216

are more common and devastating, the sea level has increased 2 to 5 inches, storm tracks are shifting northward, and arctic ice is declining.

14. *What mitigation steps could be taken to stabilize the GHG content of the atmosphere?*

"Place a worldwide cap on GHG emissions . . .; (i)nvest in and deploy an increasing percentage of energy in the form of renewable-energy technologies . . .; (r)emove fossil-fuel subsidies . . .; (e)ncourage the development of nuclear power, but only if issues concerning cost-effectiveness, reliability, spent fuel, and high-level waste are resolved; (s)top the loss of tropical forests and encourage the planting of trees and other vegetation . . .; (m)ake energy conservation rules more stringent; (r)educe the amount of fuels used in transportation . . .; (s)equester CO_2 emitted from burning fossil fuels. . .; and (m)ake a greater effort to slow the growth of the human population."

15. *Trace the political history of the FCCC and the Kyoto Protocol. What is the next international step in reaching agreement on climate change mitigation?*

The Framework Convention on Climate Change was "signed by heads of state at the UNCED Earth Summit in Rio de Janeiro in 1992. This convention agreed to the goal of stabilizing greenhouse gas levels in the atmosphere, starting by reducing greenhouse gas emission to 1990 levels by the year 2000 in all industrialized nations. Countries were to achieve the goal by voluntary means. Five years later, it was obvious that the voluntary approach was failing. All the developed countries except those of the European Union increased their greenhouse gas emissions by 7 to 9% in the ensuing five years. The developing countries increased theirs by 25%!"

"Prompted by a coalition of island nations (whose very existence is threatened by global climate change), the third Conference of Parties to the FCCC met in Kyoto, Japan, in December 1997 to craft a binding agreement on reducing greenhouse gas emissions. In Kyoto, 38 industrial and former Eastern bloc nations agreed to reduce emissions of six GHGs to 5.2% below 1990 levels, to be achieved by 2012. As of August 2005, more than 164 parties have ratified, thus meeting the first requirement for the protocol."

"The targeted reductions of the Kyoto Protocol will not stabilize atmospheric concentrations of GHGs. The IPCC calculates that it would take immediate reductions in emissions of at least 60% worldwide to stabilize greenhouse gas concentrations at today's levels."

"Parties to the FCCC and the Kyoto Protocol met in December 2005, in Montreal, Canada, to consider what to do when the Kyoto process expires in 2012. The U.N. Climate Control Conference, as it was called, reached agreement on two principles. First, there would be future meetings aimed at producing a new, tougher set of binding limits on GHG emissions that would take effect after 2012; second, there would be broader dialogues towards reaching nonbinding accords addressing global climate change."

16. *Describe recent U.S. climate change policy, and compare it with those of other developed countries.*

"Early in March 2001, U.S. representatives signed a statement with the Group of Eight industrial countries that reaffirmed our commitment to uphold the Kyoto Protocol and expressed concern about the serious threat of global climate change. A week later, in a letter responding to a query from four senators about his administration's view on global climate change, President George W. Bush state that he opposed the Kyoto Protocol for two reasons: 1. It exempts the developing countries and thus is unfair and, 2. It would cause serious harm to the U.S. economy. He also cited the 'incomplete state of scientific knowledge of the causes of, and solutions to, global climate change....' Later in March, EPA administrator Christine Whitman officially notified the world that the United States would withdraw from the Kyoto agreement."

"The move away from the Kyoto Protocol does not mean that the United States is doing nothing about climate change. Instead, we are committed to going our own way. In February 2002, that way became clearer with the release of the administration's Global Climate Change Initiative (GCCI). The flagship policy of this initiative is a reduction of 18% in emissions intensity over the next 10 years. What is emissions intensity? It is not the same as emissions; it is the ratio of greenhouse gas emissions to economic output, the latter measured as gross domestic product (GDP)."

"In July 2003, the Bush administration released a report that provides guidelines for the government's Climate Change Science Program (CCSP) and puts a sharper image on the government's approach to climate research. The plan seeks to address a number of issues in climate science such as the natural variability in climate, a quantitative approach to forces causing climate change, projections of future climate change, and the sensitivity and adaptability of human and natural ecosystems to climate change."

Germany has made a significant change in carbon emissions (–17.1%); the other developed nations have smaller decreases, for example, –0.2% for the European Union and –4.1 for the United Kingdom. Australia increased its emissions by 32.3% while Canada increased its emissions by 11.5% and Japan by 10.8%.

17. *What are some adaptation steps that should be taken to anticipate inevitable changes in climate?*

See Table 18-6 for a list of adaptation strategies that could be used in all countries as well as specifically in developing countries. Examples include changes in agriculture, infrastructure, and emergency preparedness, reducing risks by making wise choices, promoting development, controlling diseases, and enhancing economic progress.

Thinking Environmentally: Possible Answers

1. *What steps could you take to lower your climate impact? Check the Union of Concerned Scientists web site for suggestions.*

The responses to this question will be very individual. Personal changes to lower an individual's contribution to climate change would include all aspects of energy and resource conservation. Taking shorter showers, taking showers instead of baths, and turning off water while brushing teeth and shaving save energy (water heating, pumping, and water and sewage treatment), turning off lights and other electrical equipment saves electricity (especially important if the energy source is coal), reducing the quantity of food wasted (less fuel needed for production, processing, transport, cooking, etc.), when appliances are purchased, purchasing the most energy efficient model, walking or riding a bicycle, car pooling, taking the bus or train, reducing air travel, considering if a purchase is even necessary (saves resources and energy in extraction, production, use, and disposal), living in a smaller house, and planting native plants (fewer pesticides and fertilizer, no water).

2. *Research the skeptics of global climate change. What evidence do they offer in support of their views? How does it compare with the evidence from the IPCC? On balance, what do the data indicate?*

There are other climate change (and ozone depletion) skeptics than the four listed below. Their arguments are similar. For the most part they are arguing that the climatic changes we are seeing are normal. Others arguments distort the data.

Patrick Michael is a well-known skeptic. He is a Research Professor of Environmental Sciences at the University of Virginia. He claims that the climatic changes will be minor and are likely to be beneficial. He argues that the warming caused by increasing concentrations of greenhouse gases is linear and each incremental increase in greenhouse gases results in less and less warming. He also criticized the predictions of thinning of the ozone layer of the Arctic, and increasing UV radiation reaching earth. He is a fellow at the Cato Institute.

Fred Singer is a skeptic about global climate change and ozone depletion. He favors natural variation over anthropogenic causes to explain global warming. (He is also a skeptic when it comes to secondhand cigarette smoke and cancer risks.) He states in a letter to Natural Science.com on January 29, 1998, that, "The weather satellite data, the only truly global data set we have, actually show a global cooling trend during the past 19 years." Singer is referring to the satellite data that have now been shown to be incorrect. "Climate science does not support the Kyoto Protocol and its emission controls on carbon dioxide. As will become apparent from my testimony, the climate is not warming and climate models used to predict a future warming have not been validated. In any case, a warmer climate would be generally beneficial for agriculture and other human activities." Source: Transcript, S. Fred Singer's testimony before House Small Business Committee, July 29, 1998. "The current warming trend is not unusual: Climate is always either warming or cooling, and ice is either melting or accumulating.... The human contribution to global warming appears to be quite small and natural climate factors are dominant." Source: *Wall Street Journal*, June 20, 2006.

Sherwood B. Idso is another skeptic. He believes that something other than CO_2 is causing warming because something other than a decrease in atmospheric CO_2 concentration caused the Little Ice age and something besides increased atmospheric concentration of CO_2 caused us to come out of the ice age, and thus the same must be true now. He also believes that any warming of the planet will be beneficial to humans.

James Inhofe, Senator from Oklahoma, is also a skeptic. He states in a speech on the Senate floor on January 4, 2005, "Paula Dobriansky, undersecretary of state for global affairs and the leader of the U.S. delegation, put it well when she told the conference, 'Science tells us that we cannot say with any certainty what constitutes a dangerous level of warming, and therefore what level must be avoided.'" He also states, "What do we really know about temperatures in the Arctic? Let's take a closer look. As Oregon State University climatologist George Taylor has shown, Arctic temperatures are actually slightly cooler today than they were in the 1930s."

3. *Even if the human role in global climate change is highly likely, but not necessarily a certainty, should our response to it be any different?*

Whether or not the climate change that we are currently experiencing is our fault, adaptation and mitigation strategies for alleviating global climate change are wise environmentally sustainable things that need to be done anyways. First and foremost, we need to wean ourselves from the use of fossil fuels since they are resources that we are using at a much higher level than the earth can restore. Making globally sustainable decisions will be beneficial for humans as well as for all species and will help ensure our place on this earth in the future.

4. *What recent developments most increase the urgency of action in the international arena?*

With the increase in global weather disasters, and the fact that global climate change tends to affect those who are most poor, increasing international crisis that can be directly linked to climate change is of major concern.

5. *Log on to www.princeton.edu/~cmi/resources/stabwedge.htm, get some friends together, and play the Stabilization Wedge Game. The Web site has instructions and materials for this activity.*

Student answers will vary. A teacher's guide for this activity can be found at http://cmi.princeton.edu/wedges/pdfs/teachers_guide.pdf .

CHAPTER 19
Atmospheric Pollution

Chapter Outline:

I.   Air-Pollution Essentials
    A.   Pollutants and Atmospheric Cleansing
        1.   Atmospheric Cleansing
    B.   Smog and Brown Clouds
        1.   Industrial Smog
        2.   Photochemical Smog
        3.   Inversions
        4.   Atmospheric Brown Clouds

II. Major Air Pollutants and Their Sources
    A.   Primary Pollutants
        1.   Tracking Pollutants
            i.   Getting the Lead Out
            ii. Toxics and Radon
    B.   Secondary Pollutants
        1.   Ozone Formation
    C.   Acid Precipitation and Deposition
        1.   Acids and Bases
            i.   pH
        2.   Extent and Potency of Acid Precipitation
        3.   Sources of Acid Deposition
            i.   Natural Versus Anthropogenic Sources

III. Impacts of Air Pollutants
    A.   Human Health
        1.   Chronic Effects
            i.   COPD
            ii. Asthma
            iii. Strong Evidence
            iv. Lead Again
        2.   Acute Effects
        3.   Carcinogenic Effects
    B.   The Environment
        1.   Crop Damage
        2.   Forest Damage
        3.   Effects on Materials and Aesthetics
        4.   Visibility
    C.   Effects of Acid Deposition
        1.   Impact on Aquatic Ecosystems

Key Topics:

1. Air-Pollution Essentials
2. Major Air Pollutants and Their Sources
3. Impacts of Air Pollution
4. Bringing Air Pollution Under Control
5. Destruction of the Ozone Layer

Instructional Goals:

1. There are several natural processes that cleanse the atmosphere. Our current activities overwhelm the natural cleansing system.

2. Air pollution adversely impacts all living things. Plants and animals experience reduced vigor and increased death rates. Humans have higher morbidity and mortality rates.

3. Primary air pollutants are produced from combustion and evaporation while secondary pollutants are a result of chemical reactions between the primary pollutants and naturally occurring compounds.

4. Air pollutants are a result of choices we have made concerning how we produce and use energy. Our choices about electricity production and transportation are the primary reasons for poor air quality. We have made choices to reduce the quantity of air pollution produced, and more work in this direction is needed.

5. The dynamic balance between ozone and oxygen in the stratosphere results from the absorption of UV radiation. The result is lower levels of UV radiation on the surface of the planet. Higher levels of UV increase the risk of protein and DNA damage.

6. CFCs and other ozone-depleting chemicals react with ozone, changing the balance between molecule oxygen and ozone. The quantity of UV radiation arriving from the sun influences the rate of the reaction.

Concepts and Connections:

For the vast majority of Americans, air pollution is frequently visible and recent changes in EPA regulations have doubled the number of counties in the United States that do not meet Federal Air Quality Standards. Each summer a large number of American cities experience high ozone levels and officials recommend that people restrict their activities. People tend to feel strongly that air pollution should be reduced. Getting people to connect their actions with air pollution production is difficult. Because we believe we benefit from the use of the automobile, we tend to not view our driving habits as a problem. Focusing on the structural impediments to living without the automobile rather than the individual's actions (e.g., the tendency to drive when walking, bicycling, or taking mass transit is possible) will increase the ability of students to see solutions and to contemplate changes in their lifestyle that would improve air quality. Connecting air pollution to land use planning helps students focus on solutions rather than laying or avoiding blame. Discussing the differences between cities that are people friendly

222

rather than car friendly (Los Angeles) can produce ideas about changes in city design that would promote more sustainable, less polluted cities.

We have been improving our ability to measure air pollution. We also have improved our ability to quantify the impact of poor air quality on human health and the health of all organisms in the biosphere. When air pollution was first recognized as a problem, starting not long after the industrial revolution, we have been attempting to eliminate it. Only recently have we begun to view the problem from a broader perspective. Our previous attempts to eliminate air pollution have been focused on particular sources or pollutants rather than to build a sustainable economic system. We eliminated the pollutants from coal by switching to petroleum but did not address the fundamental problem of an un-sustainable lifestyle. There are many people attempting to take a broader perspective to reduce the chance that we will eliminate one pollutant to only create another one.

Concepts in Context:

Air quality can be related to a diverse number of environmental issues. Land use planning (Chapter 2) is not just how we lay out our cities but also how we grow our food (Chapter 12), dispose of wastes (Chapters 20, 21, 22), and obtain energy (Chapters 14, 15, and 16). Growing food on marginal land or removing all the plants from the soil during plowing increases the risk of dust storms (Chapter 11). Our use of ecosystems as a resource (Chapter 7) can be diminished if poor air quality begins to effect biogeochemical cycles (Chapter 5). Human health (Chapter 17) is directly affected by the quantity of pollutants in the air.

Water resources (Chapters 10 and 20) are adversely impacted by contaminants in the air. Some air contaminants can change soil pH, a limiting factor (Chapter 3). Primary and secondary air pollutants can adversely impact various organisms in an ecosystem. Food webs (Chapter 3), nutrient cycles (Chapter 4), and succession (Chapter 5) may be altered due to poor air quality. If habitats or niches (Chapter 3) are damaged or destroyed, then biodiversity (Chapter 6) may be affected.

Key Terms and Vocabulary:

Air pollutants, hydroxyl radical (OH), industrial smog, photochemical smog, temperature inversion, atmospheric brown cloud (ABC), particulates, VOCs, CO, NO_x, SO_2, lead, air toxins, secondary pollutants, ozone, peroxyacetyl nitrates, sulfuric acid, nitric acid, oxides, or NO_x, Clearinghouse for Inventories and Emissions Factors, national emissions, ambient concentrations, photochemical oxidants, sulfuric acids, nitric acids, acid deposition, acid, base, pH, acid precipitation, sulfuric acid, nitric acid, chronic obstructive pulmonary disease, benzene, buffer, artifacts, Clean Air Act of 1970 (CAA), ambient standards, criteria pollutants, National Ambient Air Quality Standards (NAAQS), primary standard, National Emission Standards for Hazardous Air Pollutants (NESHAPs), National Emission Inventory, command and control, Clean Air Act Amendments of 1990 (CAAA), State Implementation Plan (SIP), maximum achievable control technology (MACT), catalytic converter, Energy Policy and Conservation Act of 1975, Energy Independence and Security Act, point sources, area sources, Tier 2 Standards, NO_x Budget Trading Program (NBP), Clean Air Interstate Rule (CAIR), Clean Air Mercury Rule (CAMR), ozone shield, Chlorofluorocarbons (CFCs), chlorine catalytic cycle, catalyst, chlorine reservoirs, Montreal Protocol, Clean Air Act Amendments of 1990

Discussion, Activities, and Labs:

1. Discuss with the class various ways in which the automobile is subsidized. Some things we pay for indirectly by gasoline tax or car registration, while some other things we pay for out of general fund taxes. Some of these include highways, surface streets, traffic and street lights, traffic police, on-street parking, state highway police, ambulance service and fire departments (in most cities the fire department and ambulances respond to automobile accidents more often than any other emergency). There are costs that result from automobile use that you do not directly pay for when you use your automobile, nor are these costs related to taxes you may pay on your automobile use. These costs may be out of pocket or, seemingly, needed for reasons other than the automobile. These include costs to control flooding (paving increases the risk of flooding); water pollution (oil, metals, etc. deposited on roads and washed into streams when precipitation occurs), damage to crops, forests, and aquatic ecosystems; health care costs (due to increased morbidity and mortality from air pollutants); and hospital emergency rooms (trauma units are used by auto accident victims).

2. An alternative to the internal combustion engine has become available recently. Hybrid vehicles alternate between the internal combustion engine and an electric engine. These vehicles capture energy that would otherwise be lost and store it in batteries. The batteries are used to drive an electric engine. Another alternative not on the market yet is hydrogen fuel cells. Discuss with the class they types of pollutants that result from cars powered using these two and other technologies. Any energy source has pollutants associated with it. What would be the most polluting method (coal, other fossil fuels) to produce hydrogen for fuel cells? Least polluting (solar, wind, etc.)? Which, if any, of the costs discussed in **In-class discussion #1** would be eliminated?

3. Divide the class into groups of three to four students. Each group is given a set of parameters describing a city (physical, social, and economic characteristics of any city can be used). The students are to plan how to create a city that does not produce more air pollution than the atmosphere can cleanse naturally. In creating this more sustainable environment, students should be asked to consider livability (how much green space exists), safety (people need to be able to get around without fear), and convenience.

4. Use the same information in the above activity but include estimated costs for each possible solution and a limited budget for implementation. This situation is closer to reality and will help the students recognize the need for individual evaluation of lifestyles. Some changes may be necessary in what we value. Individuals and groups are constantly deciding what is valuable. Including clean air as a possible value could change how other activities and things are valued.

5. For one week have each student record the type of trips (school, work, shopping, visiting, entertainment, etc.) made each day and the distances traveled and type of transportation used for each trip. All forms of transportation should be included: walking, bicycling, single-person car trip, multiple-person car trip, bus, train, and plane. (Walking within a building should not be included because the quantity of data becomes overwhelming.) At the end of the week determine the number of miles by transportation type, the number of trips by each transportation type, the number of trips by each type (grocery store, work, entertainment) of trip, the number of miles by each type of trip, total number of trips, and total number of miles. For each type of transportation used, have the student find information in the library or on the Internet about the average quantity of pollutants per mile. (It is possible to obtain information on each automobile model.) Have each student calculate her/his total contribution to air pollution by summing the quantity of pollutant produced per mile by transportation type times the number of miles by transportation type.

Suggested Lecture Format:

I. Air-Pollution Essentials

    A. Pollutants and Atmospheric Cleansing—"Air pollutants are substances in the atmosphere—certain gases and aerosols—that have harmful effects. Three factors determine the level of air pollution: The amount of pollutants entering the air, the amount of space into which the pollutants are dispersed, and the mechanisms that remove pollutants from the air." See Figure 19-2.

        1. Atmospheric Cleansing—"There are mechanisms in the biosphere that remove, assimilate, and recycle these natural pollutants." See Figure 19-3.

    B. Smog and Brown Clouds—"With the Industrial Revolution of the 1800s came crowded cities and the use of coal for heating and energy. It was then that air pollution began in earnest."

        1. Industrial Smog—Industrial smog is "a combination of smoke and fog, an irritating grayish mixture of soot, sulfurous compounds, and water vapor. This kind of smog continues to be found wherever industries are concentrated and where coal is the primary energy source; such smog events mostly occur in the winter." See Figure 19-4.

        2. Photochemical Smog—Photochemical smog "is produced when several pollutants from automobile exhausts—nitrogen oxides and volatile organic carbon compounds-are acted on by sunlight." See Figure 19-4 and also Figure 19-5.

        3. Inversions—Normally, warm air rises, carrying pollutants with it. Sometimes, though, a warm layer of air exists above a colder layer causing a temperature inversion. Inversions can be dangerous because they can trap pollution in the air above organisms. Usually sunlight breaks up the inversion quickly, but if a significant cloud cover exists it can prevent warming of the earth and trap dangerous chemicals where they can cause harm. See Figure 19-6.

        4. Atmospheric Brown Clouds—"The ABC is in fact a persistent aerosol, similar to the summer aerosol found over industrial regions in the North Temperate Zone…Unique to the ABC is the high proportion of black carbon and soot derived from biomass burning."

II. Major Air Pollutants and Their Sources

    A. Primary Pollutants—Primary pollutants are the "direct products of combustion and evaporation." See Table 19-1. See also Figure 19-8.

        1. Tracking Pollutants—"The Environmental Protection Agency (EPA) operates the Clearinghouse for Inventories and Emissions Factors, which tracks trends in national emissions of the primary pollutants from all sources."

            i. Getting the Lead Out—"Emitted with the exhaust from gasoline-burning vehicles, lead remained airborne and traveled great distances before settling as far away as the glaciers of Greenland. Since the phase out, concentrations of lead in the air of cities in the United States have declined remarkably." See Figure 19-10.

            ii. Toxics and Radon—"Some of the air's toxic compounds—benzene, for example—originate with transportation fuels. Most, however, are traceable to industries and small businesses. Radon, by contrast, is produced by the spontaneous decay of fissionable material in rocks and soils."

B. Secondary Pollutants—"Ozone and numerous reactive organic compounds are formed as a result of chemical reactions between nitrogen oxides and volatile organic carbons. Because sunlight provides the energy necessary to propel the reactions, these products are also known as photochemical oxidants."

    1. Ozone Formation—A simplified view of the major reactions in the formation of ozone and other photochemical oxidants is shown in Figure 19-12.

C. Acid Precipitation and Deposition—"Acid precipitation refers to any precipitation-rain, fog, mist, or snow-that is more acidic than usual. Because dry acidic particles are also found in the atmosphere, the combination of precipitation and dry-particle fallout is called acid deposition." See Figure 19-13.

    1. Acids and Bases—"An acid is any chemical that releases hydrogen ions when dissolved in water. A base is any chemical that releases hydroxide ions when dissolved in water." See table 19-2 for examples.

        i. pH—"The concentration of hydrogen ions is expressed as pH. The pH scale goes from 0 (highly acidic) through 7 (neutral) to 14 (highly basic)." See Figure 19-14.

    2. Extent and Potency of Acid Precipitation—"In the absence of any pollution, rainfall is normally somewhat acidic, with a pH of 5.6, because carbon dioxide in the air readily dissolves in, and combines with water to produce carbonic acid. Acid precipitation, then, is any precipitation with a pH of less than 5.5."

    3. Sources of Acid Deposition—"As we have seen, burning fuels produce sulfur dioxide and nitrogen oxides, so the source of the acid deposition problem is evident. These oxides enter the troposphere in large quantities from both anthropogenic and natural sources. Once in the troposphere, they are oxidized by hydroxyl radicals." See Figure 19-3.

        i. Natural Versus Anthropogenic Sources—"Anthropogenic sources are estimated at 100 to 130 million tons per year of sulfur dioxide and 60 to 70 million tons per year of nitrogen oxides. The vital difference between these two sources is that anthropogenic oxides are strongly concentrated in industrialized regions, whereas the emissions from natural sources are spread out and are part of the global environment." See Figure 19-9 as well as Figure 19-16.

III. Impacts of Air Pollutants

A. Human Health—"Acute exposure to some pollutants can be life threatening, but many effects are chronic, acting over a period of years to cause a gradual deterioration of physiological functions and eventual premature mortality. Moreover, some pollutants are carcinogenic, adding significantly to the risk of lung cancer as they are breathed into the lungs."

    1. Chronic Effects—"Many people living in areas of urban air pollution suffer from chronic effects."

        i. COPD—"Chronic obstructive pulmonary disease (COPD), is a slowly progressive lung disease that makes it increasingly hard to breathe." See Figure 19-17.

        ii. Asthma—"Those most sensitive to air pollution are small children, asthmatics, people with chronic pulmonary or heart disease, and the elderly. Asthma episodes are triggered by contact with allergens (dust mites, molds, pet dander) and compounds in polluted air (ozone, particulate matter, SO2)."

    iii. Strong Evidence—"In the studies, higher concentrations of fine particles were correlated with increased mortality, especially from cardiopulmonary disease and lung cancer. The more polluted the city, the higher the mortality."

    iv. Lead Again—"Learning disabilities in children, as well as high blood pressure in adults, were correlated with levels of lead in the blood. The major source of this widespread contamination was found to be leaded gasoline. (The lead exhaust fumes were inhaled directly or settled on food, water, or any number of items that are put into the mouth)." See Figure 19-10.

  2. Acute Effects—"In severe cases, air pollution reaches levels that cause death, although such deaths usually occur among people already suffering from critical respiratory or heart disease or both."

  3. Carcinogenic Effects—"The heavy-metal and organic constituents of air pollution include many chemicals known to be carcinogenic in high doses. According to the industrial reporting required by the EPS, 4.7 million tons of hazardous air pollutants are released annually into the air in the United States." See Table 19-1.

B. The Environment—"Experiments show that plants are considerably more sensitive to gaseous air pollutants than are humans."

  1. Crop Damage—"Damage to crops, orchards, and forests downwind of urban centers is caused mainly by exposure to ozone." See Figure 19-19 and also Figure 19-20.

  2. Forest Damage—"The deaths of the ponderosa and Jeffrey pines in the Sierra Nevada were attributed to western pine beetles, which invade trees weakened by ozone. Studies have shown that damage to forest trees begins at about 40 ppb and gets more intense with higher levels."

  3. Effects on Materials and Aesthetics—Surfaces and materials can be degraded must faster than would normally happen when in the presence of pollutants. See Figure 19-21.

  4. Visibility—"A clear blue sky and good visibility are matters of health, but they also carry significant aesthetic value and can have a deep psychological impact on people."

C. Effects of Acid Deposition—"Acid deposition has been recognized as a problem in and around industrial centers for over 100 years."

  1. Impact on Aquatic Ecosystems—"The pH of an environment is extremely critical because it affects the function of virtually all enzymes, hormones, and other proteins in the bodies of all organisms living in that environment." See Figure 19-13.

  2. Neutralizing Capacity—"Despite the addition of acid, a system may be protected from changes in pH by a buffer-a substance that, when present in a solution, has a large capacity to absorb hydrogen ions and thus maintain the pH at a relatively constant value." See Figure 19-22.

  3. Impact on Forests—"Much of the damage to forests from acid precipitation is due to chemical interactions within the forest soils."

  4. Impact on Human Artifacts—"The reaction between acid deposition and limestone is causing these structures to erode at a tremendously accelerated pace." See Figure 19-21.

IV. Bringing Air Pollution Under Control—**See Discussion Topic #5.**

A. Clean Air Act—"Under grassroots pressure from citizens, the U.S. Congress enacted the Clean Air Act of 1970 (CAA). Together with amendments passed in 1977 and 1990, this law, administered by the EPA, represents the foundation of the U.S. air-pollution control efforts."

   1. NAAQS—"The CAA mandated the setting of standards for four of the primary pollutants…with the addition of lead, they are known as the criteria pollutants and are covered by the National Ambient Air Quality Standards (NAAQS)." See Table 21-3.

   2. NESHAPs—"The CAA required the EPA to establish National Emission Standards for Hazardous Air Pollutants (NESHAPs) for a number of toxic substances."

B. Control Strategies—Command and control strategies to control the output of pollutants "proved difficult to implement." **See Discussion Topic #3 and #4.**

   1. 1990 Amendments—"Polluters must apply for a permit that identifies the kinds of pollutants they release, the quantities of those pollutants, and the steps they are taking to reduce pollution. Permit fees provide funds the states can use to support their air-pollution control activities."

   2. Reducing Particulates—"Prior to the 1970s, the major sources of particulates were industrial stacks and the open burning of refuse. The CAA mandated the phasing out of open burning of refuse and required that particulates from industrial stacks be reduced to 'no visible emissions'."

      i. PM—"There is overwhelming evidence that the finer particles (2.5 microns or less) go right into the lungs when breathed. Responding to this evidence, the EPA announced a revision to the NAAQs in 2006, reducing the 24-hour primary standard."

   3. Controlling Air Toxics—"Under the CAAA, Congress identified 187 toxic pollutants. It then directed the EPA to identify major sources of these pollutants and to develop maximum achievable control technology (MACT) standards. The EPA has mobilized over 300 monitoring sites to track emissions of the affected substances." See Figure 19-23.

   4. Limiting Pollutants from Motor Vehicles—"Cars, trucks, and buses release nearly half of the pollutants that foul our air. Vehicle exhaust sends out VOCs, carbon monoxide, and nitrogen oxides that lead to ground-level ozone and PANs." See Figure 19-24. **See also Discussion Topics #1 and #2.**

      i. CAAA Changes—The CAAA regulated standards more tightly for card and emissions and reduced emissions to 30% less VOCs. See Figure 19-25.

      ii. CAFE Standards—"Under the authority of the Energy Policy and Conservation Act of 1975 and its amendments, the National Highway Traffic Safety Administration was given the authority to set corporate average fuel economy standards for motor vehicles."

      iii. Getting Around—"All of the major automakers are jumping on the hybrid bandwagon, and higher prices of gasoline have boosted hybrid sales in the United States. Another encouraging trend is the increase in mass-transit ridership."

   5. Managing Ozone—"Because ozone is a secondary pollutant, the only way to control ozone levels is to address the compounds that lead to its formation. Recent understanding of the

complex chemical reactions involving NO$_x$, VOCs, and oxygen has thrown some uncertainty into this strategy of simply emphasizing a reduction in VOCs."

    i. New Ozone Standards—"The new ozone standard is expected to prevent a substantial number of premature deaths, but only a third of those that the lower standard would have prevented. No prevention will happen, however, unless the standard is accompanied by regulations that reduce the source compounds that produce ozone."

    ii. Down with NO$_x$—"In a response to petitions from states in the Northeast that were having trouble achieving ozone and smog ambient standards because of out-of state emissions, the EPA has implemented regulations to reduce NO$_x$ emissions from mobile sources, and from power plants and large industrial boilers and turbines." See Figure 19-26.

    iii. CAIR?—"The Clean Air Interstate Rule (CAIR) set new lower caps on SO$_2$ and NO$_x$ in 28 states, many of which are upwind of eastern states experiencing nonattainment of ozone and particulate matter. CAIR would reduce SO$_2$ emissions 50% beginning in 2010 and 65% beginning in 2015."

    iv. New Source Review—"Factories and power plants would no longer be required to update their pollution controls unless the improvements or changes involved more than 20% of the entire facility's value."

C. Coping with Acid Deposition—"Scientists working on acid-rain issues calculated that a 50% reduction in acid-causing emissions in the United States would effectively prevent further acidification of the environment."

    1. Political Developments—"Although evidence of the link between power-plant emissions and acid deposition was well established by the early 1980s, no legislative action was taken until 1990."

        i. Action—"Two decades of action were lost because of political delays. In the wake of the passage of the 1990 act, Canada and the United States signed a treaty stipulating that Canada would cut its sulfur dioxide emissions by half and cap them at 3.2 million tons by the year 2000."

        ii. Title IV of the Clean Air Act Amendments of 1990—"Title IV of the CAAA addressed the acid-deposition problem by mandating reductions in both sulfur dioxide and nitrogen oxide levels."

        iii. Accomplishments of Title IV—"To carry out Title IV of the CAAA, the EPA initiated a two-phase approach." See Figure 19-27.

        iv. Field News—"Under the Acid Rain Reduction Program, air quality has improved, with significant benefits to human health, reductions in acid deposition, some recovery of freshwater lakes and streams, and improved forest conditions."

D. Costs and Benefits—"Satisfying all of the needs and wants (of Americans) is what drives the American economy—and it produces millions of tons of pollutants in the process."

V. Destruction of the Ozone Layer—"Environmental scientists have traced the problem (reduction of the ozone layer) to a widely used group of chemicals: the chlorofluorocarbons or CFCs." See Table 19-4.

229

A. Radiation and Importance of the Shield—"We are spared the more damaging effects from UV rays because most UV radiation (more than 99%) is absorbed by ozone in the stratosphere. For that reason, stratospheric ozone is commonly referred to as the ozone shield." See Figure 19-28 and Figure 19-29.

B. Formation and Breakdown of the Shield—"Ozone is formed in the stratosphere when UV radiation acts on oxygen molecules…the amount of ozone in the stratosphere is dynamic."
   1. Halogens in the Atmosphere—"At room temperature, CFCs are gases under normal (atmospheric pressure), but they liquefy under modest pressure, gibing off heat in the process and becoming cold. When they revaporize, they reabsorb the heat and become hot. These attributes led to the widespread use of CFCs."
      i. Rowland and Molina—CFCs were released into the atmosphere "where they mixed with the normal atmospheric gases and eventually reached the stratosphere." See Figure 19-3.
      ii. EPA Action—"After studying the evidence, the EPA became convinced that CFCs were a threat and, in 1978 banned their use in aerosol cans in the United States. Atmospheric scientists reasoned that any substance carrying reactive halogens to the stratosphere has the potential to deplete ozone."
      iii. The Ozone "Hole"—"In the fall of 1985, British atmospheric scientists working in Antarctica reported a gaping 'hole' in the stratospheric ozone layer over the South Pole. There, in an area the size of the United States, ozone levels were 50% lower than normal." See Figure 19-30.
      iv. Polar Vortex—"When the Antarctic winter arrives in June, it creates a vortex in the stratosphere, which confines stratospheric gases within a ring of air circulating around the Antarctic." See Figure 19-31.
   2. Further Ozone Depletion—"Polar ozone depletion and the subsequent mixing of air masses are responsible for much of this (ozone) loss. The good news from the network is that ozone levels are no longer decreasing."

C. Coming to Grips with Ozone Depletion—"The dramatic growth of the hold in the ozone layer (Fig 19-31) has galvanized a response around the world. Scientists and politicians in the United States and other countries have achieved treaties designed to avert a UV disaster."
   1. Montreal Protocol—In 1987 "member nations reached an agreement, known as the Montreal Protocol, to scale CFC production back 50% by 2000. To date, 194 countries (including the United States) have signed the original agreement." See Figure 19-32.
   2. Action in the United States—"The Clean Air Act Amendments of 1990 also address this problem, in Title VI, Protecting Stratospheric Ozone. Title VI is a comprehensive program that restricts the production, use, emissions, and disposal of an entire family of chemicals identified as ozone depleting."
   3. Final Thoughts—"The ozone story is a remarkable episode in human history. From the first warnings in 1974 that something might be amiss in the stratosphere because of a practically inert and highly useful industrial chemical, through the development of the Montreal Protocol and the final steps of CFC phase out, the world has shown that it can respond collectively and effectively to a clearly perceived threat."

Review Questions: Possible Answers

1. *What naturally occurring cleanser helps to remove pollutants from the atmosphere? Where does it come from? What other mechanisms also act to cleanse the atmosphere of pollutants?*

   The hydroxyl radical, sea salts, and sunlight are natural cleansers of pollutants in the atmosphere. Ozone is the major source of the hydroxyl radical.

2. *Describe the origins of industrial smog and photochemical smog, and atmospheric brown clouds. What are the differences in the cause and appearance of each?*

   Industrial smog is typically generated by the use of coal and occurs in cold cloudy areas. It is an "irritating, grayish mixture of soot, sulfurous compounds, and water vapor." Photochemical smog is typically generated by burning of gasoline in internal combustion engines. Local weather conditions are usually warm and sunny. Automobile exhaust, nitrogen oxides, and volatile organic compounds react with sunlight to create photochemical smog.

3. *What are the major primary air pollutants and their sources?*

   Suspended particulate matter (PM): Sources are soot, smoke, metals, and carbon from combustion; dust, salts, metal, and dirt from wind erosion; atmospheric reactions of gases. Volatile organic compounds (VOC): Sources are incomplete combustion of fossil fuels; evaporation of solvents and gasoline; emissions from plants. Carbon monoxide (CO): Sources are incomplete combustion of fuels. Nitrogen oxides (NO_x): Source is from nitrogen gas due to high combustion temperatures when burning fuels. Sulfur oxides (SO_x): Source is primarily from the combustion of sulfur-containing fuels. Lead: Sources are combustion of leaded fuels and solid wastes. Air toxics: Sources are industry and transportation. Radon: Sources are rocks and soil; natural breakdown of radium and uranium.

4. *What are the secondary pollutants, and how are they formed?*

   Ozone is a secondary pollutant formed as a result of a reaction between nitrogen oxides and volatile organic compounds with sunlight as the energy source to run the reaction. Other photochemical oxidants (aldehydes, ketones, PAN) are formed under the same conditions as ozone. Sulfur and nitric acids are also secondary pollutants. These chemicals are formed when sulfur dioxide or nitrogen oxides react with "atmospheric moisture and oxidants such as hydroxyl."

5. *Distinguish between emissions and ambient concentrations. How are they measured?*

   Emissions are the release of primary pollutants from their sources. The emissions we measure show how much of each pollutant is released from a source. Ambient concentrations are the amount of each pollutant measured in the air. There are "thousands of monitoring stations across the country" that measure the amount of each pollutant in the ambient air.

6. *What is the difference between an acid and a base? What is the pH scale?*

   ". . . (A)n acid is any chemical that releases hydrogen ions when dissolved in water. A base is any chemical that releases hydroxide ions (OH⁻, oxygen-hydrogen groups with an extra electron) when dissolved in water." pH is "(t)he concentration of hydrogen ions. . . ." The pH scale is a way of measuring the amount of Hydrogen or Hydroxide ions in a solution. It ranges from 0 to 14. Numbers below 7 represent acids, and numbers above 7 represent bases.

7. *What two major acids are involved in acid deposition? Where does each come from?*

The two major acids involved in acid deposition are nitric acid and sulfuric acid. Nitric acid primarily comes from tailpipe emissions (56%) and fuel combustion at fixed sites (39%), and sulfuric acid primarily comes "from fuel combustion (mostly from coal-burning power plants)" (86%).

8. *What impacts does air pollution have on human health? Give the three categories of impact and distinguish among them.*

"Every one of the primary and secondary air pollutants is a threat to human health, particularly the health of the respiratory system. Acute exposure to some pollutants can be life threatening, but many effects are chronic, acting over a period of years to cause a gradual deterioration of physiological functions. Moreover, some pollutants are carcinogenic, adding significantly to the risk of lung cancer as they are breathed into the lungs."

    a) Chronic effects are effects that occur due to long-term exposure. Health impacts include bronchitis, fibrosis of the lung, reduced capacity of blood to carry oxygen, impaired lung function, and adversely impacted immune system.

    b) Acute affects occur when exposed to high levels of pollutants over a short period of time. Health impacts include death and heart attacks.

    c) Carcinogenic effects are typically a result of low level exposure over a long period of time.

9. *Describe the negative effects of pollutants on crops, forests, and other materials. Which pollutants are mainly responsible for these effects?*

Negative effects of air pollution on crops, forests, and other materials include the following: "(t)he dying off of vegetation in large urban areas and the damage to crops, orchards, and forests downwind of urban centers are caused mainly by exposure to ozone and other photochemical oxidants. Estimates of crop damage by ozone range from $2 billion to $6 billion per year, with an estimated $1 billion in California alone. The negative impact of air pollution on wild plants and forest trees may be even greater than on agricultural crops. Significant damage to valuable ponderosa and Jeffrey pines occurred along the entire western foothills of the Sierra Nevada in California. Forests under stress from pollution are more susceptible to damage by insects and other pathogens than unstressed forests. Walls, windows, and other exposed surfaces turn gray and dingy as particulates settle on them. Paints and fabrics deteriorate more rapidly, and the sidewalls of tires and other rubber products become hard and checkered with cracks because of oxidation by ozone. Metal corrosion is increased dramatically by sulfur dioxide and acids derived from sulfur and nitrogen oxides, as are weathering and deterioration of stonework."

The pollutants mainly responsible for these effects are ozone and sulfuric and nitric acid.

10. *How can a shift in environmental pH affect aquatic ecosystems? In what other ecosystem can acid deposition be observed? What are its effects?*

"The pH of an environment is extremely critical, because it affects the function of virtually all enzymes, hormones, and other proteins in the bodies of all organisms living in that environment. Ordinarily, organisms are able to regulate their internal pH within the narrow limits necessary to function properly. A consistently low environmental pH, however, often overwhelms the regulatory mechanisms in many life-forms, thus weakening or killing them. Most freshwater lakes, ponds, and streams have a natural pH in the range from 6 to 8, and organisms are adapted accordingly. Most are severely stressed, and many die, if the environmental pH shifts as little as one unit from the optimum. As aquatic ecosystems become acidified (pH 5 and below), higher organisms die off, either because the acidified water kills them or because it keeps them from reproducing."

"From the Green Mountains of Vermont to the San Bernardino Mountains of California, the die-off of forests trees in the 1980s caused great concern. Red spruce forests are especially vulnerable. In New England, 1.3 million acres of high-elevation forests were devastated. Commonly, the damaged trees lost needles as acidic water drew calcium from them, rendering them more susceptible to winter freezing. Sugar maples, important tress in the Northeast, have shown extensive mortality, ranging from 20–80% of all trees in some forests. Much of the damage from acid precipitation to forests is due to chemical interactions within the forests soils. Sustained acid precipitation at first adds nitrogen and sulfur to the soils, which stimulate tree growth. In time, though, these chemicals leach out large quantities of the buffering chemicals (usually calcium and magnesium salts). When these buffering salts no longer neutralize the acid rain, aluminum ions, which are toxic, are dissolved from minerals in the soil. The combination of aluminum and the increasing scarcity of calcium, which is essential to plant growth, leads to reduced tree growth."

11. *What are the criteria pollutants and the National Ambient Air Quality Standards, and how are they used?*

The Clean Air Act required that the most widespread pollutants be identified, ambient standards—"levels that need to be achieved to protect environmental and human health"—be set, and "control methods and timetables to meet the standards" be established.

The six criteria pollutants that are covered by the National Ambient Air Quality Standards are carbon monoxide, nitric oxides, sulfur dioxide, particulates, ozone, and lead. The primary standards are quantities of the pollutants that can be found in air and are "based on the presumed highest level that can be tolerated by humans without noticeable ill effects, minus a 10% to 50% margin of safety."

12. *Discuss ways in which the Clean Air Act Amendments of 1990 addressed the failures of previous legislation.*

"The Clean Air Act Amendments (CAAA) of 1990 target specific pollutants more directly and enforce compliance more aggressively, through such means as the imposition of sanctions. As with the earlier law, the states do much of the work in carrying out the mandates of the 1990 act. Each state must develop a State Implementation Plan (SIP) that is required to go through a process of public comment before being submitted to the EPA for approval. One major change is a permit application process (already in place for the release of pollutants into waterways). Polluters must apply for a permit that identifies the kinds of pollutants they release, the quantities of those pollutants, and the steps they are taking to reduce pollution. Permit fees provide funds the states can use to support their air-pollution control activities. The amendments also afford more flexibility than the earlier command-and-control approach, by allowing polluters to choose the most cost-effective way to accomplish the goals. In addition, the legislation uses a market system to allocate pollution among different utilities."

13. *What are the major steps being taken to reduce emissions from passenger vehicles?*

The use of catalytic converters in cars has reduced emissions dramatically. In addition, new cars sold in 1994 were required to emit 30% less VOCs and 60% less nitrogen oxides. In 1992, oxygen began to be added to gasoline to reduce carbon monoxide emissions. After 1990, inspections began to be required for measuring emissions. Finally, CAFE standards have set fuel economy standards for motor vehicles.

14. *How do the NO$_x$ Budget Trading Program and CAIR address ozone pollution*

The NO$_x$ Budget Trading Program is the "cap and trade" system has allowed companies some "flexibility in how they were to attain their target budgets" for emissions that could lead to ozone pollution. CAIR reduced the allowable amounts of SO$_2$ and NO$_x$ which lead to ozone pollution.

15. *What has been happening in the United States to reduce acid deposition and how successful it has been?*

The Title VI of the Clean Air Act Amendments of 1990 aims at reducing pollutants and acid producing compounds. "Under the Acid Rain Reduction Program, air quality has improved, with significant benefits to human health, reductions in acid deposition, some recovery of freshwater lakes and streams, and improved forest conditions."

16. *How is the protective ozone shield formed? What causes its natural breakdown?*

"Ozone is formed in the stratosphere when UV radiation acts on oxygen molecules. The high-energy radiation first causes some molecular oxygen to split apart into free oxygen atoms, and these atoms then combine with molecular oxygen to form ozone." This reaction is reversible. "When ozone absorbs UVB, it is converted back to free oxygen and molecular oxygen."

233

17. *How do CFCs affect the concentration of ozone in the stratosphere and contribute to the formation of the ozone hole?*

CFCs release chlorine atoms and damage the stratospheric ozone layer. CFCs combine with the ultraviolet rays of the sun to release Chlorine that can combine with ozone and cause it to break down. "Chlorine acts as a catalyst, a chemical that promotes a chemical reaction without itself being used up in the reaction." This catalytic response of Chlorine can cause the damage of untold amount of ozone, leading to significant areas of depletion.

18. *Describe the international efforts that are currently in place to protect our ozone shield? What evidence is there that such efforts have been effective?*

The Montreal Protocol, signed by 194 countries, has been a significant stride forward in protection of ozone. CFCs have been reduced to the point that they are barely produced at all anymore. "The results of the protocol can be seen clearly in Figure 19-32, which shows the time course of production of ozone-depleting chemicals and the abundance of those chemicals in the stratosphere."

Thinking Environmentally: Possible Answers

1. *Motor vehicles release close to half the pollutants that dirty our air. What alternatives might be introduced to encourage a decrease in our use of automobiles and other vehicles with internal combustion engines?*

Various alternatives could be introduced, including subsidies for mass transit and installation of bike and walking paths. Car pooling could be encouraged on a large scale. A carbon tax on gasoline could be implemented to provide funds for alternative transportation, to encourage gas efficient cars, and to reduce driving. A tax could be imposed on automobiles (similar to what is done in European countries), making cars very expensive to own. Cities and other municipalities could be encouraged (subsidies, etc.) to change land use planning to discourage sprawl and increase the proximity of homes to work and shopping. Parking lots could be taxed at a higher rate than other land uses. Fuel efficiency of cars should be increased, and cars with hybrid engines could be subsidized. Anything that would decrease car use and increase alternative transportation that does not directly or indirectly produce air pollution should be encouraged.

2. *How would our pattern of life be different in the absence of the Clean Air Act and its amendments? Write a short essay describing the possibilities.*

Without the Clean Air Act and its amendments the air we breathe would be very deadly. The death rate for children and older adults would be higher than it is currently. There would be more people who are unable to participate in society because of disabilities caused by poor air quality. The number of days of school missed by children would be higher due to increased incidence of asthma and other lung-related diseases. School absenteeism decreases the level of education among affected children. The cost of health care would be much higher.

Some industries that require clean air would have to spend money to filter the air prior to use. The rate of decay of materials would be faster, and the cost of building, bridge, and highway maintenance would be higher. Food would cost more because more crops would be damaged or destroyed due to poor air quality. More forests would be damaged and the cost of forest products would be higher. The number of lakes that would be dead would be higher, and those people who depend upon forests and lakes for their livelihoods would be unemployed. Employers would have to deal with a higher illness rate among workers.

3. *The wind blows across Country A and into Country B. Country A has fossil-fueling-burning power plants, but a relatively low level of air pollution. Country B has power plants run by moving water (hydroelectric plants), but a higher level of pollution. What's happening? What could the two countries do to correct the situation? Explain how this pertains to international air-pollution laws.*

The wind can scatter pollutants from the area where they are produced elsewhere. If the wind is blowing pollutants from Country A into Country B, then even though Country B is acting more sustainably they may suffer the consequences of Country A's less responsible actions. It would be important to establish a clear connection between the pollution in Country B and the actions of power plants in Country A before the countries correct the situation. Possible resolutions might be reimbursements for Country B or resolutions for Country A to reduce emissions by a certain percentage per year until reasonable standards were met. International air-pollution laws are complicated, since some countries may be taking on a pollution responsibility that is not necessarily their own. Flexibility for such issues has to be built into international law.

4. *A large amount of air pollution is attributed to manufacturing. Some would argue that it is not technologically possible, or economically efficient, to eliminate this pollution. How would you respond to this argument?*

   Student answers will vary. Arguments should include the eventual economic cost of illnesses and loss of materials and infrastructure associated with pollution, which many times are not considered in the "economic" argument.

5. *What arguments might the auto and utility industries present to delay regulatory action on particulates and ozone? How would health officials respond to their arguments?*

   "Recent understanding of the complex chemical reactions involving NO_x, VOCs, and oxygen has thrown some uncertainty into simply emphasizing a reduction in VOCs." Since there may be many possible chemical combinations leading to the production of dangerous pollutants, the auto and utility industries may argue that their role in the production of pollution may be less than previously thought. Despite this possible reduced role on the part of industries, dramatic health benefits have been demonstrated since the reductions from these industries have occurred.

CHAPTER 20
Water Pollution and Its Prevention

Chapter Outline:

I. Perspectives on Water Pollution
    A. Water Pollution: Sources and Type
        1. Pathogens
            i. Public Health
            ii. Sanitation = Good Medicine
        2. Organic Wastes
            i. BOD
        3. Chemical Pollutants
        4. Sediments
            i. Bed Load
        5. Nutrients
        6. Water Quality Standards
            i. Criteria Pollutants
            ii. Arsenic
            iii. Other Applications
II. Wastewater Treatment and Management
    A. The Pollutants in Raw Wastewater
        1. Types of Pollutants
    B. Removing the Pollutants from Wastewater
        1. Primary Treatment
        2. Secondary Treatment
        3. Biological Nutrient Removal
            i. Nitrogen
            ii. Phosphorus
        4. Final Cleansing and Disinfection
            i. Final Effluent
    C. Treatment of Sludge
        1. Anaerobic Digestion
        2. Composting
        3. Pasteurization
    D. Alternative Treatment Systems
            i. Septic System Primer
            ii. Composting Toilet Systems
        1. Using Effluents for Irrigation
            i. Growing Crops
        2. Reconstructed Wetland Systems
III. Eutrophication

236

    A. Different Kinds of Aquatic Plants
       i. Benthic Plants
       ii. Phytoplankton
    B. The Impacts of Nutrient Enrichment
      1. The Process of Eutrophication
      2. Shallow Lakes and Ponds
      3. Natural Versus Cultural Eutrophication
    C. Combating Eutrophication
      1. Attacking the Symptoms
        i. Applying Herbicides
        ii. Aerating
        iii. Harvesting
        iv. Drawing Water Down
      2. Getting at the Root Cause
        i. Ecoregional Nutrient Criteria
        ii. NPDES: Control Strategy for Point Sources
        iii. TMDL: Control Strategy for Nonpoint Sources
        iv. Best Management Practices
      3. Recovery
        i. Lake Washington
IV. Public Policy and Water Pollution
        i. Reauthorization
        ii. Problems and Progress

Key Topics:

1. Perspectives on Water Pollution
2. Wastewater Treatment and Management
3. Eutrophication
4. Public Policy and Water Pollution

Instructional Goals:

1. Most water pollution can be described as resources out of place.

2. Water pollutants are pathogenic organisms, chemicals, substances that alter habitat, and various kinds of nutrients.

3. Sewage management and treatment, along with sludge treatment, have been extremely effective in the elimination of a variety of forms of pollution and improving public health.

4. Sewage treatment can be accomplished using methods that enhance wetlands and groundwater.

5. Natural eutrophication occurs much less often than cultural eutrophication.

6. Eliminating eutrophication is most effective if we eliminate the root causes.

Concepts and Connections:

Having clean water is essential for human survival and the survival of any other organism on Earth. Of the substances essential for survival—air, water, and food—only air is more important than water. We can live minutes without oxygen, days without water, and weeks without food.

Despite the fact that little of the Earth's water is accessible to humans and is fresh, we have polluted large amounts of accessible freshwater. Not only does the polluting of water reduce the available water per person but population size increases and settlements in regions of the world where water is scarce put pressure on water resources.

Water, because of its physical characteristics, is easy to pollute; it is a universal solvent. By making connections between the human tendency not to think about the consequences of our actions with the tendency of water to dissolve many chemicals and our need to have clean and accessible freshwater, we can help students to understand our tenuous position when it comes to water. Air pollution, disposal of solid and hazardous waste, and non-sustainable agricultural practices all create situations that may result in water pollution.

Concepts in Context:

Limiting factors, habitats, niches (Chapter 3); biogeochemical cycles, especially the nitrogen and phosphorus cycles (Chapter 4); population dynamics; ecological succession (Chapter 5); and ecosystem sustainability are integral to any discussion of water pollution and prevention. The hydrological cycle (Chapter 10) is integral to both how water is purified and how it can be polluted. The variety of aquatic ecosystems on Earth provides biodiversity (Chapter 6) that could not be duplicated on land; unfamiliar life forms abound in aquatic environments.

Human population size (Chapter 8) creates a potential for water pollution due to our waste products. How we practice agricultural (Chapter 11, 12, and 13), use ecosystems for goods and services (Chapter 7), produce and use energy (Chapter 14, 15, and 16), and dispose of solid (Chapter 21) and hazardous waste (Chapter 22) create a potential for water pollution. Atmospheric pollution (Chapter 19) can result in local and remote water pollution. Human health (Chapter 17) is dependent upon clean water.

Key Terms and Vocabulary:

The Federal Water Pollution Control Act of 1948, Clean Water Act of 1972 (CWA), point sources, nonpoint sources, pathogens, biochemical oxygen demand (BOD), inorganic chemicals, organic chemicals, bed load, National Recommended Water Quality Criteria, criteria pollutants, Drinking Water Standards and Health Advisories, Safe Drinking Water Act (SDWA), maximum contaminant levels (MCLs), National Pollution Discharge Elimination System (NPDES), total maximum daily load (TMDL), raw sewage, raw wastewater, bar screen, grit chamber, raw sludge, secondary treatment, trickling-filter system, activated sludge system, activated sludge, secondary clarifier

238

tank, biological nutrient removal (BNR), denitrification, anaerobic digestion, biogas, treated sludge, biosolids, sludge cake, composing, pasteurized, benthic plants, submerged aquatic vegetation (SAV), emergent vegetation, eutrophication, best management, Clean State Revolving Fund (SRF)

Discussion, Activities, and Labs:

1. Ask the students to describe water pollution they have seen. Ask each respondent to explain why they believe that what they saw was pollution. What sensory cues did they use? Why did this information tell them that they were seeing pollution?

2. Ask the students any or all of the following questions to prompt them to think about water. What substances will and will not dissolve in water? What substances can be suspended in water and therefore make the water cloudy, cutting off light required for photosynthesis? Is it possible to be alive and not produce waste products? What is the difference between waste products and pollution? Do some substances have a greater pollution potential than other substances? Why?

3. Ask the students to speculate as to why we don't combine storm water drains with our sanitary sewers. What would be the consequences of combining these two systems when it rains? Ask the students to speculate as to the impact of combining industrial effluent with the sewage from our homes. What are the differences in the kinds and quantities of materials that people put down their drains and the kinds and quantities of things industries might dispose of in the sewer system? (The combining of industrial and home-generated wastes has resulted in difficulties by some communities in the reuse of bio-solids due to heavy metal or organic solvent contamination from industrial sources. Industrial pretreatment is a possible solution.)

4. The hypoxic area in the Gulf of Mexico is an excellent topic of discussion. Begin with asking the students to describe the problem. The idea is to get at the quantity of nutrients being dumped into the gulf from the Mississippi River and the impact on the coastal ecosystem. Next, ask where and why these nutrients are in the Mississippi River when it flows into the gulf. The idea is to get the students to mention nutrient sources such as fertilizer on farmland from as far north as the head waters of the Mississippi; nutrients from livestock operations, fertilizer, pet wastes, and so forth from suburbs and cities; and wastewater effluent from the towns and cities along the Mississippi River. Additionally, the levees along the Mississippi River have contributed to the problem because nutrients that would have been deposited on the land before reaching the gulf. The final part of the discussion should focus on the solutions. How can we address the problem? Solutions range from tertiary wastewater treatment and reduced fertilizer application to the creation of seasonal wetland areas to handle spring floods.

5. Most students know substances can be dissolved in water but they have never thought about why or what the limitations might be. In this exercise create groups of two to three students and ask the groups to formulate testable questions about common substances. After formulating 10 testable questions, have each group perform experiments that would attempt to answer two of the questions. Different substances have different potential for dissolving in water. Various soluble and insoluble substances can be assembled (oil, salt, sugar, isopropyl alcohol, silt, sand, compost, instant coffee, etc.), and students can be asked to discover what will dissolve in water, how much can be dissolved, and why some materials are more soluble than other materials. If a substance does not dissolve in water, what kind of harm/benefit can result? If a substance does dissolve in water, what kind of harm/benefit can result? Does water temperature affect how much of a substance can dissolve in water?

6. The settling process used in primary water treatment can be demonstrated by providing each student with a glass jar, containing water and a combination of silt, sand, clay, and so on. Each jar contains a known proportion of materials such that jar A will settle faster than jar B, etc. Have each student shake the jar

containing the water and various materials and then time how long it takes before the materials have settled to the bottom. If you wish, you could at various times during the class ask the students to note if all, part (what percentage), or none of the material has settled. These data can be recorded as the class proceeds. When you reach the portion of the class on primary and secondary water treatment, stop the experiment. The portion of the material that has settled at this time is the portion that would be (hypothetically) removed by primary treatment. The remaining suspended material moves on to secondary treatment. (If you wish, you could have the student create a mixture of the materials on his or her own and formulate a hypothesis concerning the speed with which the material will settle.)

7. Assign groups of two to three students to determine the source of the local drinking water and the kinds of sewage treatment performed. If the students have the same hometown, then ask them to discover the information for their hometown. Once the source of the drinking water has been determined, if it is surface water, ask the students to investigate if a city or town releases treated effluent to the surface water upstream from the water supply intake. If the sewage treatment is a septic system, have the students investigate the possible flow of water underground and determine the closest surface water or groundwater use.

Suggested Lecture Format:

    I.   Perspectives on Water Pollution

        A. Water Pollution: Sources and Type—"Water pollutants originate from a host of human activities and reach surface water or groundwater through an equally diverse host of pathways. For purposes of regulation, it is customary to distinguish between point sources and nonpoint sources of pollutants." See Figure 20-3. **See also Discussion Topics #1 and #5.**

            1. Pathogens—"The most serious and widespread water pollutants are the infectious agents that cause sickness and death."

                i. Public Health—Standards regarding the purification and disinfection of water supplies, collection and treatment of wastes, standards in food processing facilities, and hygiene practices are "set and enforced by government public-health departments."

                ii. Sanitation = Good Medicine—"Many people attribute good health in a population to modern medicine, but good health is primarily a result of the prevention of disease through public-health measures." See Table 9-2.

            2. Organic Wastes—"Along with pathogens, human and animal wastes contain organic matter that creates serious problems if it enters bodies of water untreated."

                i. BOD—"Biochemical oxygen demand (BOD) is a measure of the amount of organic materials in water, stated in terms of how much oxygen will be required to break it down biologically, chemically, or both." See Figure 20-6.

            3. Chemical Pollutants—"Because water is such an excellent solvent, it is able to hold many chemical substances in solution that have undesirable effects." See Figure 20-7.

            4. Sediments—"Sediment entering waterways in large amounts has an array of impacts." See Figure 20-8. **See also Discussion Topic #2.**

                i. Bed Load—"As particles roll and tumble along, they scour organisms from the rocks."

            5. Nutrients—"The two most important nutrient elements for aquatic plant growth are phosphorus and nitrogen, and they are often in such low supply in water that they are the limiting factors for phytoplankton or other aquatic plants."

6. Water Quality Standards—"Pollution means any quantity that is harmful to human health or the environment, or prevents full use of the environment by humans or natural species."
   i. Criteria Pollutants—"The EPA has established the National Recommended Water Quality Criteria. On the basis of the latest scientific knowledge, the EPA has listed 167 chemicals and substances as criteria pollutants."
   ii. Arsenic—"Arsenic is listed as a known human carcinogen by the Department of Health and Human Services; it occurs naturally in groundwater, reaching high concentrations in some parts of the world."
   iii. Other Applications—"Two important applications of water quality criteria are the National Pollution Discharge Elimination System (NPDES) and the Total Maximum Daily Load (TMDL) programs."

II. Wastewater Treatment and Management—See **Discussion Topic #3.**

   A. The Pollutants in Raw Wastewater—The mixture of wastewater "collected from all drains, which flows from the end of the 'trunk' of the other collections system, is called raw sewage or raw wastewater."
      1. Types of Pollutants—Pollutants in wastewater can be considered debris and grit, particulate organic material, colloidal and dissolved organic material, and dissolved organic material.

   B. Removing the Pollutants from Wastewater—See Figure 20-10 for a summary of the waste treatment process.
      1. Primary Treatment—Removal of grit and debris with the help of screens and the settling process is the first step in waste treatment. **See Discussion Topic #6.**
      2. Secondary Treatment—"Secondary treatment is also called biological treatment because it uses organisms-natural decomposers and detritus feeders." See Figures 20-10 and 20-11.
      3. Biological Nutrient Removal—"Today, with increased awareness of the problem of cultural eutrophication, secondary activated-sludge systems have been added and are being modified and operated in a manner that both removed nutrients and oxidizes detritus in a process known as biological nutrient removal."
         i. Nitrogen—"For the biological removal of nitrogen, then, the activated-sludge system is partitioned into zones, and the environment in each zone is controlled in a manner that promotes the denitrifying process." See Figure 20-12.
         ii. Phosphorus—"In an environment that is rich in oxygen, but relatively lacking in foot, bacteria take up phosphate from the solution and store it in their bodies."
      4. Final Cleansing and Disinfection-"Although few pathogens survive the combined stages of treatment, public-health rigors still demand that the water be disinfected before being discharged into natural waterways."
         i. Final Effluent—"After all these steps, the wastewater from a modern treatment plant has a lower organic and nutrient content than many bodies of water into which it is discharged." **See Discussion Topic #7.**

   C. Treatment of Sludge—"Three commonly used methods for treating sludge and converting it into organic fertilizer are anaerobic digestion, composting, and pasteurization."

1. Anaerobic Digestion—"Anaerobic digestion is a process that allows bacteria to feed on the sludge in the absence of oxygen." See Figures 20-13 and 20-14.
2. Composting—After excess water is removed from raw sludge, it is placed in windrows to allow it to aerate. Over time decomposers break it down into a humus-like material.
3. Pasteurization—Raw sludge may be dried and thus pasteurized to kill any pathogens.
   D. Alternative Treatment Systems—"The traditional and still most common on-site system is the septic tank and leaching field. See Figure 20-15.
      i. Septic System Primer—See page 534 for suggestions about maintaining a successful septic system.
      ii. Composting Toilet Systems—"The objective of the system is to provide a sanitary means of treating human wastes that will destroy human pathogens and produce stable humus-like end product that can be safely disposed of." See Figure 10-16.
   1. Using Effluents for Irrigation—"The nutrient-rich water coming from the standard secondary- treatment process is beneficial for growing plants…why not use it for irrigating plants we do want to grow?"
      i. Growing Crops—"A number of developing countries irrigate croplands with raw (untreated) sewage effluents. This practice results in getting the bad with the good."
   2. Reconstructed Wetland Systems—"In treating waste-water, it is also possible to make use of the nutrient-absorbing capacity of wetlands in suitable areas and under suitable climatic conditions."

III. Eutrophication—**See Discussion Topic #4.**

   A. Different Kinds of Aquatic Plants—"To understand eutrophication, you need to be able to distinguish between benthic plants and phytoplankton."
      i. Benthic Plants—"Benthic plants are aquatic plants that grow attached to, or are rooted in, the bottom of a body of water."
      ii. Phytoplankton—"Phytoplankton consists of numerous species of photosynthetic algae, protists, and chlorophyll-containing bacteria that grow as microscopic single cells or in small groups or 'threads' of cells." See Figure 20-17.

   B. The Impacts of Nutrient Enrichment—"In an oligotrophic lake, the low nutrient levels limit the growth of phytoplankton and allow enough light to penetrate to support the growth of SAV, which draws its nutrients from the bottom sediments."
   1. The Process of Eutrophication—"In sum, eutrophication refers to this whole sequence of events (see Figure 20-18), starting with nutrient enrichment and proceeding to the growth and die-off of phytoplankton, the accumulation of detritus, the growth of bacteria, and finally, the depletion of dissolved oxygen and the suffocation of higher organisms."
   2. Shallow Lakes and Ponds—"In lakes and ponds whole water depth is 6 feet or less, eutrophication takes a somewhat different course." SAV grow and cover the surface of the water like a matt.
   3. Natural Versus Cultural Eutrophication—"Natural eutrophication is a normal process."

C. Combating Eutrophication—"There are two approaches to combating the problem of cultural eutrophication. One is to attack the symptoms…the other is to get at the root of the cause."

    1. Attacking the Symptoms—"Attacking the symptoms is appropriate in certain situations where immediate remediation is the goal and costs are not prohibitive."

        i. Applying Herbicides—"Herbicides are often applied to ponds and lakes to control the growth of nuisance plants."

        ii. Aerating—Aeration of the water can avert the final stages of eutrophication.

        iii. Harvesting—"Harvesting aquatic weeds may be an expedient way to improve the water's recreational potential and aesthetics." See Figure 20-19.

        iv. Drawing Water Down—"Because many recreational lakes are dammed, another option for shallow-water weed control is to draw the lake down for a period each year."

    2. Getting at the Root Cause—"Controlling eutrophication requires long-term strategies for correcting the problem, which ultimately means reducing the inputs of nutrients and sediments."

        i. Ecoregional Nutrient Criteria—"Beginning in 2001, the EPA began publishing water-quality nutrient criteria aimed at preventing and reducing the eutrophication that impacts so many bodies of water."

        ii. NPDES: Control Strategy for Point Sources—"Bans on detergents with phosphates and upgrades of sewage-treatment plants have brought about marked improvements in waterways that were heavily damaged by effluents from these plants."

        iii. TMDL: Control Strategy for Nonpoint Sources—"Remediation of nonpoint sources will involve thousands—perhaps millions—of individual property owners adopting new practices regarding land management and the use of fertilizer and other chemicals on their properties."

        iv. Best Management Practices—"Reducing or eliminating pollution from nonpoint sources will involve different strategies for different sources." See Table 20-2.

    3. Recovery—"The good news is that cultural eutrophication and other forms of water pollution can be controlled and often reversed, provided that a total watershed management approach is undertaken."

        i. Lake Washington—"One remarkable success story is Lake Washington, east of Seattle." See Figure 20-20.

IV. Public Policy and Water Pollution

        i. Reauthorization—"Reauthorization of the Clean Water Act is long overdue."

        ii. Problems and Progress—"A national sense of stewardship has been applied to the rivers, lakes, and bays that are our heritage from a previous generation, and public policy has been enacted and billions of dollars spent to bring our waters back from a polluted condition."

Review Questions: Possible Answers

1. What practices and consequences led to passage of the Clean Water Act of 1972?

"The Federal Water Pollution Control Act of 1948 was the first federal foray into water pollution, providing technical assistance to state and local governments, but otherwise leaving things up to the states and local municipalities. In the 1950s, as industrial production expanded and synthetic organics came into widespread use in the developed countries, many streams and rivers essentially became open chemical sewers as well as sewers for human waste. These waters not only were devoid of life, but also were themselves hazardous. Finally, in 1969, the Cuyahoga River, which flows through Cleveland, Ohio, was carrying so much flammable material that it actually caught on fire and destroyed seven bridges before the fire burned itself out. Worsening pollution (from both chemicals and sewage) and increasing recognition of the adverse health effects finally created a degree of public outrage that pushed Congress to pass the Clean Water Act of 1972."

2. Discuss each of the following categories of water pollutants and the problems they cause: pathogens, organic wastes, chemical pollutants, and sediments.

Waterborne disease (pathogens) reaches water through animal (including human) wastes being discharged to land or water; the basic impact is disease. Human and animal wastes reach water by either direct discharge or runoff from land; the basic impact is the addition of nutrients (limiting factors) and disease to water. Chemicals pollute water by either direct discharge to water or runoff from land; the basic impacts are rendering "water unpalatable (or dangerous) for humans and dangerous for aquatic life." Sediments reach water as a result of erosion; the basic impact is to increase turbidity and increase the nutrient load.

3. How are water quality standards determined? Distinguish between water quality criteria pollutants and maximum contaminant levels.

"On the basis of the latest scientific knowledge, the EPA has listed 158 chemicals and substances as **criteria pollutants**. The majority of these are toxic chemicals, but many are also natural chemicals or conditions that describe the state of water. The list identifies the pollutant and then recommends concentrations for fresh water, salt water, and human consumption."

"Drinking water standards are stricter. For these, the EPA has established the Drinking Water Standards and Health Advisories, a set of tables that are updated periodically. These standards, covering some 90 contaminants, are enforceable under the authority of the Safe Drinking Water Act. They are present as **maximum contaminant levels**."

4. Name and describe the facility and the process used to remove debris, grit, particulate organic matter, colloidal and dissolved organic matter, and dissolved nutrients from wastewater.

A sewage treatment plant removes debris, grit, particulate organic matter, colloidal and dissolved organic matter, and dissolved nutrients from wastewater. The **preliminary treatment** process removes debris and grit using a **bar screen**—a row of bars about 1 inch apart that blocks debris and is mechanically removed to be incinerated—and a **grit chamber**—swimming pool-like tank in which (the sewage) velocity is slowed just enough to permit the grit to settle" and to be removed mechanically prior to disposal at a landfill. The **primary treatment** process removes particulate organic matter in large tanks called **primary clarifiers**. Because the flow is slow, the water is nearly motionless for several hours. The particulate organic material, about 30–50% of the total organic material, settles to the bottom, where it can be removed. At the same time, fatty or oily material floats to the top, where it is skimmed from the surface. All the material that is removed, both particulate organic material and fatty material, is combined into what is referred to as raw sludge. **Secondary treatment** removes the colloidal and dissolved organic material. "Secondary treatment is also called biological treatment, because it uses organisms—natural decomposers and detritus feeders. Basically, an environment is created that enables these organisms to feed on colloidal and dissolved organic material and break it down to carbon dioxide and water via their cell respiration. The only thing that needs to be added to the water is oxygen to enhance the organisms' respiration and growth. Either of two systems may be used to add oxygen to the water: a trickling-filter system or an activated-sludge system. In the trickling-filter system, the water exiting from primary treatment is sprinkled onto, and allowed to percolate through, a bed of fist-sized rocks 6–8 feet deep. The spaces between the rocks provide good aeration." In the activated-sludge system (w)ater from the

244

primary treatment enters a large tank that is equipped with an air-bubbling system or a rapidly churning system of paddles. A mixture of detritus-feeding organisms, referred to as activated sludge, is added to the water as it enters the tank, and the water is vigorously aerated as it moves through the tank. (F)rom the aeration tank, the water is passed into a secondary clarifier tank where the organisms settle out and the water—now with more than 90% of all the organic material removed—flows on." **Tertiary treatment** or Biological Nutrient Removal is the removal of the dissolved inorganic material (also called biological nutrients). "For the biological removal of nitrogen . . . the activated-sludge system is partitioned into zones, and the environment in each zone is controlled in a manner that promotes the denitrifying process. In an environment that is rich in oxygen, but relatively lacking in food—the environment of zone 3—bacteria take up phosphate from solution and store it in their bodies. Thus phosphate is removed as the excess organisms are removed from the system." Chemical treatments are also used as alternatives to biological nutrient removal.

5. Why is secondary treatment also called biological treatment? What is the principle involved? What are the two alternative techniques used?

"Secondary treatment is also called biological treatment, because it uses organisms—natural decomposers and detritus feeders. Basically, an environment is created that enables these organisms to feed on colloidal and dissolved organic material and break it down to carbon dioxide and water via their cell respiration" The only thing that needs to be added to the water is oxygen to enhance the organisms' respiration and growth. Either of two systems may be used to add oxygen to the water: a trickling-filter system or an activated-sludge system. In the trickling-filter system, the water exiting from primary treatment is sprinkled onto, and allowed to percolate through a bed of fist-sized rocks 6–8 feet deep. The spaces between the rocks provide good aeration." In the activated-sludge system (w)ater from the primary treatment enters a large tank that is equipped with an air-bubbling system or a rapidly churning system of paddles. A mixture of detritus-feeding organisms, referred to as activated sludge, is added to the water as it enters the tank, and the water is vigorously aerated as it moves through the tank. (F)rom the aeration tank, the water is passed into a secondary clarifier tank where the organisms settle out and the water—now with more than 90% of all the organic material removed—flows on."

6. What are the principles involved in removing biological nutrients from waste, and what is accomplished by doing so? Where do nitrogen and phosphate go in the process?

Biological Nutrient Removal is the removal of the dissolved inorganic material (also called biological nutrients) from wastewater. This process removes the nutrients that can cause cultural eutrophication. "For the biological removal of nitrogen . . . the activated-sludge system is partitioned into zones, and the environment in each zone is controlled in a manner that promotes the denitrifying process." The nitrogen is released to the atmosphere. "In an environment that is rich in oxygen, but relatively lacking in food . . . bacteria take up phosphate from solution and store it in their bodies. Thus phosphate is removed as the excess organisms are removed from the system."

7. Name and describe the three methods of treating raw sludge, and give the end product(s) that may be produced from each method.

"**Anaerobic digestion** is the process of allowing bacteria to feed on the detritus in the absence of oxygen. The raw sludge is put into large airtight tanks called sludge digesters. The end products of this decomposition are carbon dioxide, methane, and water. Thus, a major by-product . . . is biogas, a gaseous mixture that is about two-thirds methane. After four to six weeks, anaerobic digestion is more or less complete, and what remains is called treated sludge or biosolids, consisting of the remaining organic matter, which is now relatively stable, nutrient-rich, humus-like material suspended in water. Pathogens have been largely, if not entirely, eliminated, so they no longer present any significant health hazard."

"**Composting** is another process used to treat sewage sludge. Raw sludge is mixed with wood chips or some other water-absorbing material to reduce the water content. It is then placed in windrows—long, narrow piles that allow air to circulate conveniently through the material and that can be turned with machinery. Bacteria and other decomposers break down the organic material to rich humus-like material that makes an excellent treatment for soil."

245

Pasteurization is a process through which raw sludge, once dewatered, is "put through ovens that operate like oversized laundry dryers. In the dryers, the sludge is pasteurized—that is, heated sufficiently to kill any pathogens (exactly the same process that makes milk safe to drink). The product is dry, odorless organic pellets."

8. How may sewage from individual homes be handled in the absence of municipal collection systems? What are some of the problems with these on-site systems?

Sewage from individual homes may be handled using a septic system with a leaching field. "(O)n-site systems frequently fail, resulting in unpleasant sewage backup into homes and pollution of groundwater and surface water.

9. Describe and compare submerged aquatic vegetation and phytoplankton. Where and how does each get nutrients and light?

Submerged aquatic vegetation (SAV) are benthic plants that grow under water. "Benthic plants are (submerged and emergent) aquatic plants that grow attached to, or are rooted in, the bottom of a body of water. All common aquarium plants and sea grasses are benthic plants. To thrive, SAV requires water that is clear enough to allow sufficient light to penetrate to allow photosynthesis. As water become more turbid, light is diminished. In extreme situations, it may be reduced to penetrating to just a few centimeters beneath the water's surface. Thus, increasing turbidity decreases the depth at which SAV can survive. Another important feature of SAV is that it absorbs its required mineral nutrients from the bottom sediments through the roots, just as land plants do. SAV is not limited by water that is low in nutrients. Indeed, enrichment of the water with nutrients is counterproductive for SAV, because it stimulates the growth of phytoplankton."

"**Phytoplankton** consists of numerous species of photosynthetic algae, protests, and chlorophyll-containing bacteria that grow as microscopic single cells or in small groups, or 'threads,' of cells. Phytoplankton lives suspended in water, and are found wherever light and nutrients are available. In extreme situations, water may become literally pea-soup green (or tea-colored, depending on the species involved), and a scum of phytoplankton may float on the surface and absorb essentially all the light. However, phytoplankton reaches such densities only in nutrient-rich water, because, not being connected to the bottom, it must absorb its nutrients from water. A low level of nutrients in water limits the growth of phytoplankton accordingly."

10. Explain the difference between oligotrophic and eutrophic waters. Describe the sequential process of eutrophication.

Oligotrophic waters are low in nutrients while **eutrophic** waters have high levels of nutrients. "As the water of an oligotrophic body becomes enriched with nutrients, numerous changes are set in motion. First, the nutrient enrichment allows the rapid growth and multiplication of phytoplankton, increasing the turbidity of the water. The increasing turbidity shades out the SAV that live in the water. With the die-off of SAV, there is a loss of food, habitats, and dissolved oxygen from their photosynthesis. Phytoplankton has a remarkably high growth and reproduction rate. Under optimal conditions, phytoplankton biomass may double every 24 hours, a capacity far beyond that of benthic plants. Thus, phytoplankton soon reaches a maximum population density, and continuing growth and reproduction are balanced by die-off. Dead phytoplankton settles out, resulting in heavy deposits of detritus on the lake or river bottom. In turn, the abundance of detritus supports an abundance of decomposers, mainly bacteria. The explosive growth of bacteria, consuming oxygen via respiration, creates an additional demand for dissolved oxygen. The result is the depletion of dissolved oxygen, with the consequent suffocation of fish and shellfish. In sum, eutrophication refers to this whole sequence of events, starting with nutrient enrichment, and proceeding to the growth and die-off of phytoplankton, the accumulation of detritus, the growth of bacteria, and, finally, the depletion of dissolved oxygen and the suffocation of higher organisms."

11. Distinguish between natural and cultural eutrophication.

"In nature, apart from human impacts, eutrophication is part of the process of aquatic succession, discussed in Chapter 4. Over periods of hundreds of thousands of years, bodies of water are subject to gradual enrichment

246

with nutrients. Thus, natural eutrophication is a normal process. Wherever nutrients come from sewage-treatment plants, poor farming practices, urban runoff, and certain other human activities, humans have inadvertently managed to vastly accelerate the process of nutrient enrichment. The accelerated eutrophication caused by humans is called cultural eutrophication."

12. What is being done to establish nutrient criteria?

"Beginning in 2001, the EPA began publishing water quality nutrient criteria aimed at preventing and reducing the eutrophication that impacts so many bodies of water. The agency listed its recommended criteria for causative factors—nitrogen and phosphorus—and criteria for response factors—chlorophyll as a measure of phytoplankton density and a measure of water clarity. The EPA divided the country into ecoregions and determined criteria levels deemed appropriate for the specific region. Like the other water quality criteria, the nutrient criteria are provided as targets for the states as they address their water pollution (and especially eutrophication) problems."

13. How does the NPDES program address point-source pollution by nutrients?

"The NPDES program addresses point-source pollution and issues permits that regulate discharges from wastewater treatment plants and industrial sources."

14. Describe the TMDL program. How does it address nonpoint-source pollution, and what role do water quality criteria play in the program?

"The TMDL program . . . evaluates all sources of pollutants entering a body of water, especially nonpoint sources, according to the water body's ability to assimilate the pollutant. (W)ater quality criteria provide an essential means of assessing the condition of the receiving body of water, as well as evaluating the levels of the various pollutant discharges."

15. What are some of the important public-policy issues relating to water quality?

Since the enactment of the Clean Water Act in 1972, the number of Americans served by sewage treatment plants has increased from 85 million to 173 million. Two-thirds of our "waterways are safe for fishing and swimming, double the number in 1972." Many of our "most heavily used rivers, lakes, and bays have been cleaned up and restored. EPA estimates than an additional $148 billion will be needed over the next 20 years to meet funding needs for all eligible municipal wastewater treatment systems. The amount represents a gap of about $6 billion between current annual expenditures and projected needs."

Problems in reauthorizing the act include debates "over whether requirements should be strengthened or weakened, whether additional mandates should be subjected to a cost/benefit analysis, and how regulatory relief should be provided to industries, states, cities, and individuals who are required to take actions to comply with the regulations."

"EPA has identified nonpoint-source pollution as the nation's number-one water pollution problem, with the construction of new wastewater treatment facilities not far behind. Other significant issues, including storm-water discharges, combined and separate sewer overflows, wetlands protection, and animal feeding operations, are also receiving the EPA's attention and are in Congress' sights for possible action. The continuing high percentage of the nation's water resources that fail the meet the water quality standards makes it clear that much remains to be accomplished."

Thinking Environmentally: Possible Answers

1. A large number of fish are suddenly found floating dead on a lake. You are called in to investigate the problem. You find an abundance of phytoplankton and no evidence of toxic dumpling. Suggest a reason for the fish kill.

A very likely reason for the fish kill is low oxygen level in the lake. A source for the nutrient enrichment should be located as this was the first step in the process. ("Nutrient enrichment allow(ed) the rapid growth and

247

multiplication of phytoplankton, increasing the turbidity of the water. The increasing turbidity shade(d) out the SAV that live in the water. With the die-off of SAV, there (was) a loss of food, habitats, and dissolved oxygen. . . . Thus, phytoplankton soon reache(d) a maximum population density. . . ." Dead phytoplankton settle(d) out, resulting in heavy deposits of detritus on the lake or river bottom, which supported an "abundance of decomposers, mainly bacteria. The explosive growth of bacteria, consuming oxygen via respiration, creates an additional demand for dissolved oxygen." Suffocation of the fish resulted.

2. Nitrogen pollution has damaged the San Diego Creek-Newport Bay ecosystem in California by encouraging the heavy growth of intertidal algae. Report on the TMDL for this system. Consult the EPA web site: www.epa.gov/owow/tmdl/examples/nutrients.html.

Table 1.   Total Nitrogen (TN) TMDL for Newport Bay

(expressed as allowable discharge to Newport Bay)

	Annual (lbs TN)	October 1 March 31 (lbs TN) Non-Storm Discharges	April 1 September 30 (lbs TN)
TMDL (loading capacity)	298,225	144,364	153,861
Waste Load Allocation			
Urban Runoff	72,070	55,442	16,628
Other NPDES Discharges	39,311	13,640	25,671
Total WLA	111,381	69,082	42,299
Load Allocation			
Nurseries[2]	85,646	23,060	62,586
Agricultural Discharges	49,764	38,283	11,481
Undefined Sources	51,434	13,939	37,495
Total LA	186,844	75,282	111,562

Table 2.   Total Nitrogen (TN) TMDL for San Diego Creek, Reach 2 during non-storm conditions 3

248

(expressed as allowable discharge to San Diego Creek, Reach 2)

TMDL	14 lbs/day (TN)
Waste Load Allocation (NPDES Discharge Urban Runoff)	5.5 lbs/day (TN)
Load Allocation (Nurseries, Agriculture, Open Space)	8.5 lbs/day (TN)

3. Arrange a tour to the sewage-treatment plant that serves your community. Compare it with what is described in this chapter. Is the water being purified or handled in a way that will prevent cultural eutrophication? Are sludges being converted to, and used as, fertilizer? What improvements, if any, are in order? How can you help promote such improvements?

Most communities will not have Biological Nutrient Removal, nor will they have an alternative sludge treatment. Sewage treatment will stop at secondary treatment and, typically, the sludge will be land filled. Discussions concerning the economic and health costs and benefits of leaving the system as is or altering the system to including biological nutrient removal and/or treatment of the sludge prior to use as fertilizer would be the place to begin promoting improvement.

4. Suppose a new community of several thousand people is going to be built in Arizona (with a warm, dry climate). You are called in as a consultant to design a complete sewage system, including the collection, treatment, and use or disposal of by-products. Write an essay describing the system you recommend, and give a rationale for the choices involved.

The first step in completing a sewage system would be to separate the storm-drain and sewage systems. While it does not rain frequently in Arizona, flash floods are not uncommon when it does rain. Additionally, all industrial sources would have to pretreat their wastes to remove any solvents, metals, and other incompatible material.

A sewage treatment plant with **preliminary**, **primary** and **secondary and tertiary treatment** would be built. The secondary treatment system would be an activated sludge system to allow for Biological Nutrient Removal. Tertiary treatment is the removal of the dissolved inorganic material. Sludge would be treated using anaerobic digestion, and the remaining biosolids would be solid as soil amendment.

This system would remove nutrients from the sewage and allow for the release effluent that would not provide nutrients for phytoplankton growth. The separation of the storm-drain system from the sewage system would decrease the risk of a rain event causing the release of raw sewage. The separation of industrial sewage from residential wastes would ensure that the biosolids did not contain hazardous metals and organic solvents. The use of biological nutrient removal would eliminate the inorganic material from the effluent that is typically remaining after the removal of the organic material from sewage.

CHAPTER 21
Municipal Solid Waste: Disposal and Recovery

Chapter Outline:

I. Solid Waste: Landfills and Combustion
  - A. Disposal of Municipal Solid Waste
    1. Whose job?
    2. Past Sins
  - B. Landfills
    1. Problems of Landfills
      - i. Leachate Generation and Groundwater Contamination
      - ii. Methane Production
      - iii. Incomplete Decomposition
      - iv. Settling
    2. Improving Landfills
      - i. Siting New Landfills
      - ii. Outsourcing
  - C. Combustion: Waste to Energy
    1. Advantages of Combustion
    2. Drawbacks of Combustion
    3. An Operating Facility
  - D. Costs of Municipal Solid-Waste Disposal
II. Better Solutions: Source Reduction and Recycling
  - A. Source Reduction
    1. Examples
  - B. The Recycling Solution
    1. Why Recycle?
    2. What Gets Recycled?
  - C. Municipal Recycling
    1. Economics of Recycling
    2. Paper Recycling
      - i. Markets
    3. Glass Recycling and Bottle Laws
      - i. Bottle Laws
    4. Plastics Recycling
      - i. Bottled Water
      - ii. PETE and HDPE
      - iii. Plastic Bags
  - D. Regional Recycling Options
    - i. How a MRF Works
    - ii. Composting Mixed Waste and Yard Trimmings
III. Public Policy and Waste Management
  - A. The Regulatory Perspective
  - B. Integrated Waste Management
    1. Waste Reduction
      - i. WasteWise
      - ii. PAYT

250

Key Topics:

1. Solid Waste: Landfills and Combustion
2. Better Solutions: Source Reduction and Recycling
3. Public Policy and Waste Management

Instructional Goals:

1. It is not possible to throw anything away. The First and Second Laws of Thermodynamics and the Law of Conservation of Energy rule how we use resources and energy.

2. All organisms produce waste. To live sustainably, the wastes produced must not be hazardous to other organisms due to concentration or inherent characteristics of the waste.

3. The greatest quantity of energy and resources conservation is associated with reducing waste generation followed by reusing and then recycling. When reducing, reusing, and recycling are not options, landfills and incinerators may be acceptable disposal options if operated with proper care.

4. Landfills can be operated to decrease leachate contamination of surface and groundwater, maximize the production and capture of methane, increase the rate of settling, and maximize the life of the disposal site.

Concepts and Connections:

Solid waste is the material left over from production and use of items to satisfy needs and desires. All organisms produce waste. When we generate more wastes or types of wastes than can be integrated into the Earth's cycles, we are living in a non-sustainable manner.

Rethinking what we need versus what we want can be a useful exercise. Not only can we reduce our impact on Earth when we separate our needs from our wants and focus our efforts on fulfilling our needs, we also simplify our lives. Any of us, even the most environmentally sophisticated, can re-think our needs and wants. Prompting students to begin this continual evaluation can be challenging yet rewarding.

Encouraging students to begin someplace, any place, is important. There are a thousand and one things from which to choose. It doesn't matter if the first action is simply to recycle the aluminum cans from soda or beer. Each action is important, and it is important for each person to recognize that each action is important. Resources are saved; energy is saved; air pollution is reduced; water pollution is reduced; solid waste disposal problems are reduced. Each small step adds up. The point is to choose something and stick with it. It is important to not start with too many things because it is hard to sustain big changes; small steps are just that—steps.

Creating a social system to help us act in a sustainable manner is important. Students need to understand that we have been making positive changes. Ten years ago curbside recycling was not available in most cities. Grocery stores did not encourage (and in fact discouraged) the reusing or recycling of paper and plastic bags. Through consumer protests we eliminated most Styrofoam use and the over-packaging of electronics. We now see popcorn used as packing material. Recycled paper greeting cards are common. Recycled paper products can be found in many grocery stores. The list is endless and we need to provide students with recent history so that they do not become discouraged.

Concepts in Context:

The material in this chapter can be linked with all the material on energy and resources. The First and Second Laws of Thermodynamics and the Law of Conservation of Matter (Chapter 4) are integral to understanding why it is not possible to throw something away and why we cannot obtain the same amount of energy out of an aluminum can that we put into it. The biogeochemical cycles (Chapter 4) and the hydrological cycle (Chapter 10) provide examples of how nature recycles and how humans need to think in order to live sustainably (Chapters 2 and 23).

If we use the goods and resources (Chapter 7) of ecosystems (Chapters 3, 4, and 5) in a non-sustainable manner, we adversely impact biodiversity (Chapter 6). If we do not take care with our disposal methods for solid waste, we can adversely impact soils (Chapter 11) and our ability to grow food (Chapter 12). Our use of energy (Chapters 14, 15, and 16) affects and is affected by our resources use. The size of human populations (Chapter 8) and our perceived cost of raising children (Chapter 9) influence the total quantity of waste generated by humans.

Water pollution (Chapter 21), air pollution (Chapter 19), ozone depletion, and production of greenhouse gases (Chapter 18) are influenced by the waste quantity and handling method. Human health (Chapter 17) can be adversely impacted if waste is placed into a landfill or if incinerated wastes are not processed properly.

Key Terms and Vocabulary:

Municipal solid waste (MSW), landfill, siting, LULU, NIMBY, NIMTOO, BANANA, composting, primary recycling, secondary recycling, materials recovery facilities, Solid Waste Disposal Act, Resource Recovery Act, Resource Conservation and Recovery Act (RCRA), Superfund Act, Hazardous and Solid Waste Amendments, WasteWise, Solid Waste Interstate Transportation Act

Discussion, Activities, and Labs:

1. Ask students to list the ways in which we can reduce the quantity of waste generated. Clarify that recycling does not reduce waste generated; recycling is a change to what we do with the waste once it is generated. The list could include reducing packaging; changes in manufacture to reduce resource use (lighter steel and aluminum cans); the paperless office due to computers (questionable if this is real); reusable bottles; yard sales, flea markets, and consignment clothing stores to reuse items; reduction in junk mail; and evaluating your needs versus your wants (shopping for needs rather than pleasure).

2. Ask the students to list the problems associated with the disposal of solid waste in a landfill (or waste-to-energy facility). What responsibility do we each have to reduce the wastes we generate to reduce our impact on Earth? If harm occurs because of the wastes we generate, is it ethical for someone else to bear the costs rather than ourselves.

3. Bring as many types of plastic to class as you can find. By my last count, there were at least 17 different types of plastic, plus different colors. It is possible for many plastic polymers to be either molded (like a shampoo bottle) or blown (like a plastic bag). Divide the class into groups of two to three students. Provide each group of students with a wide variety of plastic types and ask them to sort the material by the type of plastic using the recycling number, look, and feel. Then ask the groups to sort the plastic by those consumer items that do similar things. Ask the groups to decide if there is more than one type of plastic used for the same type of consumer item. As it is necessary to sort by type and color of plastic in order to recycle, ask the students to determine if they find the diversity of plastic type and color necessary as a consumer. (The sorting is necessary because combining different types of plastic can result in non-usable blobs of junk.) Ask the groups to write a list of recommendations to the plastics industry on how to better respond to consumer needs.

252

4. Have each student list all items in their possession that contain some recycled materials. Tell the students that they should be creative because not everything that contains recycled materials will say-so on the product. You might want to recommend that students research the manufacturing process for various consumer items. Have the students go to the library and search the Internet to determine what consumer items are commonly made from recycled products. Have the student differentiate between primary and secondary recycling and post- and pre-consumer waste.

5. Ask each student keep a list of everything they throw away for a week. Have them answer the following questions: Which items are recyclable and which items are not? Are some items recyclable but the local recycling program does not accept the items? Are the items that are not recyclable reusable? Could some of the items not be purchased? Is there another way to obtain what you want/need? What is the impact of disposing of the item that is not reusable or recyclable?

Suggested Lecture Format:

I. Solid Waste: Landfills and Combustion

   A. Disposal of Municipal Solid Waste—"Little attention is given to what people throw away in their trash. Even if there are restrictions and prohibitions, they can be bypassed with careful packing of the trash containers. Thus, many environmentally detrimental substances—paint, used motor oil, old TV sets, and so on—are discarded, with the feeling that they are gone forever." See Figure 21-2.
      1. Whose job?—"Customarily, local governments have had the responsibility for collecting and disposing of MSW."
      2. Past Sins—"Until the 1960s, most MSW was buried in open dumps." See Figure 21-3.

   B. Landfills—"In a landfill, the waste is put on or in the ground and is covered with earth. Because there is no burning and because each day's fill is covered with at least six inches of earth, air pollution and populations of vermin are kept down." See Figure 21-4.
      1. Problems of Landfills—Issues with landfills include possible groundwater contamination, methane production, lack of decomposition, and settling of the land over time making it difficult to build upon.
         i. Leachate Generation and Groundwater Contamination—"The most serious problem by far is groundwater contamination. As water percolates through any material, various chemicals in the material may dissolve in the water and get carried along in a process called leaching."
         ii. Methane Production—"A major by-product of the process is biogas, which is about two-thirds methane and one-third hydrogen and carbon dioxide, a highly flammable mixture." "The recovery of landfill gas has significant environmental benefits."
         iii. Incomplete Decomposition—"The commonly used plastics in MSW resist natural decomposition because of their molecular structure."
         iv. Settling—"Settling does present a problem in landfills that have been converted to playgrounds and golf courses because it creates shallow depressions (and sometimes deep holes) that collect and hold water."
      2. Improving Landfills—The features of newer landfills are summarized in Figure 21-6 and on page 549 of the text.

    i.   Siting New Landfills—"People in residential communities (where the MSW is generated) invariably reject proposals to site landfills anywhere near where they live, and those who already live close to existing landfills are anxious to close them down."

    ii.   Outsourcing—"The siting problem has some undesirable consequences. First, it drives up the costs of waste disposal, as alternatives to local landfills are invariably more expensive. Second, it leads to the inefficient and equally objectionable practice of the long-distance transfer of trash as waste generators look for private landfills whose owners are anxious to receive trash." See Table 21-1. **See also Discussion Topic #2.**

C.   Combustion: Waste to Energy—"Because it has a high organic content, refuse (especially the plastic portion) can be burned. Currently, 89 combustion facilities are operating in the United States, burning about 32 million tons of MSW annually—$12.6 of the waste stream."

1.   Advantages of Combustion—The advantages of combustion are listed on p. 550-551 of the text.

2.   Drawbacks of Combustion—The disadvantages of combustion are listed on p. 551 of the text.

3.   An Operating Facility—The operations of a waste to energy facility are summarized in Figure 21-7 and on p. 551-552 of the text. "An appreciation for the impact of such a facility can be gained from looking at the outcome of a year's operation. In one year, 1 million tons of MSW are processed, 40,000 tons of metal are recycled, and 570,000 megawatt-hours of electricity are generated-the equivalent of more than 60 million gallons of fuel oil and enough electricity to power 65,000 homes. All this comes from stuff that people have thrown away!"

D.   Costs of Municipal Solid-Waste Disposal—"Getting rid of all trash is becoming more expensive, and one sad consequence of this increasing expense is illegal dumping."

II.   Better Solutions: Source Reduction and Recycling—**See Discussion Topics #1 and #4.**

A.   Source Reduction—"Source reduction accomplishes two goals: It reduces the amount of waste that must be managed, and it conserves resources." **See Discussion Topic #5.**

1.   Examples—"Source reduction can involve a broad range of activities on the part of homeowners, businesses, communities, manufacturers, and institutions." Examples can be found on p. 553 of the text.

B.   The Recycling Solution—"Recycling is a hands-down winner in terms of energy use and pollution." It saves energy and it decreases pollution.

1.   Why Recycle?—Recycling saves energy and it decreases pollution

2.   What Gets Recycled?—"The primary items from MSW that are currently being heavily recycled are cans (both aluminum and steel), bottles, plastic containers, newspapers, and yard wastes."

C.   Municipal Recycling—"There is a great diversity of approaches to recycling in municipalities, from recycling centers requiring miles of driving to curbside recycling with sophisticated separation processes. The most successful programs have the following characteristics:" For a list of these characteristics see p. 555-556. See Figure 21-12.

1.   Economics of Recycling—"If the costs of recycling (from pickup to disposal of recyclable components) are compared with the costs of combusting waste or placing it in landfills, recycling frequently comes out second best. Markets for recyclable materials fluctuate wildly, and residents often end up subsidizing the recycling effort. Competition between

landfills and combustion facilities often lowers tipping fees, creating an even greater disincentive to recycle. Thus, critics of current recycling practices argue that unless recycling pays for itself, through the sale of materials recovered, it should not be done."

    2. Paper Recycling—"Newspapers are by far the most important item that is recycled because of their predominance in the waste stream."

        i. Markets—"After the wastepaper is incorporated into a final product, the market becomes a critical factor. Is there a demand for recycled paper?"

    3. Glass Recycling and Bottle Laws—"Non-returnable glass containers constitute 5.3% of the solid-waste stream in the United States and about 50% of the non-burnable portion; they also make up a large proportion of roadside litter."

        i. Bottle Laws—"Such laws generally call for a deposit on all beverage containers, both reusable and throwaway and both glass and plastic. Retailers are required to accept the used containers and pass them along for recycling or reuse." See Table 21-2.

    4. Plastics Recycling—"Plastics have a bad reputation in the environmental debate for several reasons. First, plastics have many uses that involve rapid throughput-for example, packaging, bottling, the manufacture of disposable diapers, and the incorporation of plastics into a host of cheap consumer goods. Second, plastics are conspicuous in MSW and litter. Finally, plastics do not decompose in the environment because no microbes (or any other organisms) are able to digest them." **See Discussion Topic #3.**

        i. Bottled Water—"Some 8.9 billion gallons of bottled water were sold in the United States in 2007, making us the world leader in consumption of bottled water."

        ii. PETE and HDPE—"The two recyclable plastics in most common use are high-density polyethylene (HDPE; code 2) and polyethylene terephthalate (PETE; code 1)"

        iii. Plastic Bags—"Hanging from trees and bushes, blowing along highways, clogging sewer pipes, drifting on ocean currents, plastic bags are everywhere on the planet—everywhere, that is, but the trash or recycling barrel. They cause thousands of deaths of marine mammals and turtles each year."

    D. Regional Recycling Options—"It is an encouraging sign that a number of the transfer stations are being converted into material recovery facilities, referred to in the trade as MRFs."

        i. How a MRF Works—"The objective of the process is to prepare materials for the recyclable-goods market." See Figure21-14.

        ii. Composting Mixed Waste and Yard Trimmings—"Taking advantage of the fact that MSW has a high organic content, a few regional facilities compost the MSW after removing large items and metals."

III. Public Policy and Waste Management

    A. The Regulatory Perspective—See p. 560 for a list of legislation that has been passed at the federal level regarding waste management.

    B. Integrated Waste Management—"Source reduction, waste-to-energy combustion, recycling, materials recovery facilities, landfills, and composting all have roles to play in waste management. A system having several processes in operation is called integrated waste management."

    1. Waste Reduction—"The modern United States leads the world in per capita energy consumption—we really are a 'throwaway society'." See Figure 21-15.

     i.   WasteWise—"The EPA sponsors the WasteWise program, targeting the reduction of MSW by establishing partnerships with not only local governments, schools, and organizations, but multinational corporations as well."

    ii.   PAYT—"Instead of using local taxes to pay for trash collection and disposal, which provides no incentive to reduce waste, communities levy curbside charges for all unsorted MSW." See Figure 21-16.

   iii.   EPR—"Extended product responsibility (EPR) is a concept that involves assigning some responsibility for reducing the environmental impact of a product at each stage of its 'life cycle', especially the end."

  2.   Waste Disposal Issues—"No human society can avoid generating solid waste."

     i.   Just Say No!—The Solid Waste Interstate Transportation Act of 2009 "is a demand for fairness to states that are working hard to deal responsibly with their own wastes, only to see the unrestricted transport of wastes from other states."

  3.   Recycling and Reuse—"Recycling is certainly the wave of the future. It should not, however, be pursued in lieu of waste reduction and reuse."

Review Questions: Possible Answers

1. List the major components of municipal solid waste (MSW).
    MSW consists of paper, yard wastes, food wastes, plastics metal, glass, and wood.

2. Trace the historical development of refuse disposal. What percentages now go to landfills, combustion, and recycling?
    "Until the 1960s, most MSW was burned in open dumps. The waste was burned to reduce its volume and lengthen of the life span of the dump, but refuse does not burn well. Smoldering dumps produced clouds of smoke that could be seen from miles away, smelled bad, and created a breeding ground for flies and rats. Some cities turned to incinerators, or combustion facilities, as they are called today—huge furnaces in which high temperatures allow the waste to burn more completely than in open dumps. Without controls, however, incinerators were prime sources of air pollution. Public objection and air pollution laws forced the phase out of open dumps and many incinerators during the 1960s and early 1970s. Open dumps were then converted to landfills. In the United States in 2003, 55.4% of MSW was disposed of in landfills, 30.6% was recovered for recycling and composting, and the remainder (14.0%) was combusted."

3. What are the major problems with placing waste in landfills? How can these problems be managed?
    There are four problems with landfills: leachate generation and groundwater contamination, methane production, incomplete decomposition, and settling. Newer landfills are built with leachate collection systems, and groundwater monitoring wells are installed so that continuous monitoring of groundwater will occur. Methane collection systems are being installed as a standard part of the landfill. To improve the cost effectiveness of methane collection systems, decomposition rates are increased by adding moisture. Two additional benefits to speeding decomposition are that leachate production does not continue for the same length of time and more rapid settling. If decomposition rates are increased, more material can be buried in the same location because decomposed material occupies less space.

4. Explain the difficulties accompanying landfill siting and outsourcing. How can these processes be handled responsibly?
    "People in residential communities (where MSW is generated) invariably reject proposals to site landfills anywhere near where they live, and those who already live close to existing landfills are anxious to close them down." Some reasons for the opposition to landfills are odors, litter from the landfill, heavy truck traffic, litter next to the roads from the garbage trucks and other users of the landfills, contamination of surface or

groundwater from leachate, seagulls and other birds attracted to the garbage, and landfill operators not following rules concerning covering wastes.

Outsourcing is the sending of wastes some distance from the place of origin. Outsourcing "leads to the inefficient and equally objectionable practice of the long-distance transfer of trash, as waste generators look for private landfills whose owners are anxious to receive trash. Often this transfer occurs across state and even national lines, leading to resentment and opposition on the part of citizens of the recipient state or nation."

5. *What are the advantages and disadvantages of WTE combustion?*

The advantages of WTE facilities include reducing trash weight "by over 70% and volume by 90%," concentrating toxic or hazardous substances into two streams of ash, eliminating the need to change "trash collection procedures or people's behavior," and generating electricity.

The disadvantages include MSW not burning cleanly, adverse health effects ("especially from older or poorly managed facilities"), cost to build the WTE facility, hazardous characteristics of the ash, options for MSW reduced, and resource and energy loss.

6. *What is the evidence for increasing source reduction, and what are some examples of how it is accomplished?*

"Source reduction is difficult to measure, because it means trying to measure something that no longer exists. The EPA measures source reduction by measuring consumer spending, which reflects the goods and products that ultimately make their way to the trash bin. After 1990, consumer spending continued to grow, but the MSW stream slowed down. If the MSW had grown at the same pace as consumer spending, some 287 million tons would have been generated in 2000 instead of 232 million. Thus, some 55 million tons never made it into the waste stream in 2000, and the EPA considers this to be due to source reduction activities."

Changes in the resources used in the manufacture of goods, the durability of consumer goods, how we package consumer items, how we use consumer items, the types of consumer items purchased, and the quantity of items purchased can all reduce waste at its source. Many changes in the quantity of materials used in the manufacture of consumer items have occurred in recent years. For years, the computer has been cited as a resource that will allow us to consume less paper. Using products longer, (e.g. reusable bottles), is an underutilized way of reducing waste at its source. While deposit legislation has not increased the use of reusable bottles, bottle deposits have increased the quantity of aluminum and plastic recycling. Rather than throwing away items, resale is a good idea. Removing your name from junk mail lists also reduces waste at its source.

7. *What are the environmental advantages of recycling?*

Some environmental advantages of recycling are that it saves energy and resources and decreases pollution.

8. *Describe the materials that are recycled and how recycling is accomplished.*

"**Paper and paperboard** can be remade into pulp and reprocessed into recycled paper, cardboard and other paper products; finely ground and sold as cellulose insulation; or shredded and composted."

"Most **glass** that is recycled is crushed, re-melted, and made into new containers; a smaller amount is used in fiberglass or 'glasphalt' for highway construction."

"Some forms of **plastic** can be re-melted and fabricated into carpet fiber, outdoor wearing apparel, irrigation drainage tiles, building materials, and sheet plastic."

"**Metals** can be re-melted and re-fabricated. Making aluminum from scrap aluminum saves up to 90% of the energy required to make aluminum from virgin ore." National recycling of aluminum saves energy, creates jobs, and reduces the trade deficit.

"**Yard** wastes can be composted to produce a humus soil conditioner."

9. *Discuss the attributes of successful recycling programs.*

"The most successful programs have the following characteristics: 1. There is a strong incentive to recycle, in the form of pay-as-you-throw charges for general trash and no charge for recycled goods.
2. Recycling is not optional; mandatory regulations are in place, with warnings and sanctions for violations.
3. Residential recycling is curbside with free recycling bins distributed to households. 4. Drop-off sites are provided for bulky goods like sofas, appliances, construction and demolition materials, and yard waste.

5. Recycling goals are ambitious, yet clear and feasible. Some percent of the waste stream is targeted, and progress is followed and communicated. 6. A concerted effort is made to involve local industries in recycling. 7. The municipality employs an experienced and committed recycling coordinator."

10. *Discuss MRFs, mixed waste processing, and mixed waste co-composting.*

"Basic sorting takes place when waste is collected, either through curbside collection or by town recycling stations (sites to which townspeople can bring wastes to be recycled). The waste is then trucked to the **MRF** and handled on three tracks—one for metal cans and glass containers, another for paper products, and a third for plastics. The materials are moved through the facility by escalators and conveyor belts, tended by workers who inspect and sort further. The objective of the process is to prepare materials for the recycled-goods market. Glass is sorted by color, cleaned, crushed into small pebbles, and then shipped to glass companies, where it replaces the raw materials that go into glass manufacture—sand and soda ash—and saves substantially on energy costs. Cans are sorted, flattened, and sent either to de-tinning plants or to aluminum-processing facilities. Paper is sorted, baled, and sent to reprocessing mills. Plastics are sorted into four categories, depending on their color and type of polymer, and then sold. The facility's advantages are its economy of scale and its ability to produce a high-quality end product for the recycled materials market."

"Less common the conventional MRFs, the **mixed waste processing** facility receives MSW just as if it were going to a landfill or a WTE facility. The waste is loaded on a conveyer and is sorted for recovery of recyclable materials before being landfilled or combusted."

"Taking advantage of the fact that MSW has a high organic content; a few regional facilities compost the MSW after removing large items and metals. Often, they will mix treated sewage sludge with the MSW (called **co-composting**), which provides a rich source of bacteria and nutrients."

11. *What laws has the federal government adopted to control solid-waste disposal?*

There are six federal laws governing solid-waste disposal: Solid Waste Disposal Act of 1965, Resource Recovery Act of 1970, Resource Conservation and Recovery Act (RCRA) of 1976), Superfund Act of 1980, Hazardous and Solid Waste Amendments of 1984, and Solid Waste Interstate Transportation Act of 2005.

12. What is e-waste, and how is it being managed?

E-waste includes "discarded televisions, computers, DVD players, VCRs, cell phones, printers, copiers, and video game systems." "E-waste has numerous toxic components and is classified as hazardous waste. Federal law regulates the transport, treatment, and disposal of such hazardous wastes under RCRA. To date, only 14 states have implemented any kind of e-waste management, and there is broad consensus on the need for federal legislation to manage this waste."

13. *What is integrated waste management? What decisions would be part of a stewardly and sustainable solid-waste management plant?*

Source reduction, waste-to-energy combustion, recycling, material recovery facilities, landfills, and composting are all a part of integrated waste management—"a system having several processes in operation . . . ." A stewardly and sustainable solid waste management plan would start with source reduction. A second, equally important component would be to establish a system of "'unit pricing' or charging households and other 'customers' for the waste they dispose." A third policy would be to "establish a program of extended product responsibility (EPR), a concept that involves assigning some responsibility for reducing the environmental impact of a product at each stage of its 'lifecycle,' especially the end. For example, Hewlett-Packard and Xerox make it easy for customers to return spent copier cartridges, and the two companies recycle the components of the cartridges." Some portion of our waste will be burned in a waste-to-energy facility, some component (the largest) would be recycled, and some component would be landfilled. Once a component of the waste is recycled, we need to encourage the purchasing of goods with recycled content.

"Here is one ideal stewardly waste management plan: (1) emphasize source reduction wherever possible; (2) employ mandatory curbside recycling and a PAYT collection program; (3) if feasible, establish a MRF for efficient handling of recyclables (and possible MS); (4) employ co-composting of remaining MSW with treated sewage sludge; (5) deposit residual materials in a local landfill; and (6) prohibit all interstate transfer of MSW."

Thinking Environmentally: Possible Answers

1. *Compile a list of all the plastic items you used and threw away this week. Was it more than you expected? How can you reduce the number of items on the list?*

   Plastic items are likely to include plastic bags (shopping and produce), water and soda bottles, shampoo and liquid soap/detergent containers, shrink wrap and other packaging material, and disposable pens, razors, and so on.

   Plastic bags can be reused, as can water bottles. Shampoo and liquid soaps/detergents can be purchased in larger containers, and reusable pens and razors can be purchased. Rather than accepting a plastic bag to hold your purchases, a canvas bag could be used.

2. *How and where does your school dispose of solid waste? E-waste? Is a recycling program in place? How well does it work?*

   The office to call to have these questions answered is maintenance or physical plant. There typically is an administrator who is in charge of the buildings and grounds. This office will have made the decisions about recycling, composting, and other solid waste handling.

3. *Suppose your town planned to build a combustion facility or landfill near your home. Outline your concerns, and explain your decision to be for or against the site.*

   One issue that students should address is how wastes should be handled, not just where they should (not) be placed. While a combustion facility or a landfill might be inappropriate for a particular location, it is necessary to process our wastes. There are additional impacts (e.g., air quality, noise, resource use from transportation) to be considered if wastes are to be transported away from an area because it is too "sensitive" for use as a disposal or recycling site.

4. *Does your state have a bottle law? If not, what has prevented the bill from being adopted?*

   Most students will live in states without deposit legislation. Bills requiring deposits on beverage containers have been successfully fought in most states. The arguments against deposit legislation include rodent, ant, and other pest problems in grocery stores and consumer reluctance to return bottles.

5. *Consider the stewardly waste management plan described in the "Stewardship" section of "Revisiting the Themes". How many of these components does your city or town employ?*

   Many towns will not employ any of these tactics. Source reduction is not likely to be mentioned and recycling is likely to be voluntary. It could be useful to evaluate why the city or town has not employed the "ideal" waste management plant suggested by the author.

CHAPTER 22
Hazardous Chemicals: Pollution and Prevention

Chapter Outline:

I. Toxicology and Chemical Hazards
   A. Dose Response and Threshold
      1. Threshold Level.
   B. The Nature of Chemical Hazards: HAZMATs
   C. Sources of Chemicals Entering the Environment
      1. Toxics Release Inventory
   D. The Threat from Toxic Chemicals
      1. Heavy Metals
      2. Organic Compounds
         i. Dirty Dozen
      3. PERC
         i. Issues with Other Organics
   E. Involvement with Food Chains
II. Hazardous-Waste Disposal
   A. Methods of Land Disposal
      1. Deep-Well Injection
      2. Surface Impoundments
      3. Landfills
   B. Mismanagement of Hazardous Wastes
      1. Midnight Dumping and Orphan Sites
      2. Scope of the Mismanagement Problem
         i. Occidental?
III. Cleaning Up the Mess
   A. Ensuring Safe Drinking Water
      1. Groundwater Remediation
   B. Superfund for Toxic Sites
      1. Setting Priorities
      2. Cleanup Technology
         i. Bioremediation
         ii. Plant Food?
      3. Evaluating Superfund
         i. Progress
         ii. Who Pays?
         iii. Critics
      4. Brownfields
      5. Leaking Underground Storage Tanks (LUSTs)
IV. Managing Current Toxic Chemicals and Wastes

A. The Clean Air and Clean Water Acts

B. The Resource Conservation and Recovery Act (RCRA)

C. Reduction of Accidents and Accidental Exposures

    1. Department of Transportation Regulations

    2. Worker Protection: OSHA and the "Worker's Right to Know"

    3. Community Protection and Emergency Preparedness: SARA, Title III

       i. EPCRA Rules

    4. The Toxic Substances Control Act

       i. REACH

V. Broader Issues

A. Environmental Justice and Hazardous Wastes

    1. Federal Response

    2. International EJ

B. Pollution Prevention for a Sustainable Society

    1. Green Chemistry

    2. Reuse

    3. You, the Consumer

Key Topics:

1. Toxicology and Chemical Hazards
2. Hazardous-Waste Disposal
3. Cleaning Up the Mess
4. Managing Current Toxic Chemicals and Wastes
5. Broader Issues

Instructional Goals:

1. The dose of a chemical will determine its toxicity. The hazard of a chemical is determined by toxicity and exposure. Whether a chemical is considered toxic is dependent upon the outcome of interest. Before we recognized the ability of exogenous chemicals to be hormonally active we could have determined a hormonally active chemical to be nontoxic.

2. A substance is legally defined as hazardous if it is flammable, corrosive, reactive, or toxic.

3. Persistence, bio-accumulation, and ease of absorption increase a substance's ability to cause harm.

Concepts and Connections:

The disposal of hazardous substances on land in response to laws eliminating the discharge of hazardous substances to air and water is an example of humans not thinking through the consequence of our actions. Most hazardous waste sites are not a result of malice. We did not know we were creating a problem. When we passed the Clean Air and Clean Water acts, we moved the waste from one media to the next, creating new problems in the

261

process; we did not eliminate the problem because we did not eliminate the production of the pollutants. When we eliminated the burning of trash in open dumps, we moved pollutants from the disposal of municipal wastes from the air to the land and water. When we built taller smokestacks to eliminate local air pollution, we created the conditions for acid deposition miles from the pollutant source. We need to remember that the Laws of Thermodynamics and the Law of Conservation of Matter govern human actions. We cannot throw things away because nothing ever goes away.

Because we have begun to recognize the need to look at the full life cycle of a product we are moving toward pollution prevention rather than "command and control" technologies. To build a sustainable society we need to improve our ability to prevent pollution.

Concepts in Context:

The concepts in this chapter on hazardous chemicals can be related to the limiting factors (Chapter 3) as hazardous chemicals, when found in too high a concentration, will result in the immediate death of an organism. The inappropriate handling of hazardous substances can result in the destruction of niches and habitats (Chapter 2), disruption of the food web (Chapter 3), and disruption of the biogeochemical cycles (Chapter 4). The disposal of hazardous substances is dependent upon the Laws of Thermodynamics and the Law of Conservation of Matter (Chapter 4). The presence of a hazardous substance in an ecosystem can alter the environmental resistance factors influencing population growth (Chapter 5). If a hazardous substance disrupts an ecosystem, then succession can be influenced (Chapter 5). If an ecosystem is adversely impacted by how we handle hazardous substances, then biodiversity (Chapter 6) may be reduced.

The quantity of hazardous waste produced is influenced by the number of people (Chapter 8) and the kinds of economic choices we make (Chapter 2). Many of the goods and resources we obtain from ecosystems (Chapter 7) are adversely impacted by our use of hazardous substances. We use hazardous substances in agriculture (Chapters 12 and 13) and in the extraction of energy (Chapters 14, 15, and 16).

Air (Chapter 19), water (Chapters 10 and 20), and land (Chapter 11) may be adversely influenced by the disposal and use of hazardous substances. Our production, use, and disposal of hazardous chemicals can affect human health (Chapter 17).

Key Terms and Vocabulary:

toxicology, acute, chronic, carcinogenic, dose, response, exposure, threshold level, hazardous material (HAZMAT), total product life cycle, Toxics Release Inventory (TRI), Emergency Planning and Community Right-to-Know Act of 1986 (EPCRA), Pollution Prevention Act of 1990, halogenated hydrocarbons, chlorinated hydrocarbons, organic chlorides, Stockholm Convention of Persistent Organic Pollutants, Resource Conservation and Recovery Act (RCRA), best-demonstrated available technologies (BDATs), secure landfill, midnight dumping, orphan sites, Drinking Water Act of 1974, maximum contaminant levels, groundwater remediation, Comprehensive Environmental Response, Compensation, and Liability Act of 1980 (CERCLA), Superfund, Superfund Amendments and Reauthorization Act of 1986 (SARA), National Priorities List, bioremediation, phytoremediation, American Recovery and Reinvestment Act of 2009, brownfields, Brownfield Act, underground storage tank (UST), discharge permit, Department of Transportation Regulations (DOT Regs), Occupational Safety and Health Act of 1970, hazard communication standard, "worker's right to know", material safety data sheet (MSDS), Toxic Substances Control

Act of 1976 (TSCA), REACH, environmental justice, Basel Convention, pollution control, pollution prevention, wet cleaning, green products

Discussion, Activities, and Labs:

1. A controversial aspect of Superfund has been the amount of money spent to determine the Responsible Parties (RPs). The Superfund legislation required that RPs be identified and costs to perform site remediation be assigned to the RPs. Ask the students to consider why this might have been required. Why did we not first clean up the site and worry about assigning responsibility later, if at all?

2. Ask the students to speculate about how we can create a society that does not produce hazardous wastes. If you discussed pollution prevention strategies earlier in the class, have them think about how these ideas could be implemented.

3. Phthalates are used in plastics to create a flexible product. Recent data from the CDC indicates that Americans have measurable levels of some phthalates in their bodies. Some phthalates have been linked to endocrine activity and the levels sufficient to cause activity in humans are equivalent to exposure levels experienced by Americans. Discuss with the students the ubiquity of plastics, the impacts that would result from the elimination of plastics (economic, consumer goods, etc.), and the possible problems that could result to current and future generations if phthalates do disrupt endogenous hormone activity. Discuss possible solutions to this dilemma. Challenge the students to be creative with their solutions because it is creativity (thinking outside the box) that we need to solve this problem.

4. Ask each student to make a list of all items in her/his home that are hazardous. One way to determine this is if the label indicates the product should be disposed of properly. Hazardous substances would include pesticides, antibiotics and other medicines, smoke detectors, printer cartridges, and batteries. Discuss the lists compiled by the students in class.

5. Form groups of two to three students. Have each group choose a consumer product, (e.g. computer, television, stereo, etc.) to investigate. The investigation should focus on the hazardous materials needed during manufacture and the hazardous waste produced during manufacture and use. Each group then divides up the investigation tasks and individuals report their findings back to the group. Each group appoints a spokesperson to report on their findings to the class.

Suggested Lecture Format:

I. Toxicology and Chemical Hazards

    A. Dose Response and Threshold—"Human exposure to a hazard is a vital part of its risk characterization, and such exposure can come through the workplace, food, water, or the surrounding environment."

        1. Threshold Level—In the dose-response relationship, there is usually a threshold. Organisms are able to deal with certain levels of many substances without suffering ill effects. The level below which no ill effects are observed is called the threshold level." See Figure 22-1.

263

B. The Nature of Chemical Hazards: HAZMATs—"A chemical that presents a certain hazard or risk is known as a hazardous material (HAZMAT). The EPA categorizes substances on the basis of the following hazardous properties." See Figure 22-2.

C. Sources of Chemicals Entering the Environment—"To understand how HAZMATs enter our environment, we need to look at how people in our society live and work." See Figure 22-3.
   1. Toxics Release Inventory—"Requires industries to report releases of toxic chemicals to the environment, and the Pollution Prevention Act of 1990 mandates collection of data on toxic chemicals that are treated on-site, recycled, or combusted for energy." See Figure 22-4.

D. The Threat from Toxic Chemicals—"Fortunately, a large portion of the chemicals introduced into the environment are gradually broken down and assimilated by natural processes. After that, they pose no long-term human or environmental risk, even though they may be highly toxic in acute doses."
   1. Heavy Metals—"The most dangerous heavy metals are lead, mercury, arsenic, cadmium, tin, chromium, zinc, and copper."
   2. Organic Compounds—"Petroleum-derived and synthetic organic compounds are the chemical basis for all plastics, synthetic fibers, synthetic rubber, modern paint-like coatings, solvents, pesticides, wood preservatives, and hundreds of other products."
      i. Dirty Dozen—"Most of the 'dirty dozen' POPs (Table 22-1) are halogenated hydrocarbons."
   3. PERC—"Perchloroethylene, or PERC, is a colorless and nonflammable and is the major substance in dry-cleaning fluid. Breathing PERC for short periods can bring on dizziness, fatigue, headaches, and unconsciousness. Over longer periods, PERC can cause liver and kidney damage." See Figure 22-5.
      i. Issues with Other Organics—Phthalates, BPA, and Perchlorate "have been in the news recently because of concerns about health effects." **See Discussion Topic #3.**

E. Involvement with Food Chains—"The trait that makes heavy metals and non-biodegradable synthetic organics particularly hazardous is their tendency to accumulate in organisms."

II. Hazardous-Waste Disposal

A. Methods of Land Disposal—"In the early 1970s, there were three primary land disposal methods: (1) deep-well injection, (2) surface impoundments, and (3) landfills."
   1. Deep-Well Injection—"Deep-well injection involves drilling a borehole thousands of feet below groundwater into a porous geological formation." See Figure 22-6.
   2. Surface Impoundments—"are simple excavated depressions (ponds) into which liquid wastes are drained and held." See Figure 22-7.
   3. Landfills—"Some 403 million pounds of hazardous wastes were delivered to on-site landfills in 2007, and an additional 341 million pounds were deposited in off-site landfills." See Figure 22-8.

B. Mismanagement of Hazardous Wastes—Throughout the years many hazardous wastes have been disposed of improperly, causing pollution.
   1. Midnight Dumping and Orphan Sites—Locations where hazardous wastes were dropped off illegally are known as orphan sites and are very difficult to clean up. See Figure 22-9 and 22-10.
   2. Scope of the Mismanagement Problem—The surface of Love Canal, New York "began to collapse, exposing barrels of chemical wastes." See Figure 22-11.
      i. Occidental?—"Occidental Petroleum eventually spent more than $233 million on the cleanup and subsequent lawsuits" at Love Canal.

III. Cleaning Up the Mess

   A. Ensuring Safe Drinking Water—"To protect the public from the risk of toxic chemicals contaminating drinking water supplies, Congress passed the Safe Drinking Water Act of 1974."
      1. Groundwater Remediation—"Techniques involve drilling wells, pumping out the contaminated groundwater, purifying it, and injecting the purified water back into the ground or discharging it into surface waters." See Figure 22-12.

   B. Superfund for Toxic Sites—"Through a tax on chemical raw materials, this legislation provides a trust fund for the identification of abandoned chemical waste sites, protection of groundwater near the sites, remediation of groundwater if it has been contaminated, and cleanup of the sites." **See Discussion Topic #1.**
      1. Setting Priorities-"Resources are insufficient to clean up all sites at once. Therefore, a system for setting priorities has been developed."
      2. Cleanup Technology—"The VOD (valley of the drums) site was situated in a poorly drained shale and limestone deposit. The EPA determined that the most feasible treatment was simply to contain the contaminated soil and groundwater." See Figure 22-13.
         i. Bioremediation—"In bioremediation, oxygen and organisms are injected into contaminated zones. The organisms feed on and eliminate the pollutants and then die when the pollutants are gone."
         ii. Plant Food?—"When the soil contaminants are heavy metals and non-biodegradable `organic compounds, phytoremediation has been employed with some success."
      3. Evaluating Superfund—"More than 11,300 sites remain on the master list-a figure that is assumed, now includes most (if not all) of the sites in the United States that pose a significant risk."
         i. Progress—"As of 2009, 1,264 sites were still on the NPL."
         ii. Who Pays?—"When liability is difficult to track down or the responsible parties are unable to pay, the Superfund trust fund kicks in. However, over 70% of the cleanup costs to date have been paid by the polluters."
         iii. Critics—"Many feel that the overly stringent standards of cleanup are costing large sums of money without providing any additional benefit to public health."
      4. Brownfields—The Brownfield Act "provides grants for site assessment and remediation work and authorized $250 million/year for the ensuing five years for the program." See Figure 23-1.

265

5. Leaking Underground Storage Tanks (LUSTs)—"One consequence of our automobile-based society is the millions of underground fuel-storage tanks at service stations and other facilities. Putting such tanks underground greatly diminishes the risk of explosions and fires, but it also hides leaks.

IV. Managing Current Toxic Chemicals and Wastes

   A. The Clean Air and Clean Water Acts—"Discharge permits are a means of monitoring who is discharging what. Establishments with discharge permits are required to report all discharges of substances covered by the TRI. The renewal of permits is then made contingent on reducing pollutants to meet certain standards within certain periods."

   B. The Resource Conservation and Recovery Act (RCRA)—"The 1976 RCRA and its subsequent amendments are the cornerstone legislation designed to prevent unsafe or illegal disposal of all solid wastes on land." See Figure 22-14.

   C. Reduction of Accidents and Accidental Exposures—"A considerable number or laws bear on reducing the probability of accidents and on minimizing the exposure of both workers and the public if accidents should occur."
      1. Department of Transportation Regulations—"As modern society uses increasing amounts and kinds of hazardous materials, the stage is set for accidents to become wide-scale disasters." See Figure 22-2.
      2. Worker Protection: OSHA and the "Worker's Right to Know"—"The law requires businesses, industries, and laboratories to make available both information regarding hazardous materials and suitable protective equipment."
      3. Community Protection and Emergency Preparedness: SARA, Title III—"After the Bhopal disaster, Congress passed legislation to address the problem of accidents." See Figure 22-15.
         i. EPCRA Rules—"The task of the committee is to draw up scenarios for accidents involving the chemicals on-site and to have a contingency plan for every case."
      4. The Toxic Substances Control Act—"Requires that, before manufacturing a new chemical in bulk, manufacturers submit a 'pre-manufacturing notice' to the EPA in which the potential environmental and human health impacts of the substance are assessed."
         i. REACH—"REACH regulation has resulted in a process of registering an estimated 30,000 chemical substances out of the 100,000 or so in use in European societies." See Figure 22-16.

V. Broader Issues

   A. Environmental Justice and Hazardous Wastes—"Several recent studies have shown that, all across the United States, waste sites and other hazardous facilities are more likely than not to be located in towns and neighborhoods where most of the residents are non-Caucasian."
      1. Federal Response—"The federal government has taken the problem (of environmental justice) seriously."

266

2. International EJ—"The Basel Convention is an international agreement that bans most international toxic-waste trade when it is not in conformity with the convention."

B. Pollution Prevention for a Sustainable Society—"involves changing the production process, the materials used, or both so that harmful pollutants won't be produced in the first place." **See Discussion Topic #2.**
   1. Green Chemistry—"A second angle of pollution avoidance is substitution—finding non-hazardous substitutes for hazardous materials."
   2. Reuse—Is the process of "cleaning up and recycling solvents and lubricants." See Figure 22-4.
   3. You, the Consumer—"Pollution avoidance can also be applies to the individual consumer. So far as you are able to reduce or avoid the use of products containing harmful chemicals, you are preventing those amounts of chemicals from being released into the environment." **See Discussion Topics #4 and #5.**

Review Questions: Possible Answers

1. How do toxicologists investigate hazardous chemicals? How is this information disseminated to health practitioners and the public?
   "In investigating a suspected chemical, a toxicologist would conduct animal tests, investigate human involvement with the chemical, and present the information linking the dose (the level of exposure multiplied by the length of time of which exposure occurs) with the response (some acute or chronic effect or the development of tumors)." Toxicologists may also use cell cultures to study mutagenicity, carcinogenicity, or endocrine activity. Data from epidemiological studies will also be utilized if available. The overall goal is to link the quantity of exposure to the degree of response to a specified outcome. The outcome can be a measure of morbidity (nausea, edema, headache, tremor) or mortality (immediate or delayed).

2. What four categories are used to define hazardous chemicals?
   The categories are ignitability, corrosivity, reactivity, and toxicity.

3. Define total product life cycle and describe the many stages at which pollutants may enter the environment.
   "Our use constitutes only one step in the total product life cycle, a term that encompasses all steps, from obtaining raw materials to final disposal of the product. Implicit in our use of hair spray, for example, is that raw materials were obtained and various chemicals were produced to make both the spray and its container. Chemical wastes and by-products are inevitable in production processes. In addition, consider the risk of accidents or spills occurring in the manufacturing process and in the transportation of raw materials, the finished product, or wastes. Finally, what are the risks of breathing hair spray? What happens to the container you throw into the trash, which still holds some of the hair spray when the propellant is used up?"

4. What are the two classes of chemicals that pose the most serious long-term toxic risk, and how do they affect food chains?
   The two classes of chemicals are heavy metals and persistent organic compounds.

   "Heavy metals are extremely toxic because, as ions or in certain compounds, they are soluble in water and may be readily absorbed into the body, where they tend to combine with and inhibit the functioning of

267

particular vital enzymes. Even very small amounts can have severe physiological or neurological consequences."

"The trait that makes heavy metals and non-biodegradable synthetic organics particularly hazardous is their tendency to accumulate in organisms."

5. *What are the "dirty dozen" POPs? Why are they on a list?*

"A particularly troublesome class of synthetic organics is the halogenated hydrocarbons, organic compounds in which one or more of the hydrogen atoms have been replaced by atoms of chlorine, bromine, fluorine, or iodine. Most of the so-called 'dirty dozen' POPs are halogenated hydrocarbons. All are toxic to varying extents, and most are known animal carcinogens. Many are also suspected endocrine disruptors at very low levels." Several of the organic compounds bio-accumulate in living tissue.

6. *What two laws pertaining to the disposal of hazardous wastes were passed in the early 1970s? Describe how the passage of the laws shifted pollution from one part of the environment to another.*

"The Clean Air and Clean Water Acts and their subsequent amendments remain cornerstones of environmental legislation. However, their passage in the early 1970s left an enormous loophole. If you can't vent wastes into the atmosphere or flush them into waterways, what do you do with them? Industry turned to land disposal, which was essentially unregulated at the time, as an expedient alternative. Indiscriminate air and water disposal became indiscriminate land disposal. Thus, in retrospect, we see that the Clean Air and Clean Water Acts, for all their benefits in improving air and water quality, also succeeded in transferring pollutants from one part of the environment to another."

7. *Describe three methods of land disposal that were used in the 1970s. How has their use changed over time?*

"In the early 1970s, there were three primary land-disposal methods: (1) deep-well injection, (2) surface impoundments, and (3) landfills. With the conscientious implementation of safeguards, each of these methods has some merit, and each is still heavily used for hazardous-waste disposal. Without adequate regulations or enforcement, however, contamination of groundwater is inevitable. The total amount of deep-well injection has declined over the years, from 685 million tons in 1988 to 116 million tons in 2001 (representing 5.4% of on-land disposal)."

8. *What law was passed to cope with the problem of abandoned hazardous-waste sites? What are the main features of the legislation?*

"The Comprehensive Environmental Response, Compensation, and Liability Act of 1980 (CERCLA), popularly known as Superfund, initiated a major federal program aimed at cleanup of abandoned chemical waste sites. Through a tax on chemical raw materials (the authorization for collecting more tax monies expired in 1995), this legislation provides a trust fund for the identification of abandoned chemical wastes sites, protection of groundwater near the site, remediation of groundwater if it has been contaminated, and cleanup of the site." Because "resources are insufficient to clean up all sites at once . . . a system for setting priorities was developed." "As sites are identified—note that many abandoned sites had long since been forgotten—their current and potential threat to groundwater supplies is initially assessed. . . . If a threat to human health does exist, the most expedient measures are taken immediately to protect the public. The worst sites (those presenting the most immediate and severe threats) are put on the National Priorities List and scheduled for total cleanup."

9. *What is being done about leaking underground storage tanks and brownfields?*

"Underground storage tank (UST) regulations, part of RCRA, now require strict monitoring of fuel supplies, tanks, and piping so that leaks may be detected early. When leaks are detected, remediation must begin within 72 hours. Rules now require all USTs to be upgraded with interior lining and cathodic protection (to retard electrolytic corrosion of the steel), and new tanks must be provided with the same protection if they are steel."

"Brownfields are 'abandoned, idled, or underused industrial and commercial facilities where expansion or redevelopment is complicated by real or perceived environmental contamination' (EPA definition). The Brownfield Act in 2002 (passed with bipartisan support) provides grants for the assessment of sites and remediation work and authorized $200 million for the ensuing five years of the program. The brownfields program 'limits liability for owners and prospective purchasers of contaminated land, thus clearing the way for more cleanup of the estimated 450,000 sites that would qualify as brownfields.' Frequently, the rehabilitation of brownfield sites provides industries and municipalities with centrally located, prime land for facilities that would otherwise have been carved out of suburban or 'greenfield' land (land occupied by natural ecosystems). A further advantage is that new developments go back on the tax rolls, turning a liability into a community asset that lightens the load of residential taxpayers."

10. *What law was passed to ensure safe land disposal of hazardous wastes? What are the main features of the legislation?*

"The 1976 RCRA and its subsequent amendments are the cornerstone legislation designed to prevent unsafe or illegal disposal of all solid wastes on land. The RCRA has three main features. First, it requires that all disposal facilities, such as landfills, be sanctioned by permits. Second, the RCRA requires that toxic wastes destined for landfills be pretreated to convert them to forms that will not leach. For whatever is still going to disposal facilities, the third major feature of RCRA is to require 'cradle-to-grave' tracking of all hazardous wastes."

11. *What laws exist to protect the public against exposures resulting from hazardous chemical accidents? What are the main features of the legislation?*

"Transport is an area that is particularly prone to accidents. As modern society uses increasing amounts and kinds of hazardous materials, the stage is set for accidents to become wide-scale disasters. To reduce this risk, Department of Transportation Regulations (DOT Regs) specify the kinds of containers and methods of packing to be used in the transport of various hazardous materials."

"In the past, it was not uncommon for industries to require workers to perform jobs that entailed exposure to hazardous materials without informing the workers of the hazards involved. This situation is now addressed by certain amendments to the Occupational Safety and Health Act (OSH Act of 1970). These amendments make up the hazard communication standard or 'worker's right to know.' Basically, the law requires businesses, industries, and laboratories to make available both information regarding hazardous materials and suitable protective equipment. One form taken by this information is the material safety data sheet (MSDS)."

"Title III of SARA (Superfund Amendments and Reauthorization Act of 1986) is better known as Emergency Planning and Community Right-to-know Act (EPCRA). EPCRA requires companies that handle in excess of 5 tons of any hazardous material to provide a 'complete accounting' of storage sites, feed hoppers, and so on. The information goes to a local emergency planning committee, which is also required in every governmental jurisdiction. The committee is made up of officials representing local fire and police departments, hospitals, and any other groups that might be involved in case of an emergency, as well as the executive officers of the companies in question. The task of the committee is to draw up scenarios for accidents involving the chemicals on-site and to have a contingency plan for every case."

12. *What role does the Toxic Substances Control Act play in the hazardous waste arena?*

"The Toxic Substances Control Act (TSCA) . . . requires that, before manufacturing a new chemical in bulk, manufacturers must submit a 'pre-manufacturing report' to the EPA in which the environmental and human health impacts of the substance are assessed (including those that may derive from the ultimate disposal of the chemical). Depending on the results of the assessment, the manufacturer may be required to test the effects of the product on living things. Following the results of the testing, a product's uses may be restricted or a product may be kept off the market altogether."

269

13. *Why does the EPA have an environmental justice program?*

   "The EPA defines environmental justice as 'the fair treatment and meaningful involvement of all people regardless of race, color, national origin, or income with respect to the development, implementation, and enforcement of environmental laws, regulations, and policies. Fair treatment means that no group of people, including racial, ethnic, or socioeconomic group(s), should bear a disproportionate share of the negative environmental consequences resulting from industrial, municipal, and commercial operations or the execution of federal, state, local, and tribal programs and policies. Several recent studies have shown that, all across the United States, waste sites and other hazardous facilities are more likely than not to be located in towns and neighborhoods where most of the residents are non-Caucasian. These same towns and neighborhoods are also less affluent, a further element of environmental injustice."

14. *Describe the advantages of pollution prevention efforts.*

   "Pollution control and pollution prevention are not the same. Pollution control involves adding a filter or some other device at the 'end of the pipe' to prevent pollutants from entering the environment. The disposal of the captured pollutants still has to be dealt with, and this entails more regulation and control. Pollution prevention, by contrast, involves changing the production process, the materials used, or both so that harmful pollutants won't be produced in the first place."

   "Pollution prevention often results in better product or materials management—that is, less wastage. Thus, pollution prevention frequently creates a cost savings. A second angle on pollution avoidance is substitution— that is, finding nonhazardous substitutes for hazardous materials. A third approach is reuse—that is, cleaning up and recycling solvents and lubricants. Some military bases, for example, have been able to distill solvents and reuse them, instead of discarding them into the environment. Finally, pollution avoidance can also be applied to the individual consumer. So far as you are able to reduce or avoid the use of products containing harmful chemicals, you are preventing those amounts of chemicals from going into the environment. You are also reducing the by-products resulting from producing those chemicals."

Thinking Environmentally: Possible Answers

1. *Select a chemical product or drug you suspect could be hazardous, and investigate it, using the resources made available on the Internet by federal agencies and Environmental Defense.*

   The answers to this question will vary by the chemical or drug product. If the product or drug chosen by the student is not hazardous you might ask them to look at the manufacturing process for the product or drug. It is not unusual for there to be some hazardous materials used in production.

2. *Before the 1970s, it was not illegal to dispose of hazardous chemicals in unlined pits, and many companies did so. Should they be held responsible today for the contamination those waste are causing, or should the government (taxpayers) pay for the cleanup? Give a rationale for your position.*

   If a student proposes that companies should not be held responsible for contamination caused by legal disposal practices, ask about who benefited from those practices. While the consumer might have benefited by lower prices, the company would have also benefited from higher profits.

   If a student proposes that companies should be held responsible for contamination caused by legal disposal practices, ask about why the consumers who benefited should not also pay. Additionally, the company may have limited funds available for cleanup if it is to remain in business. What will happen to the community if jobs are lost and the taxes from the company disappear?

3. *Use the Toxic Release Inventory on the Web to investigate the location and amounts of toxic chemicals released in your state or region.*

Responses to this question will differ. You might consider asking students to do their search using their home county or zip code. This will provide more data to compare betweens students. The number of businesses with toxic chemical releases will be surprising to many. Even counties or zip codes with little industry are likely to have data. A number of different reports can be generated: (1) by quantity of each chemical or by industry (by chemical), (2) trends in chemical releases by county or zip code, (3) chemical releases by geographic region (state, all counties, counties within a state), and (4) by industry type for the whole country, within a state, or within a county. Additionally, maps can be generated for the United States and for each state (by county).

4. *List three toxic items in your house. What do you do to keep them out of the environment? How do you dispose of such chemicals?*

Student responses will vary based on the chemicals found in their homes and their experiences with those chemicals.

CHAPTER 23
Sustainable Communities and Lifestyles

Chapter Outline:

I. Urban Sprawl
- A. The Origins of Urban Sprawl
  - 1. Suburbs
    - i. Housing Boom
  - 2. Highways
    - i. Vicious Cycle
    - ii. Exurbs Too
- B. Measuring Sprawl
- C. Environmental Impacts of Urban Sprawl
  - 1. Energy Resources
  - 2. Air Pollution
  - 3. Water Resources
  - 4. Loss of Agricultural Land
  - 5. Loss of Landscapes and Wildlife
- D. Impacts of Sprawl on Quality of Life
  - 1. Higher Vehicle Ownership and Driving Mileages
  - 2. Less Physical Activity and Greater Health Risks
  - 3. Congestion and Higher Costs
- E. The Benefits of Urban Sprawl
  - 1. Net Benefits?
  - 2. Common Good?
- F. Reigning in Urban Sprawl: Smart Growth
  - 1. Initiatives
  - 2. Raiding the Fund

II. Urban Blight
- A. Economic an Ethnic Segregation
- B. The Vicious Cycle of Urban Blight
  - 1. Economic Dysfunction
  - 2. Economic Exclusion of the Inner City
- C. Urban Blight in Developing Countries
  - 1. The Needs
- D. What Makes Cities Livable?
  - 1. A Matter of Design
    - i. Charinkos
    - ii. Portland
    - iii. The Big Dip
  - 2. Livable Equals Sustainable

Key Topics:

1. Urban Sprawl
2. Urban Blight
3. Moving Toward Sustainable Communities
4. Lifestyles and the Common Good

Instructional Goals:

1. Urban sprawl was made possible by the automobile and high-speed highways.

2. Urban sprawl and blight are flip sides of the same coin. When a city becomes un-livable, people leave if they can. Those who leave the city are car owners. Urban flight worsens urban blight by taking money out of the city and bringing the suburban/rural area all the problems that people were attempting to escape.

3. Urban sprawl creates new environmental problems or makes existing ones worse. Air pollution, increased energy use, water pollution, water resource degradation, and loss of landscapes, wildlife, and agricultural lands are some of the adverse consequences of urban sprawl.

4. Addressing the problems of urban decay creates livable cities. When cities are livable a more sustainable, less environmentally damaging lifestyle is possible.

Concepts and Connections:

  The most important new idea presented is the impact of urbanization on the environment and the need to create sustainable and livable cities. In the United States, we began moving out of cities after World War II because of some unpleasant aspects of urban living. Unfortunately, moving to the suburbs did not eliminate the problems we were attempting to escape, (e.g., crime, pollution, noise, and lack of space), and created or exacerbated a number of problems, (e.g., air and water pollution, loss of landscapes, wildlife and agricultural land, and faster rates of energy depletion). Urban flight increased urban decay and created new locations for urban decay. The problems people are (were) trying to avoid by leaving the city are (were) real, and to reverse urban decay and address the problems created by urban flight we need to create livable cities. Livable cities are reasonably safe and relatively noise free,

273

contain many trees and other greenery, and have convenient transportation and nearby retail business, restaurants, physicians, and other professionals.

Many of the problems discussed throughout the semester can be tied together using the issue of suburban sprawl. Students, if given the opportunity, can identify all the characteristics of a livable city and all the problems created by suburban sprawl. Challenging students to define the most immediate changes that are possible and the justification for the changes will help them leave the class knowing that we are moving towards solutions. Challenging students to "think outside the box" and create cities that are livable will help them see that many things are possible and that we can achieve sustainability. It will be their generation that will move us closer to sustainability and in this process they will see problems and solutions that we currently cannot see.

Concepts in Context:

The discussion of urban sprawl can be linked to the all the concepts learned about ecosystems (Chapters 3, 4, and 5). As we have moved out of urban areas in search of a better life, we have encroached on the habitats of many species. Loss of habitat is the most important cause of biodiversity loss (Chapter 6). It can be useful to point out that human population growth (Chapters 8 and 9) has not been the force behind the spread of cities in the developed world; the availability of automobiles and the building of roads made sprawl possible.

Urban sprawl has had an adverse impact on agriculture as we have paved land. This can be discussed in the context of soil and soil erosion (Chapter 11) and food production (Chapter 12). Pesticide (Chapter 13) use has been important, as we have decreased the availability of prime agriculture land. Urban sprawl has led to increased air pollution (Chapter 19), increased quantities of greenhouse gases (Chapter 18), and substantial releases of ozone depletion chemicals from our automobile air conditioners (Chapter 20). Water pollution (Chapter 20), groundwater depletion (Chapter 10), and various impacts on aquatic ecosystems can be linked to the massive amount of paving that has accompanied urban sprawl.

As we have decreased the population density of urban areas by urban sprawl, we have increased the amount of energy (Chapters 14, 15, and 16) needed to perform necessary tasks. The amount of energy lost to heat during the transport of energy is greater because the users of the energy are more dispersed, necessitating greater transportation distances. Goods and services have to be delivered to a greater area. Human health (Chapter 17) is adversely impacted by urban sprawl because of increases in air pollution and water pollution. The pesticide use (Chapter 13) in urban areas also increases the risk to human health.

Living sustainably also includes choices about how and what we consume. The use of hazardous materials and their disposal (Chapter 22) will need evaluation to insure sustainability. The quantity of materials used and how they are disposed (Chapter 21) also influence sustainability.

Key Terms and Vocabulary:

Highway Trust Fund, exurban migration, exurbs, Intermodal Surface Transportation Efficiency Act (ISTEA), Transportation Equity Act for the 21st Century (TEA-21), Safe, Accountable, Flexible, Efficient, Transportation Equity Act-A Legacy for Users (SAFETEA-LU), eroding, declining, tax base, urban blight, Shack/Slum Dwellers International (SDI), Sustainable Communities Network, Smart Communities Network, Chattanooga Venture

Discussion, Activities, and Labs:

1. Discuss why we have changed from a rural to an urban people. What attracts people to suburbs? What makes suburbs possible? What are the impacts of suburbanization on society and the environment?

2. Ask the students what they find most and least livable about the urban/suburban/rural area where they currently live. What suggestions do they have to improve the livability of the area? What changes would each student need to make?

3. Divide the students into groups of four to five individuals. Have each group evaluate how livable your city is. The students in the group should divide up tasks to determine livability. (See the section in the chapter on what makes a city livable.) Each group should determine, in their opinion, if the city can be considered livable. Their opinion should be justified based upon the information gathered. For any items that are considered to not help the city's livability, the group is to develop a plan to improve the situation.

Suggested Lecture Format:

I. Urban Sprawl

    A. The Origins of Urban Sprawl—"Until the end of World War II, a relatively small percentage of people owned cars." Because of this, people lived within walking distance of most of the places that they needed to go. **See Discussion Topic #1.**

        1. Suburbs—"When mass production of cars resumed as the end of the war, people flocked to buy them. Their cars would allow them to drive back and forth easily to their jobs, shopping, recreation, and so on."

            i. Housing Boom—As veterans returned from the war, there was a great demand for new housing. The government provided low-interest mortgages and property taxes became tax deductible. With all of this, suburban development came up quickly and without much planning. See Figure 23-4.

        2. Highways—"The influx of commuters into previously rural areas soon resulted in traffic congestion, creating a need for new and larger roads."

            i. Vicious Cycle—"New highways that were intended to reduce congestion actually fostered the development of open land and commuting by more drivers from distant locations." See Figure 23-5.

            ii. Exurbs Too—"In broad perspective, then, urban sprawl is a process of exurban migration-that is, a relocation of residences, shopping areas, and workplaces from their traditional spots in the city to outlying areas."

    B. Measuring Sprawl—Sprawl is "the process in which the spread of development across the landscape far outpaces population growth." An index that averages to 100 points is given to each city in regards to sprawl. See Figure 23-7 and Table 23-2.

    C. Environmental Impacts of Urban Sprawl—"The environmental impacts of urban sprawl are many and serious."

1. Energy Resources—With more cars comes more air pollution from the burning of fossil fuels and is leading to climate change.
2. Air Pollution—"Vehicles are responsible for an estimated 80% of the air pollution in metropolitan areas."
3. Water Resources—"All the highways, parking lots, driveways, and other paved areas associated with urban sprawl lead to a substantial increase in runoff, resulting in increased flooding and erosion of stream banks."
4. Loss of Agricultural Land—"With so many farms turned into housing developments, it is estimated that food now travels an average of 1,000 miles from where it is produced…to where it is eaten." See Figure 23-8.
5. Loss of Landscapes and Wildlife—"The fragmentation of wildlife habitat due to urban sprawl has led to marked declines in many species, ranging from birds to amphibians."

D. Impacts of Sprawl on Quality of Life—See the impacts listed below.
   1. Higher Vehicle Ownership and Driving Mileages—"In the top 10 sprawl areas, there were 180 vehicles per 100 households, while in the lowest 10 there were 162."
   2. Less Physical Activity and Greater Health Risks—"People living in high-sprawl areas drive more, while those in more compact communities walk and take mass transit more."
   3. Congestion and Higher Costs—"There was no difference in commute times between high-and low-sprawl areas. This indicates that moving out to the suburbs or exurbs to get away from traffic congestion does not work."

E. The Benefits of Urban Sprawl—"In general, sprawl involves lower-density residential living, larger lot sizes, larger single-family homes, better quality public schools, lower crime rates, better social services, and greater opportunity for participation in local governments."
   1. Net Benefits?—It is arguable when the benefits and disadvantages of living in the suburbs are considered that there are net benefits.
   2. Common Good?—"The environmental costs of sprawl are very real, but these are seldom perceived as decisive by the people moving to the sprawling suburbs."

F. Reigning in Urban Sprawl: Smart Growth—"The recently emerged concept of smart growth is inviting communities and metropolitan areas to address sprawl and purposely choose to develop in more environmentally sustainable ways." See Table 23-3.
   1. Initiatives—"Smart growth initiatives are appearing on the ballot in many states and municipalities." See p. 598 for the key strategies involved in smart growth.
   2. Raiding the Fund—"In addition to foregoing key strategies, there have been successful attempts to break the cycle created by the Highway Trust Fund by allowing revenues to be used for purposes other than the construction of more highways."

II. Urban Blight

A. Economic and Ethnic Segregation—"Historically, U.S. cities have included people with a wide diversity of economic and ethnic backgrounds. However, moving to the suburbs required some degree of affluence-at least the ability to manage a down payment and mortgage on a home and the ability to buy and drive a car."

B. The Vicious Cycle of Urban Blight—"Affluent people moving to the suburbs set into motion a vicious cycle of exurban migration and urban blight that continues today."
    1. Economic Dysfunction—With exurban migration come lowered property values in the city and a declining tax base. "This downward spiral of conditions is referred to as urban blight or urban decay."
    2. Economic Exclusion of the Inner City—"The exurban migration includes more than just individuals and families: The flight of affluent people from the city removes the purchasing power necessary to support stores, professional establishments, and other enterprises."

C. Urban Blight in Developing Countries—"UN-HABITAT estimates that one out of every three people in the developing world cities lives in slums."
    1. The Needs—"The vast slums surrounding the cities are a tremendous challenge to the institutional structure of developing countries."

D. What Makes Cities Livable?—"Livability is a general concept based on people's response to the question "do you like living here, or would you rather live somewhere else?" **See Discussion Topics #2 and #3.**
    1. A Matter of Design—"The world's most livable cities are not those with 'perfect' auto access between all points. Instead, they are cities that have taken measures to reduce outward sprawl, diminish automobile traffic, and improve access by foot and bicycle in conjunction with mass transit." See Figures 23-13 and 23-14.
        i.   Charinkos—"In Tokyo, millions of people ride charinkos, or bicycles, either all the way to work or to subway stations from which they catch fast, efficient trains, including the 'bullet train' to their destination." See Figure 23-15.
        ii. Portland—"Portland, Oregon, is a pioneering U.S. city that has taken giant steps to curtail automobile use."
        iii. The Big Dip—Many highways that were funded by the Highway Fund are now being torn down or buried to allow neighborhoods to connect to each other and to livable areas of the city.
    2. Livable Equals Sustainable—"Even though cities are a concentration of energy use, resource sue, and pollution, there are certain environmental benefits to urbanization." See Figure 23-17.
        i.   To the Point—"The decay of our cities is hastening the degradation of our larger environment."

III. Moving Toward Sustainable Communities

A. Sustainable Cities—The Sustainable Cities Program "defines a sustainable city as a city in which 'achievements in social, economic and physical development are made to last'."
    1. Bottom Up—Bottom up programs call for "the involvement of people at all economic and social levels and reconciling their interests when conflicts are evident." See Figure 23-18.

2. SustainLane—"In the United States, the 50 most populous cities have been ranked for sustainability by the organization SustainLane."

B. Sustainable Communities—"What is termed a sustainable communities movement is taking root in cities around the United States. The Sustainable Communities Network and the Smart Communities Network provide a cornucopia of information, help, case studies, and linkages, demonstrating that the movement is gaining ground throughout the nation."

    i. Chattanooga—40 years ago Chattanooga, Tennessee was considered the dirtiest city in America. "Then the Chattanooga Venture, a nonprofit organization founded by community leaders, launched Vision 2000, the first step of which was to bring people from all walks of life together to build a consensus about what the city could be like."

    ii. Revision—"Chattanooga has changes its reputation from one of the worst to one of the best places to live." See Figure 23-19.

IV. Lifestyles and the Common Good

A. Our Dilemma—"When 2015 arrives, will we be able to say that we have met all the Millennium Development Goals, alleviating much of the developing world's grinding poverty and its consequences?"

1. Human Decisions—"Making stewardly decisions is not a simple task. Decision making is affected by our personal values and needs, and competing values and needs exist at every turn."

2. The Common Good—The common good in the context of public policy is "to improve human welfare and to protect the natural world."

B. Lifestyle Changes—"There are a number of levels on which we can participate to work toward a sustainable society: individual lifestyle choices, political involvement, membership and participation in nongovernmental environmental organizations, volunteer work, and career choices."

Review Questions: Possible Answers

1. What problems do Trenton and Waitakere City illustrate, and how are they organizing to deal with those problems?
    "Waitakere City has been experiencing the typical problems of urban growth, such as urban sprawl, traffic congestion, and pressure on natural areas within the city. In addition, the city reflects a diverse ethnic makeup: a distinctly European ethnic majority and minorities of several cultural groups, but especially the native Maori. This city formally adopted Agenda 21 in 1993 and became New Zealand's first ecocity. Adopting the Agenda 21 goal of protection the indigenous people and cultures of countries while meeting other goals of sustainable development, Waitakere City focused on Maori principles and values first and then on New Zealand legislation and Agenda 21 principles to develop the guidelines for the city's efforts. Using the Maori perspective of tangata whenua, or 'people of the land,' which incorporates ecological and stewardship principles into the relationship between people and land, the city developed a strategic plan called Greenprint. With input for the Maori, the city council has developed a Green Network Plan with the objective of 'protection, restoring, and

278

enhancing the natural environment across the whole city, while increasing human enjoyment and appreciation of that environment. This goal places human beings within the natural world, as stewards of its natural and spiritual health.' The whole community is enlisted in 'greening the city': restoring native plants, providing corridors for wildlife, and providing access to the parks and reserves that will maintain people's safety (from crime)."

"On the other side of the world, citizens of Trenton, New Jersey, have made remarkable progress in rehabilitating their city, with the aid of Isles, Inc. (from the concept of neighborhood-scale 'islands of redevelopment'), an urban-planning company. Trenton, with a multicultural population of 89,000, is the capital of New Jersey. Isles, Inc., was founded in 1981 by nearby Princeton University personnel, but quickly evolved into a locally owned and controlled development organization. A thriving industrial city a century ago, Trenton was suffering from the all-too-common problems of a decaying urban center, ethnic segregation, and urban blight. To date, Isles has fostered the following changes: Vacant land has been transformed into 15 community garden sites; almost 300 units of affordable housing have been created; numerous unemployed young people have been given job training in connection with the affordable housing projects; a career center provides academic and job training, counseling, and leadership training to at-risk, inner city youths; environmental education programs are provided yearly to 3,000 students; a recent capital campaign raised funding for an urban environmental education center and an endowment; and the city is redeveloping nearly 60 'brownfield' sites."

2. *How did the structure of cities begin to change after World War II? What factors were responsible for the changes?*

Cities began to expand into suburbs where people had larger houses and larger yards. Roads became more numerous and stores were grouped together rather than scattered within the housing area. Since World War II more and more people have purchased automobiles and have driven ever-increasing numbers of miles per year. Starting in the mid-1950s, we have built an endless number of miles of roads to accommodate the automobile. Cars and roads made urban sprawl possible because people could move from cities and still get to their jobs. People moved from the cities because the surroundings were not perceived to be pleasant. In the process of exurban migration people move residences and shopping areas and jobs moved with them. Because the causes of urban blight have not been addressed, these "new" suburbs decay and people move again.

3. *Why are the terms "car dependent" and "urban sprawl" used to describe our current suburban lifestyle and urban layout?*

In suburban layout, houses are spread apart; stores are away from housing; schools may be distant from housing; work sites are not near homes; and roads, many roads, connect everything. The distances from schools, housing, work, and shopping are great. To get from one place to another, a person needs to use a car; it is not possible to walk because of distances and lack of sidewalks and pedestrian-friendly locations. Time, not distance, is the limiting factor in a suburb because of cars and the highways built for them.

4. *What federal laws and policies tend to support urban sprawl?*

"The government aided this trend (purchasing of houses by returning GIs) by providing low-interest mortgages through the Veterans Administration and the Federal Housing Administration, and interest payments on mortgages (but not rent) were made tax deductible. Property taxes in suburbs were much lower than in the city. Congress passed the Highway Revenue Act of 1956, which created the Highway Trust Fund. This legislation placed a tax on gasoline and earmarked the revenues to be used exclusively for building new roads. Ironically, the Highway Trust Fund perpetuates development. A new highway not only alleviates existing congestion, but also encourages development at farther locations, because time, not distance, is the limiting factor for commuters."

5. *Compare the costs and benefits of urban sprawl, looking at the environmental impacts and the impacts on quality of life.*

279

Environmental impacts—

Depletion of energy resources: "Shifting to a car-dependent lifestyle has entailed an ever-increasing demand for petroleum. . . ." Delivering goods and services to a less concentrated area requires more energy. **Air pollution:** Because of the increased use of the car the improvements in per mile emissions has not resulted in improved air quality. As urban sprawl increases, the need for driving increases. **Water pollution and degradation of water resources:** "All the highways, parking lots, driveways, and other paved areas associated with urban sprawl lead to a substantial increase in runoff resulting in increased flooding and erosion of stream banks." ". . . (W)ater quality is degraded by runoff of fertilizers, pesticides, crankcase oil, pet droppings, and so on." **Loss of landscapes and wildlife:** "New developments are consuming land at an increasing pace. The result is the sacrifice of aesthetic, recreation, and wildlife values in metropolitan areas, the very places where they are most important." Habitat fragmentation also occurs. Loss of biodiversity and increases in the number of road kill animals may also result from urban sprawl. **Loss of agricultural land:** "In the United States alone, sprawling development is eating up 590,000 acres of prime agricultural land a year."

Impacts on the quality of life—

Higher vehicle ownership and driving mileages: "Cars are driven greater distances per person in high-sprawl areas. Chauffeuring kids to and from school or after-school activities requires more driving in sprawl areas." **Greater risk of fatal accidents:** "The higher rates of vehicle use lead to higher highway fatalities. In Riverside, California, at the top of the sprawl index, 18 of every 100,000 people die each year in highway accidents." **Lowered rates of walking and lessened use of mass transit facilities:** "The percentage of commuter trips by mass transit in the 10 highest sprawl areas was 2%, compared with 7% in the 10 lowest sprawl areas." **No change in congestion delays:** "There was no difference in commute times between high- and low sprawl areas. This indicates that moving out to the suburbs or exurbs to get away from traffic congestion does not work." **Higher costs for municipal services:** "The developments in outlying regions of metropolitan areas all have to be serviced with schools, sewers, water, electricity, roads and other infrastructure elements, often forcing county and town budgets to escalate. More compact forms of development are less expensive to service." **Higher incidence of obesity and high blood pressure:** "People living in high-sprawl areas drive more, while those in more compact communities walk more. Walking and other moderate physical activity have many health benefits."

Benefits of urban sprawl: Benefits include low density residential living, larger lots sizes, larger single-family homes, better quality public schools, lower crime rates, better social services, and greater opportunity for participation in local government.

6. *What is "smart growth"? What are the four smart growth strategies that address urban sprawl?*
   "The concept (of smart growth) recognizes that growth will occur and focuses on economic, environmental, and community values that together will lead to more sustainable communities. Zoning laws are being changed in many localities, and a new generation of architects and developers is beginning to focus on creating integrated communities, as opposed to disassociated facilities." Four smart growth strategies are 1. Setting boundaries on urban sprawl 2. Saving open space 3. Developing existing urban space 4. Creating new towns. In 1991 the Intermodal Surface Transportation Efficiency Act was passed by Congress; ". . . almost half of the money levied by the Highway Trust Fund is . . . eligible to be used for other modes of transportation, including cycling, walking, and mass-transit."

7. *What services do local governments provide, and what is their prime source of revenue for these services?*

"... local governments (usually city or county agencies, although the particular entities vary from state to state) are responsible for providing public schools, maintaining local roads, furnishing police and fire protection, collecting and disposing of refuse, maintaining public water and sewers, and providing welfare services, libraries, and local parks." Local governments also have to pay electric bills to keep streetlights and traffic lights running.

The "... major source of revenue to pay for these services is local property taxes, a yearly tax proportional to the market value of the property and home or other buildings on it."

8. *What is meant by "erosion of a city's tax base"? Why does it follow from exurban migration? What are the results?*

Erosion of a city's tax base is the "declining tax revenue resulting from falling property values." Property values fall when the affluent citizens of the city leave to the suburbs because the demand for property in the city declines. As property values decline some individuals abandon property dropping property values even more. The result is the city government is forced "... to cut local services, increase the tax rate, or, generally, both."

9. *How do exurban migration, urban sprawl, and urban decay become a vicious cycle?*

"Affluent people moving to the suburbs set into motion a vicious cycle of exurban migration and urban blight. ..." Affluent people move to the suburbs, causing property values in the city to fall. As property values decline, the government services decline and/or the rate of taxation increases. More deterioration occurs because the city lacks money to pay for services, thus more people leave the city.

10. *What is meant by "economic exclusion"? How is it related to the problems of crime and poverty in cities?*

Economic exclusion is a result of exurban migration because existing jobs in the city are lost when people move to the suburbs and new jobs created in the suburban and exurban areas are not accessible to the people in the city because of the lack of public transportation. Jobs decline in the city because the people with the money to support a diversity of businesses have moved to the suburbs and exurbs. "Therefore, not only are people who remain in the inner city poor from the outset, but the cycle of exurban migration and urban decay has led to their economic exclusion from the mainstream. As a result, drug dealing, crime, violence, and other forms of deviant social behavior are widespread and worsening in such areas."

11. *What are the reasons for urban blight in the cities of many developing countries? What do the people in the shantytowns need most?*

"The economies of rural areas, often based only on subsistence farming, simply do not provide the jobs needed by a growing population. So people move to the cities, where they at least have the hope of employment. The city housing is overwhelmed by the influx of migrants, who could not afford the rents even if housing were available. The slums actually represent a great deal of entrepreneurial energy, because the residents build the dwellings and erect their own infrastructure, usually including food stands, coffee shops, barber shops, and, in some cases, schools for their children."

"A great need in such neighborhoods is home security. People live in fear of bulldozers coming at any time and leveling the shantytown. Providing this level of security to the inhabitants is often the key to mobilizing further assets, such as acquiring access to credit and negotiating with the city government or utilities for additional services. People will improve their living conditions if they are given the assurance that they can stay where they are. The people in the shantytowns also need more jobs. And again, local governments could provide employment at low cost to accomplish many improvements in their own neighborhoods and elsewhere. ... Providing cheap transportation is another need. Perhaps the greatest need of people living in the informal neighborhoods of city slums is government representation."

12. *What are some characteristics of livable cities?*

There are three important characteristics of a livable city: "(1) maintaining a high population density; (2) preserving heterogeneity of residences, businesses, stores, and shops; and (3) keeping layouts on a human dimension, so that people can meet, visit, or conduct business incidentally over coffee at a sidewalk café or stroll on a promenade through an open area. In short, the space is designed for, and devoted to, people. The world's most livable cities are not those with 'perfect' auto access between all points. Instead, they are cities that have taken measures to reduce outward sprawl, diminish automobile traffic, and improve access by foot and bicycle in conjunction with mass transit."

13. *How does the U.N.'s Sustainable Cities Program and Localizing Agenda 21 work?*
    The U.N.'s Sustainable Cities Program (SCP) "is designed to foster the planning and management needed to move cities in the developing countries toward the objective of sustainability. The program defines a sustainable city as one in which 'achievements in social, economic, and physical development are made to last.'" The SCP is viewed as a 'capacity-building program,' meaning that it is intended to help cities and countries mobilize resources and capabilities that are mostly available within the cities themselves (building management capacity).

14. *What is the Sustainable Communities Program? How does Chattanooga illustrate the program?*
    "Revitalizing urban economies and rehabilitating cities requires coordinated efforts on the part of all sectors of society." This is termed the "sustainable communities movement. . . . Chattanooga, Tennessee, is . . . regarded as a prototype of what can occur with such a movement. . . . Chattanooga Venture, a nonprofit organization founded by community leaders, launched Vision 2000, the first step of which was to bring people from all walks of life together to build a consensus about what the city could be like. Literally thousands of ideas were gradually distilled into 223 specific projects. Then, with the cooperation of all sectors—including government, business, lending institutions, and average persons—work on the projects began, providing employment in construction for more than 7,300 people and permanent employment for 1,380 and investing more than $800 million. Among the projects were the following: . . local government clamped down hard on industries to control pollution, …building or renovation of more than 4,600 units of low- and moderate-income housing…, a recycling center employing mentally handicapped adults…, urban greenway demonstration farm…, zero emissions industrial park was built. With these and numerous other projects, many of them still ongoing, Chattanooga has moved its reputation from one of the worst to one of the best places to live."

15. *What are some stewardship virtues, and what role could they play in fostering sustainability?*
    "We can identify a number of values (indeed, virtues) that can be the basis of stewardship and help us in our ethical decisions involving both public policies and personal lifestyles: **Compassion for those less well off** —those suffering from extreme poverty or other forms of deprivation. Compassion can become a major element of our foreign policy, energizing our country's efforts in promoting sustainable development in countries that are most in trouble." "**A concern for justice**—just policies can become the norm in international economic relations, and a concern for justice can also move people to protest the placement of hazardous facilities in communities of color. **Honesty** or a concern for the truth— in a sense of keeping the laws of the land and in openly examining issues from different perspectives." "**Sufficiency**—rather than ever-increasing consumption, using no more than is necessary of Earth's resources." "**Humility**—instead of demanding our rights, being willing to share and even defer to others." "**Neighborliness**—being concerned for other members of our communities (even the global community), such that we do not engage in activities that are harmful to them, but instead make positive contributions to their welfare."

16. *State five levels on which people can participate in working toward a sustainable future.*
    People can participate in working toward a sustainable society by individual lifestyle changes, political involvement, membership and participation in nongovernmental environmental organizations, volunteer work, and career choices.

Thinking Environmentally: Possible Answers

1. *Interview an older person (say, 75 years or older) about what his or her city or community was like before 1950 in terms of meeting people's needs for shopping, participating in recreation, getting to school, work, and so on. Was it necessary to have a car?*

   Several good locations to meet people who are 65 or older are senior citizen centers, nursing homes, and churches, synagogues, and other religious institutions. One could volunteer to work with an organization that brings in cats or dogs to visit with individuals living in senior facilities. Asking a person in a friendly way about what life was like 50 years ago or more will generally elicit a great deal of information.

2. *Do a study of your region. What aspects of urban sprawl and urban blight are evident? What environmental and social problems are evident? Are they still going on? Are efforts being made to correct them?*

   Answers to this question will vary by region. Many small towns do not have the same visible symptoms of urban sprawl or urban blight, but the problems that plague urban areas are not unique because they are human constructs. In small towns or rural areas look for situations and actions that if allowed to continue for many years would produce what we observe in urban areas.

3. *Identify nongovernmental organizations in your region that are working toward reining in urban sprawl or toward preserving or bettering the city. What specific projects are underway in each of these areas? What roles are local governments playing in the process? How can you become involved?*

   Nongovernmental organizations that will address urban sprawl tend to include those interested in habitat preservation, road development, land use planning, and so on. If there is a local Audubon Society, this organization is typically interested in preserving parts of the urban area where birds can be observed.

4. *Suppose you are a planner or developer. Design a community that is people oriented and that integrates the principles of sustainability and self-sufficiency. Consider all the fundamental aspects: food, water, energy, sewage, solid waste, and how people get to school, shopping, work, and recreation.*

   This answer will vary tremendously among students. One possibility is below. Trying to mimic how an ecosystem is structured is a good start for creating a sustainable city. Food needs to be grown as locally as possible to reduce transportation and facilitate the movement of compost from the city to the farm. A sewage treatment system that separates industrial waste from municipal waste is essential so pasteurized sludge can be returned to farmland. Minimal amounts of water could be extracted from the surrounding ecosystem if water was recycled. This would require treatment to remove pharmaceuticals from sewage. Landscaping throughout the city would need to be native species to reduce any irrigation necessary and to assist in minimizing the impact of human habitation on other species. All housing would have to be built to maximize energy efficiency and minimize exposure to hazardous compounds. Common, noise-proof walls would be standard construction to decrease the footprint occupied by housing and decrease heat loss in the winter and cooling needs in the summer. Houses would be oriented to take advantage of solar heating and cooling and would include overhangs and landscaping to aid in energy efficiency. Large amounts of land surrounding the community would be available for community gardens and natural areas would be preserved for recreation. Bicycle paths and sidewalks would connect all housing, work, and shopping areas. Stores would be integrated into housing and work areas to reduce travel distances. For those whose work site is too far to walk or ride a bicycle, mass transit would be available. Car accessible areas would be kept to a minimum. Electric carts (with drivers) would be available for those with disabilities and to move large or heavy objects. Cultural events would occur frequently.